THEORETIC ARITHMETIC

THOMAS TAYLOR

THE
THEORETIC
ARITHMETIC

OF THE
PYTHAGOREANS

BY THOMAS TAYLOR

INTRODUCTORY ESSAY
BY MANLY HALL

SAMUEL WEISER, INC.
York Beach, Maine

First published in London in 1816
Reissued, with an introduction by Manly P. Hall
by the Phoenix Press, California, 1934

First Weiser imprint, 1972
Reprinted 1975, 1978

First paperback edition, including an
introduction by Manly P. Hall, 1983

Samuel Weiser, Inc.
Box 612
York Beach, Maine 03910

Cover illustration: courtesy of Manly P. Hall.
This illustration by J.A. Knapp appears on page
64 of *An Encyclopedic Outline of Masonic,
Hermetic, Qabbalistic and Rosicrucian Sym-
bolical Philosophy* published by the
Philosophical Research Society.

Library of Congress Catalogue
Card No.: 82-83818
ISBN 0-87728-558-6

Printed in the U.S.A. by
Maple-Vail, Binghamton, New York

INTRODUCTION

By

MANLY P. HALL

APPROACH YE GENUINE PHILOSOPHIC FEW,
THE PYTHAGORIC LIFE BELONGS TO YOU:
BUT FAR, FAR OFF YE VULGAR HERD PROFANE;
FOR WISDOM'S VOICE IS HEARD BY YOU IN VAIN:
AND YOU, MIND'S LOWEST LINK, AND DARKSOME END,
GOOD RULERS, CUSTOMS, LAWS, ALONE CAN MEND.

I

THOMAS TAYLOR, the author of this remarkable treatise on the philosophy of numbers, was the greatest Platonist of the modern world. He was a prodigy of erudition and industry. He translated into English the complete works of Plato and Aristotle, the *Commentaries of Proclus on the Theology of Plato*, the philosophical and mathematical *Commentaries of Proclus on Euclid*, and numerous smaller but scarcely less important fragments of classical learning. In addition to these translations Mr. Taylor composed several original works, of which his *Theoretic Arithmetic* is the most important. No other Greek scholar since Proclus, named the Platonic Successor, has so perfectly understood the Orphic theology. The superiority of Thomas Taylor's ability is best evidenced by the esteem in which his writings and translations are now held, the ever increasing demand for them, and the prices they bring whenever offered for sale. The most sought after of Thomas Taylor's works are his *Aristotle,* in ten volumes, and his *Theoretic Arithmetic.* Of this last work but few copies are known. We feel that the republication of this famous and valuable book will render available a quantity of rare and little known material on a profound and fascinating subject.

Thomas Taylor, "The Modern Plato," "The Apostle of Paganism," and "The Gentile Priest of England," was born in London on the 15th of May, 1758. As is so often the case with truly great men, his life was a constant struggle against physical and financial limitations. About his sixth year he developed symptoms of tuberculosis. During the most productive years of his life he suffered from a painful and incurable malady and did a great part of his voluminous and tedious writing after having lost the use of the forefinger of his right hand. In spite of his infirmities of health, which were greatly aggravated by overwork and malnutrition, he lived to the age of seventy-seven. Impecuniousness was termed by an ancient philosopher "the disease of the wise." For some time Thomas Taylor's income was seven shillings, less than two dollars, a week. He was a rapid worker for he translated the complete writings of Plato, with voluminous commentaries of the most abstruse nature, in less than two years. The manuscript when completed made five large folio volumes. He was miserably paid for his work. For example, for translating Sallust *On the Gods and the Worlds,* the *Pythagoric Sentences of Demophilus,* five *Hymns of Proclus,* two *Orations of the Emperor Julian,* and five books of Plotinus he received twenty pounds.

Thomas Taylor believed the Platonic philosophy as preserved in the writings of its genuine disciples to be the noblest revelation of divine truths ever imparted to man. He regarded Platonism as a workable philosophy of life, an illumined code of thought and action, which, if studied and lived, would bring man to a noble and enlightened state. Mr. Taylor was termed an impractical man because he chose to live in a world of high ideals and noble thoughts. His life was a rare example of absolute devotion to the words and thoughts of the classical philosophers whom he regarded as personifications of divinely enlightened learning. He wrote not for his own age but for other ages which were to come.

In his *Miscellanies* Mr. Taylor predicted that "the sublime theology which was first obscurely promulgated by Orpheus, Pythagoras and Plato, and was afterward perspicuously unfolded by other legitimate disciples, a theology which, however, though it may be involved in oblivion in *barbarous* and derided in *impious* ages, will again flourish for very extended periods, through all the infinite revolutions of time."

II

Unfortunately no complete system of numerical divination has descended to this age from the old Mystery Schools. The Pythagorean philosophers, after the martyrdom of their master, were scattered throughout the Mediterranean countries and left to posterity no complete account of their numerical tradition.

The third book of the *Theoretic Arithmetic* is devoted to philosophizing on the virtues of numbers, and contains practically all of the fragments of genuine Pythagorean onomancs which have survived the ruin of time. From these fragments it will be evident that to the Samian Initiate numbers were the elements of a sublime theological symbolism. Through the study of mathematics Pythagoras invited all men to a communion with the gods.

Pythagoras is known to have practiced divination and to have instructed his disciples in the rudiments of the oracular arts. Plutarch mentions that Pythagoras interpreted omens;

Porphyry that he practiced divination by frankincense and smoke; Cicero that he foretold events from the flight of birds; and Diogenes Laertius that he prophesied by cledonism, that is by the euphony of words and the accidental speeches of those around him. According to Iamblichus the miracles performed by Pythagoras exceeded ten thousand. From Apuleius comes comes the tradition that Pythagoras was well versed in judicial astrology which he had learned from the Chaldeans. Varro notes that Pythagoras practiced hydromancy, that is prediction from the agitation of water.

Numerology as it is practiced today derives its premise from a short statement of Iamblichus to the effect that Pythagoras perfected a system of divination by numbers, based upon the secret traditions which had descended from Orpheus. In the sixth and seventh centuries before Christ it was customary for the ancient Greeks to perform divinations from the entrails of especially sacrificed animals and birds. Pythagoras condemned this practice and substituted therefor *arithmomancy,* the oracular use of numbers, as more acceptable to the gods and not harmful to any living creature. It should not be inferred, however, from the words of Iamblichus, that Pythagoras actually invented numerology. The use of numbers for symbolical and divinatory purposes was common to nearly all ancient religious systems. Well developed systems of numerology are to be found in the older writings of the Chinese, Hindus, Egyptians, and Jews. Numerical cabbalism is usually found closely associated with astrology and magic.

Two serious obstacles confront modern students of numerology. In the first place there have been numerous changes in alphabets and languages since the devisement of the original systems, and in the second place the ancient method by which numerological values were bestowed upon letters and words is apparently irretrievably lost. Pitifully few fragments remain from which to restore the vast structure of numerical philosophy. Although he lived many centuries after the death of the master, Apollonius of Tyana claimed to be a genuine Pythagorean and practiced the austerities of the order. Apollonius claimed to possess the genuine Pythagorean numerical "globe" by the use of which an infinite diversity of problems regarding life, death, litigations, victories, defeats, etc. could be solved. The globe referred to by Apollonius seems to have been actually a circle made up of letters and numbers. It is variously termed a ring, sphere or wheel and is unquestionably the most ancient form of numerical divination which may be ascribed to the Greeks or Egyptians.

Charles Singer, in his recent publication *From Magic to Science,* describes a MS. written in the 9th century—probably the earliest medical text by an English hand—in which the Pythagorean sphere was used to discover whether a sick person would recover. Mr. Singer notes: "The sphere of Pythagoras is a recognized magical device. It is possibly of Egyptian origin, but it certainly spread to Europe through Greek intermediaries. It is translated from Greek and is known in that language from a third century papyrus (Leyden v.) and in Latin from a large number of early Mss. from the 8th century onward. During the Dark and Middle Ages this diagram is common in the English Mss., where it is variously attributed to Hippocrates, Democritus, Apuleius, Apollonius, Pythagoras, Culumcille, Bede, Petosiris, Nechepso, and Plato! Quite a number of specimens date from Anglo-Saxon times."

From this it is quite evident that the wheel of Pythagoras has probably the greatest claim to authenticity of any form of numerical divination ascribed to Pythagoras. While there is no definite proof as to its authenticity, there is, conversely, no definite proof that it is not authentic. In choosing an example of the Pythagorean wheel it has been deemed advisable to make use of the fine example published by Robert Fludd in 1619. Fludd thus describes the wheel: "On the composition of this wheel and the true positions of the numbers upon it, the older authors have written so variously that the correct composition cannot be surely known but only conjectured. I have inspected the spheres composed by these authors and following those that agree most closely, have drawn the accompanying figure in conformity with the original wording and design according to their own doctrine."

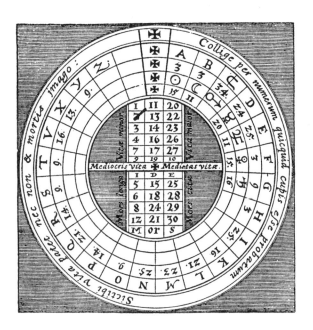

In addition to the wheel itself it is necessary to make use of a specially devised alphabet. In his *De Numero et Numeratione,* Robert Fludd sets forth what he claims to be the Pythagorean numerical correspondences to the letters of the alphabet, the seven planets, the days of the week, and the signs of the zodiac. Robert Fludd was a high Rosicrucian initiate and it is not impossible that he might have had access to records hidden from the general public. If this numerological table be authentic it is obviously a priceless key to the old doctrine.

A	3		M	23
B	3		N	15
C	12		O	8
D	14		P	13
E	22		Q	21
F	3		R	13
G	4		S	8
H	6		T	8
I (J)	20		V (U)	5
K	15		X	6
L	12		Y	3
		Z	4	

Sun	1		Sunday	24
Venus	2		Monday	26
Mercury	3		Tuesday	5
Moon	4		Wednesday	20 & 29
Saturn	5		Thursday	17
Jupiter	6		Friday	30 & 32
Mars	7		Saturday	24

Aries	1 & 2	Libra	17, 18 & 19
Taurus	3, 4 & 5	Scorpio	20 & 21
Gemini	6, 7, 8 & 9	Sagittarius	22 & 23
Cancer	10, 11, & 12	Capricorn	24, 25 & 26
Leo	13 & 14	Aquarius	27 & 28
Virgo	15 & 16	Pisces	29 & 30

The method of consulting the Wheel of Pythagoras is briefly as follows:

Find the numerical value of the Christian name of the person with whom the question is concerned. Then in the table of numerical correspondences find the number corresponding to the day of the week upon which the incident will take place. Also find from an almanac the number of days of the Moon's age upon the particular day under consideration. Add all these sums together and divide by 30. Search for the number remaining in the vertical panel in the center of the Wheel. If the number appears above the central line, the answer is affirmative; if below, negative.

III

In his second book of Occult Philosophy, the celebrated magician Sir Henry Cornelius Agrippa devotes a section to the numbers which are attributed to letters and the art of divining therefrom. According to Agrippa, who speaks the opinions of Aristotle and Ptolemy, the very elements of letters have certain divine numbers associated with them by which, from the proper names of things, it is possible to draw reasonable conjectures concerning the hidden things which are to come to pass. Agrippa's work contains several alphabets with their numerical equivalents, two of which are sufficiently different from those generally accepted to warrant consideration.

A	B	C	D	E	F	G	H	I	K	L	M	N	O
1	2	3	4	5	6	7	8	9	10	20	30	40	50

P	Q	R	S	T	V	X	Y	Z	J	U	HI	HU
60	70	80	90	100	200	300	400	500	600	700	800	900

A simple system of Greek numeration assigns numbers to the letters in the following order:

1	2	3	4	5	6	7	8	9	10	11	12	13	14	15
α	β	γ	δ	ε	ζ	η	θ	ι	κ	λ	μ	ν	ξ	ο

16	17	18	19	20	21	22	23	24
π	ρ	σ	τ	υ	φ	χ	ψ	ω

Agrippa also gives an English alphabet which follows the principle of the Hebrew numeration but, of course, does not follow the order of the letters. He also notes that in both the Greek and Hebrew systems letters were generally divided into three classes: first the units, second the tens, and third the hundreds. The units pertain to divine matters, the tens to celestial concerns, and the hundreds to such qualities as are terrestrial. In Agrippa also is to be found the rudiments of the modern numerical theory called the Fadic system which will be considered more in detail in the following section.

IV

John Heydon, who designated himself "the servant of God, and secretary of nature," in a little work called *The Harmony of the World,* written in 1662, set forth what he claimed to be the Rosicrucian key to numbers. An extensive work by the same author entitled *The Holy Guide* may be consulted by those who desire an elaborate exposition of this system. Heydon's opinions are of especial interest from an astrological standpoint for he gives a method of associating the degrees of the zodiac with numbers so that from the positions and configurations of the planets in the horoscope various names may be deduced. He assigns the primary aspects and positions of the planets to the vowels, thus:

> The conjunction to *a*; the sextile to *e*; the square to *i*; the trine to *o*; and the opposition to *u*.

He then describes a method of assigning the letters to the degrees of the zodiacal signs by attributing *a* to the 1st degree of Aries, *b* to the 2nd degree of Aries, etc. The sign of Taurus begins with *b* and continues through the alphabet, ending with *a*. The sign of Gemini begins with *c* and continues through the alphabet, ending with *b*. The 30 degrees of the zodiacal sign leaves the last 4 degrees of each sign without a letter assigned to them. According to Heydon the last 4 degrees are sacred to the cabbalistic names of God and are divine degrees, not used in terrestrial calculations. To some measure this agrees with astrological opinion that there is a peculiar strength and virtue in the last 4 degrees of signs. Planets in these degrees have exceptional power. According to Heydon, it is possible to calculate from these tables and degrees, the names of the angels and celestial spirits called the genii or daemons which are assigned to the soul at birth and are its guardians and to which prayers and supplications should be addressed by magical formulas.

V

Godfrey Higgins devoted over thirty years of his life to the preparation of his massive work *Anacalypsis* which he subtitled "An Enquiry into the Origin of Languages, Nations and Religions." Mr. Higgins makes frequent use of the numerical equivalents of words in order to trace derivations of terms, roots, origins and forgotten meanings. No one can fail to be impressed by the value of numbers in this recondite work. While *Anacalypsis* contains no material relating to divination by numbers and letters, it reminds the thoughtful investigator that the names and words used in ancient writings and pagan and Christian scriptures often have a secret significance. The Holy Bible was written in Hebrew and Greek, and both these languages were involved in an elaborate cabbalism. Nearly all proper names in both the Old and New Testament have hidden meanings which can be unlocked by numerology, often clearing up confusion and contradiction and correcting obvious misunderstandings in the literal text.

Godfrey Higgins makes use of what may be termed the standard table of numerical equivalents for both the Greek and Hebrew alphabets. There is abundant evidence that these tables were employed for cabbalistic purposes during the periods

1	2	3	4	5	6	7	8
Aleph	א	א	1	A α	*	Alpha	A
Beth	ב	ב	2	B β	*	Beta	B
Gimel	ג	ג	3	Γ γ	*	Gamma	G
Daleth	ד	ד	4	Δ δ	*	Delta	D
He	ה	ה	5	E ε	*	Epsilon	E
Vau	ו	ו	6	F	*	Digamma	Fv
Zain	ז	ז	7	Z ζ		Zeta	
Heth	ח	ח	8	H η		Eta	
Teth	ט	ט	9	Θ ϑ θ		Theta	
Jod	י	י	10	I ι	*	Iota	I
Caph	כ	כ	20	K κ	*	Kappa	C
Lamed	ל	ל	30	Λ λ	*	Lambda	L
Mem	מ	מ	40	M μ	*	Mu	M
Nun	נ	נ	50	N ν	*	Nu	N
Samech	ס	ס	60	Ξ ξ		Xi	
Oin	ע	ע	70	O o	*	Omicron	O
Pe	פ	פ	80	Π π	*	Pi	P
Tzadi	צ	צ	90	Ϛ		Episemon bau ἐπίσημον ϐαυ	
Koph	ק	ק	100				
			100	P ρ	*	Rho	R
Resh	ר	ר	200				
			200	Σ σ	*	Sigma	S
Shin	ש	ש	300				
			300	T τ	*	Tau	T
Tau	ת	ת	400				
			400	Υ υ	*	Upsilon	U
			500	Φ φ		Phi	
			600	X χ		Chi	
			700	Ψ ψ		Psi	
			800	Ω ω		Omega	
			900	ϡ		Sanpi	

of Scriptural compilations. For research purposes in philosophical numerology, Mr. Higgin's table is by far the best and most practical. But it will be observed that the English equivalents to the Greek and Hebrew letters are very incomplete. In order to decode English words from these tables it is first necessary to reduce them to their Greek or Hebrew equivalents. All students of classical Greek literature and the Christian Scriptural writings will find this table of the utmost value. It fits in directly with Thomas Taylor's line of research, but unfortunately, it does not contribute a great deal to arithmomancy. Its purpose is the analysis of the divine meaning of words and not prediction from names.

VI

Modern systems of numerology, though claiming for themselves an ancient and exalted origin, are really without much background beyond the field of speculation. Some success is recorded by modern numerologists but it is always an open question as to how great a part intuition plays in the results achieved. An intuitive person with a poor system may accomplish apparent miracles, while another person, lacking intuition but equipped with a precise method, may accomplish little.

The simplest and most common system of modern numerology is that which distributes the numbers among the letters as follows:

1	2	3	4	5	6	7	8	9
a	b	c	d	e	f	g	h	i
j	k	l	m	n	o	p	q	r
s	t	u	v	w	x	y	z	

In addition to this there is another system called the Fadic which has also been successfully operated. In this method the numbers are arbitrarily distributed among the letters according to the following order:

A	= 1	I or J	= 1	S	= 3
B	= 2	K	= 2	T	= 4
C	= 3	L	= 3	U	= 6
D	= 4	M	= 4	V	= 6
E	= 5	N	= 5	W	= 6
F	= 8	O	= 7	X	= 5
G	= 3	P	= 8	Y	= 1
H	= 5	Q	= 1	Z	= 7
		R	= 2		

The Fadic system also assigns numbers to the planets and the days of the week, thus:

Sunday	1—4	Sun	1
Monday	2—7	Moon	2
		Jupiter	3
Tuesday	9	Uranus	4
Wednesday	5	Mercury	5
Thursday	3	Venus	6
		Neptune	7
Friday	6	Saturn	8
Saturday	8	Mars	9

It appears that this system is built up, at least in part, from the writings of Agrippa whose opinions in magical matters have colored metaphysics since 1533.

It is hardly necessary here to interpret the meanings or readings for the numbers, as Book Three of Thomas Taylor's treatise is devoted almost exclusively to this subject and represents the most authentic compilation possible. Mr. Taylor not only examined all of the published writings of the Greek authors but had access to the earliest original Mss. in the British Museum. His treatment is thorough, comprehensive, and, although a century has elapsed since its first publication, practically nothing now can be added, for scholarship has waned in the last hundred years. Men's minds today are little given to exploring the mysteries of classical philosophy.

THEORETIC ARITHMETIC

IN THREE BOOKS;

CONTAINING

THE SUBSTANCE
OF ALL THAT HAS BEEN
WRITTEN ON THIS SUBJECT BY
THEO OF SMYRNA, NICOMACHUS, IAM-
BLICHUS, AND BOETIUS.—TOGETHER WITH
SOME REMARKABLE PARTICULARS RESPECT-
ING PERFECT, AMICABLE, AND OTHER NUMBERS,
WHICH ARE NOT TO BE FOUND IN THE WRITINGS
OF ANY ANCIENT OR MODERN MATHEMATICIANS.
LIKEWISE, A SPECIMEN OF THE MANNER IN
WHICH THE PYTHAGOREANS PHILOSOPHI-
ZED ABOUT NUMBERS; AND A DEVEL-
OPEMENT OF THEIR MYSTI-
CAL AND THEOLOGI-
CAL ARITHMETIC.

BY THOMAS TAYLOR.

"It will be proper then Glanco, to establish by law this discipline (arithmetic), and to persuade those who are to manage the *greatest affairs* of the city to apply to computation and study it, *not in a common way*, but till by intelligence itself they arrive at the survey of the nature of numbers, *not for the sake of buying nor of selling, as merchants and shopkeepers,* but both for war, *and for facility in the energies of the soul itself, and its conversion from generation (or the whole of a visible nature) to truth and essence, (or real being)."* Plato, Repub. Bk. vii.

LONDON:

PRINTED FOR THE AUTHOR,

NO. 9, MANOR PLACE, WALWORTH,

BY A. J. VALPY, TOOKE'S COURT, CHANCERY LANE.

1816

INTRODUCTION

IF philosophy, properly so called be, according to Plato, and as I am firmly persuaded it is, *the greatest good that was ever imparted by divinity to man,*** he who labours to rescue it from oblivion, and transmit it to posterity, must necessarily be endeavouring to benefit his country and all mankind, in the most eminent degree. To accomplish this grand object, has been the aim of the greater part of my life; and the present work was solely written with a view to promote its accomplishment.

In consequence of the oblivion indeed, into which genuine Philosophy has fallen, through the abolition of her schools,

---

* The Pythagoreans were so deeply convinced of the truth of this assertion, that one of them beautifully observes: των κατα φιλοσοφιαν θεωρηματων απολαυστεον εφ' οσον οιον, καθαπερ αμβροσιας και νεκταρος. ακηρατον τε γαρ το απ' αυτων ηδυ και θειον· το μεγαλοψυχον δυναται τε ποιειν, και ει μη αιδιους αιδιων τε επιστημονας. Iamblic. Protrept. p. 4. i. e. "The theorems of philosophy are to be enjoyed as much as possible, as if they were ambrosia and nectar. For the pleasure from them is genuine, incorruptible and divine. They are also capable of producing magnanimity, and though they cannot make us eternal beings, yet they enable us to obtain a scientific knowledge of eternal natures."

III

the mathematical disciplines have been rather studied with a view to the wants and conveniences of the merely animal life, than to the good of intellect in which our very being and felicity consist. Hence, the Pythagoric enigma "a figure and a step, but not a figure and three oboli," has been entirely perverted. For the whole attention of those who have applied to the mathematics, has been directed to the oboli, and not to the steps of ascent; and thus as their views have been groveling, they have crept where they should have soared. Hence, too, the greatest eye of the soul has been blinded and buried, "though, as Plato elegantly observes, it is purified and resuscitated by the proper study of these sciences, and is better worth saving than ten thousand corporeal eyes, since truth becomes visible through this alone."

This observation particularly applies to Theoretic Arithmetic, the study of which has been almost totally neglected: for it has been superseded by practical arithmetic, which though eminently subservient to vulgar utility, and indispensably necessary in the shop and the counting house, yet is by no means calculated to purify, invigorate, and enlighten the mind, to elevate it from a sensible to an intellectual life, and thus promote the most real and exalted good of man. Indeed, even with respect to geometry itself, though the theory of it is *partially* learnt from the Elements of Euclid, yet it is with no other view than that of acquiring a knowledge of the other parts of mathematics which are dependant on it, such as astronomy, optics, mechanics, etc. or of becoming good guagers, masons, surveyors, and the like, without having even a dreaming perception of its first and most essential use, that of enabling its votary, like a bridge, to pass over the obscurity of a material nature, as over some dark sea to the luminous regions of perfect reality; or as Plato elegantly expresses it, "conducting them as from some benighted day, to the true ascent to incorporeal being, which is genuine philosophy itself."* I have said, that the theory of geometry is only *partially* studied; for the 10th book of Euclid, which is on incommensurable quantities, and the 13th, 14th, and 15th, which are on the five regular bodies, though they are replete with the most interesting information, in the truest sense of the word, yet they are for the most part sordidly neglected, in this country at least, because they neither promote the increase of a commerce which is already so extended, nor contribute anything to the further gratification of sensual appetite, or the unbounded accumulation of wealth.

If the mathematical sciences, and particularly arithmetic and geometry, had been studied in this partial and ignoble manner by the sagacious Greeks, they would never have produced a Euclid, an Apollonius, or an Archimedes,† men who carried geometry to the acme of *scientific* perfection, and whose

---

* τουτο δη ως εοικεν, ουκ οστρακου αν ειη περιστρφη, αλλα ψυχης περιαγωγη, εκ νυκτερινης τινος ημερας εις αληθινην του οντος επανοδον, ην δη φιλοσοφιαν αληθη φησομεν ειναι. Platonis De Repub. lib. 7.

† Plutarch, in his life of Marcellus, informs us, that the reason why Archimedes did not vouchsafe to leave any account of the admirable machines which he invented, in writing, was because "he considered the being busied about mechanics, and in short every art which is connected with the common purposes of life, as ignoble and illiberal; and that those things alone were objects of his ambition, with which the beautiful and the excellent were present, unmingled with the necessary." αλλα την περι τα μηχανικα πραγματειαν, και πασαν ολως τεχνην χρειας εφαπτομενην, αγεννη και βαναυσον ηγησαμενος, εκεινα καταθεσθαι μονα την αυτου φιλοτιμιαν, οις το καλον και περιττον αμιγες του αναγκαιου προσεστιν. The great accuracy and elegance in the demonstrations of Euclid and Archimedes, which have not been equalled by any of the greatest modern mathematicians, were derived from a deep conviction of this important truth. On the other hand, modern mathematicians, through a profound ignorance of it, and looking to nothing but the wants and conveniences of the animal life of man, as if the gratification of his senses was his only end, have corrupted pure geometry, by mingling with it algebraical calculations, and through eagerness to reduce it as much as possible to practical purposes, have more anxiously sought after conciseness than accuracy, facility than elegance of geometrical demonstration.

works, like the remains of Grecian art, are the models by which the unhallowed genius of modern times has been formed, to whatever mathematical excellence it may possess. Newton himself, as may be conjectured from what he says of Euclid, was convinced of this when it was too late, and commenced his mathematical career with the partial study only of these geometrical heroes. "For he spoke with regret, says Dr. Hutton,* of his mistake at the beginning of his mathematical studies, in applying himself to the works of Des Cartes, and other algebraic writers,† before he had considered the Elements of Euclid with that attention, which so excellent a writer deserves."

Having premised thus much, I shall in the next place present the reader with some observations on the essence of mathematical genera and species, on the utility of the mathematical science, and on the origin of its name, derived from

* See the article Newton in Hutton's Mathematical Dictionary.

† Dr. Halley also, who certainly as a mathematician ranks amongst the greatest of the moderns, appears to have had the same opinion of the transcendency of the Grecian genius in the mathematical sciences. For in the preface to his translation of Apollonius de Sectione Rationis, (for which work he conceived so great an esteem, that he was at the pains to learn Arabic, in order to accomplish its translation into Latin) he says: "Methodus hæc cum algebra speciosa facilitate contendit, evidentia vero et demonstrationum elegantia eam longe superare videtur: ut abunde constabit, si quis conferat hanc Apollonii doctrinam de Sectione Rationis cum ejusdem Problematis Analysi Algebraica, quam exhibuit clarissimus Wallisius, tom. 2. Operum Math. cap. 54. p. 220." i.e. "This method contends with specious algebra in facility, but seems far to excel it in evidence and elegance of demonstrations; as will be abundantly manifest, if this doctrine of Apollonius De Sectione Rationis, is compared with the algebraic analysis of the same problem which the most celebrated Wallis exhibits in the second volume of his mathematical works, chap. 54. p. 220." And in the conclusion of his preface, he observes, "Verum perpendendum est, aliud esse problema aliqualiter resolutum dare, quod modis variis plerumque fieri potest, aliud methodo elegantissima ipsum efficere: analysi brevissima et simul perspicua; synthesi concinna, et minima operosa. i.e. "It is one thing to give the solution of a problem some how or other, which for the most part may be accomplished in various ways, but another to effect this by the most elegant method; by an analysis the shortest, and at the same time perspicuous; by a synthesis elegant, and in the smallest degree laborious."

the admirable commentaries of Proclus on Euclid, as they will considerably elucidate many parts of the following work, and may lead the well-disposed mind to a legitimate study of the mathematical disciplines, and from thence to all the sublimities of the philosophy of Plato.

With respect to the first thing proposed, therefore, if it should be said that mathematical forms derive their subsistence from sensibles, which is the doctrine of the present day, the soul fashioning in herself by a secondary generation, the circular or trigonic form from material circles or triangles, whence is the accuracy and certainty of definitions derived? For it must necessarily either be from sensibles or from the soul. It is, however, impossible it should be from sensibles; for these being in a continual flux of generation and decay, do not for a moment retain an exact sameness of being, and consequently fall far short of the accuracy contained in the definitions themselves. It must therefore proceed from the soul which gives perfection to things imperfect, and accuracy to things inaccurate. For where among sensibles shall we find the impartible, or that which is without breadth or depth? Where the equality of lines from a center, where the perpetually stable ratios of sides, and where the exact rectitude of angles? Since all divisible natures are mingled with each other, and nothing in these is genuine, nothing free from its contrary, whether they are separated from each other, or united together. How then can we give this stable essence to immutable natures, from things that are mutable, and which subsist differently at different times? For whatever derives its subsistence from mutable essences, must necessarily have a mutable nature. How also from things which are not accurate, can we obtain the accuracy which pertains to irreprehensible forms? For whatever is the cause of a knowledge which is perpetually mutable, is itself much more mutable than its effect. It must be admitted, therefore, that the soul is the generator of mathematical forms, and the source of the productive principles with which the mathematical sciences are replete.

If, however, she contains these as paradigms, she gives them subsistence essentially, and the generations are nothing else than the projections of the forms which have a prior existence in herself. And thus we shall speak conformably to the doctrine of Plato, and discover the true essence of mathematical objects. But if the soul, though she neither possesses nor causally contains these productive principles, yet weaves together so great an immaterial order of things, and generates such an admirable theory, how will she be able to judge whether her productions are stable, or things which the winds may dissipate, and images rather than realities? What standard can she apply as the measure of their truth? And how, since she does not possess the essence of them, can she generate such a variety of principles productive of truth? For from such an hypothesis we shall make their subsistence fortuitous, and not referred to any scientific bound.

In the second place, therefore, if by a downward process, and from sensibles we collect mathematical principles, must we not necessarily say, that those demonstrations are more excellent, which derive their composition from sensibles, and not those which are always framed from more universal, and more simple forms. For we say, in order to the investigation of the thing sought, that the causes should be appropriate and allied to the demonstrations. If, therefore, partial natures are the causes of universals, and sensibles of the objects of the reasoning power, why does the boundary of demonstration always refer to that which is more universal, instead of that which is partial? And how can we evince that the essence of the objects of the reasoning power is more allied to demonstrations

than the essence of sensibles? For, as Aristotle* says, his
knowledge is not legitimate, who demonstrates that the isosceles, the equilateral, or the scalene triangle, have angles equal
to two right, but he who demonstrates this of every triangle,
and simply, has essentially a sceintific knowledge of this pro-
position. And again, he says, that universals, for the purpose
of demonstration are superior to particulars; that demonstrations concern things more universal; and that the principles
of which demonstrations consist, have a priority of existence,
and a precedency in nature to particulars, and are the causes of
the things which are demonstrated. It is very remote, therefore, from demonstrative sciences, that from converse with
things of posterior origin† (υστερογενη κοινα) and from the
more obscure objects of sensible perception, they should collect their indubitable propositions.

In the third place, the authors of this hypothesis, make the
soul to be more ignoble than the material forms themselves.
For if matter indeed, receives from nature things which are
essential, and which have a greater degree of entity and evidence, but the soul by a posterior energy abstracts the resem-
blances and images of these from sensibles, and fashions in
herself forms which have a more ignoble essence, by taking
from matter things which are naturally inseparable from it, do
they not evince the soul to be more inefficacious than, and sub-
ordinate to matter itself? For matter is the place of material
productive principles, and the soul of immaterial forms. On
this hypthesis, however, matter would be the recipient of primary; but the soul of secondary forms. The one would be
the seat of things which have a precedency among beings; but

* In his Posterior Analytics.

† These υστερογενη κοινα in modern language are called *abstract ideas.*
Hence the doctrine of Mr. Locke on this subject was well known to Proclus; but
the hypothesis that the soul has no other ideas than these, was justly exploded
by him, and the best of the Platonists.

the other of such as are fashioned from these. And the former of things which have an essential subsistence; but the latter,of such as exist only in conception. How, therefore, can the soul which is a participant of intellect, and the first intellectual essence, and which is from thence filled with knowledge and life, be the receptacle of the most obscure forms, the lowest in the order of things, and participating the most imperfect existence.*

* In addition to the above excellent arguments from Proclus, I shall present the liberal reader with what Syrianus the preceptor of Proclus says on the same subject, in his commentary on the 13th book of Aristotle's Metaphysics, and which is as follows: "We neither behold all the figures, nor all the numbers contained in sensibles, nor is it possible for things derived from sensibles, to possess mathematical accuracy and certainty. But if it should be said, that we add what is wanting, and make the things abstracted from sensibles more certain, and after this manner consider them; in the first place, indeed, it is requisite to say whence we derive the power of thus giving them perfection. For we shall not find any cause more true than that assigned by the ancients; I mean that the soul prior to the energies of sense, essentially contains the reasons of all things. But in the next place, by adding something to the things abstracted from sensibles, we do not make them more certain and true, but, on the contrary more fictitious. For, if any one blames the person of Socrates, while he accurately preserves in his imagination the image which he has received from the sensible Socrates, he will have an accurate knowledge of his person; but if he wishes to transform it into a more elegant figure, he will rather consider the transformed figure than the form of Socrates. Nothing, however, of this kind takes place in equal and similar numbers and figures; but by how much the nearer we bring them to the more certain and perfect, they become by so much the more manifest and known, in consequence of approaching so much the nearer to their own impartible form. We may say indeed that we are excited to the perception of mathematical truths by sensible objects; but it must by no means be admitted that they derive their subsistence by an abstraction from sensibles. For the forms indeed, which are transmitted to us through the senses may proceed as far as to the imagination, in which they wish to retain an individual subsistence, and to continue such as they entered. When intellect, however, afterwards passes beyond these to universal, and to things which are apprehended by scientific reasoning, it plainly evinces that it considers objects allied to itself, and which indeed are its legitimate progeny. Hence, this energy is emulous of divine energy, and not laborious, and has a power of exciting, purifying, and enlightening the rational eye of the soul. But how could this be effected, if it were employed about things, which alone subsist by a denudation from sensibles?

In short, one of these two things must follow; either that mathematical demonstrations are less certain than physiological arguments; or that the mathematical sciences are conversant with things which possess more reality than the objects of physics. For it is not reasonable to suppose that things which have more of reality

By no means, therefore, is the soul a smooth tablet, void of productive principles, but she is an ever-written tablet, herself inscribing the characters in herself, of which she derives an eternal plenitude from intellect. For soul also is an intellect evolving itself conformably to a prior intellect, of which it is the image, and external type. If therefore intellect is all things intellectually, soul will be all things psychically; (or in a manner adapted to soul) if the former is all things paradigmatically, the latter will be all things iconically or conformably to an image; and if the former, contractedly, the latter, with expansion and divisibly. This, Plato also perceiving, constitutes the soul of the world, (in the Timaeus) from all things, divides it according to numbers, binds it by analogies and harmonic ratios, inserts in it the primary principles of figures, the right and circular line, and intellectually moves the circles which it contains. Hence all mathematical forms have a primary subsistence in the soul; so that prior to sensible she contains self-motive numbers, vital figures prior to such as are apparent, harmonic ratios prior to things harmonized, and invisible circles prior to the bodies that are moved in a circle. Soul also is a plenitude of all things, and another order, herself producing herself, and at the same time produced from her proper principle, filling herself with life, and being filled by her fabricator, incorporeally and without interval. When therefore she produces her latent principles, she unfolds into light all sciences and virtues.

Hence, the soul is essentialized in these forms, and neither

should be more obscurely known, nor that things which are less real should be more manifestly known. But whenever this happens in the speculation of any intelligible essence, it is the consequence of our imbecility, and does not arise from the thing itself. For the assertion of Plato in this respect is most true, that every thing participates of splendor and knowledge, in proportion as it participates of truth and being. The same thing also is manifestly asserted by Aristotle in the second book of his Metaphysics; for he there expressly says, *"as is the being of every thing, such also is its truth."*

must her inherent number be supposed to be a multitude of monads or units, nor must her idea of natures that are distended with interval, be conceived to subsist corporeally; but all the paradigms of apparent numbers and figures, ratios and motions, must be admitted to exist in her, vitally and intellectually, conformably to the Timaeus of Plato, who gives completion to all the generation and fabrication of the soul, from mathematical forms, and in her establishes the causes of all things. For the seven boundaries* of all numbers, pre-exist in soul according to cause. And again, the principles of figures, are established in her in a fabricative manner. The first of motions also, and which comprehends and moves all the rest, are consubsistent with soul. For the circle, and a circular motion, are the principle of every thing which is moved. The mathematical productive principles therefore, which give completion to the soul, are essential, and self-motive; and the reasoning power exerting and evolving these, gives subsistence to all the variety of the mathematical sciences. Nor will she ever cease perpetually generating and discovering one science after another, in consequnce of expanding the impartible forms which she contains. For she antecedently received all things causally; and she will call forth into energy all-various theorems, according to her own infinite power, from the principles which she previously received.†

* Viz. 1. 2. 4. 8. 3. 9. 27, concerning which see the Introduction to the Timæus, in the 2nd Vol. of my translation of Plato.

† The sagacious Kepler has not only inserted the above extract from the Commentaries of Proclus, in his treatise On the Harmonic World, but also gives it the following encomium: "At quod attinet quantitates continuas, omnino adsentior Proclo; etsi oratio fluit ipsi torrentis instar, ripas inundans, et cæca dubitationum vada gurgitesque occultans, dum mens plena majestatis tantarum rerum, luctatur in angustiis linguæ, et conclusio nunquam sibi ipsi verborum copia satisfaciens, propositionum simplicitatem excedit." i.e. "With respect to what pertains to continued quantities, I entirely assent to Proclus, though his language flows like a torrent inundating its banks, and hiding the dark fords and whirlpools of doubt, while his mind, full of the majesty of things of such a magnitude, struggles in

With respect to the utility of the mathematical science which extends from the most primary knowledge, to that which subsists in the lowest degree, it must be observed that Timaeus in Plato calls the knowledge of the mathematical disciplines the path of erudition, because it has the same ratio to the science of wholes, and the first philosophy, or meta-physics, which erudition has to virtue. For the latter disposes the soul for a perfect life by the possession of unperverted manners; but the former prepares the reasoning power and the eye of the soul to an elevation from the obscurity of objects of sense. Hence Socrates in the Republic rightly says "that the eye of the soul which is blinded and buried by other studies, is alone naturally adapted to be resuscitated and excited by the mathematical disciplines. And again, "that it is led by these to the vision of true being, and from images to realities, and is transferred from obscurity to intellectual light, and in short is extended from the caverns [of a sensible life] and the bonds of matter, to an incorporeal and impartible essence." For the beauty and order of the mathematical reasonings, and the sta-bility of the theory in these sciences, conjoin us with and per-fectly establish us in intelligibles, which perpetually remain the same, are always resplendent with divine beauty, and pre-serve an immutable order with reference to each other.

But in the Phaedrus, Socrates delivers to us three characters who are led back from a sensible to an intellectual life, viz. the philosopher, the lover, and the musician. And to the lover indeed, the beginning and path of elevation, is a progression from apparent beauty, employing as so many steps of ascent, the middle forms of beautiful objects. But to the musician who is alloted the third order, the transition is from the har-mony in sensibles, to unapparent harmony, and the productive

the straits of language, and the conclusion never satisfying him, exceeds by the copia of words the simplicity of the propositions."

principles existing in these. And to the one sight, but to the
other hearing is the organ of recollection. To him, therefore,
who is naturally a philosopher, whence, and by what means is
the recollection of intellectual knowledge, and the excitation
to real being and truth? For this character also, on account of
its imperfection, requires a proper principle; since physical
virtue is alloted an imperfect eye, and imperfect manners. He
therefore, who is naturally a philosopher, is excited indeed
from himself, and surveys with astonishment real being.
Hence, says Plotinus, he must be disciplined in the mathematical sciences, in order that he may be accustomed to an incorporeal nature, and led to the contemplation of the principles of
all things. From these things, therefore, it is evident that the
mathematics are of the greatest utility to philosophy.

It is necessary, however, to be more explicit, and to enumerate the several particulars to which they contribute, and evince
that they prepare us for the intellectual apprehensions of theology. For whatever to imperfect natures appears difficult and
arduous in the truth, pertaining to divinity, these the mathematical sciences render through images credible, manifest, and
irreprehensible. For in numbers they exhibit the representa-
tions of superessential peculiarities, and unfold in the proper
objects of the reasoning part of our nature, the powers of intellectual figures. Hence Plato teaches us many admirable
theological dogmas, through mathematical froms; and the
philosophy of the Pythagoreans, employing these as veils, con-
ceals through them the mystic tradition of divine dogmas. For
such is the whole of the *Sacred Discourse,** what is said by
Philolaus in his Bacchics, and the whole method of the Pytha-

* Concerning this valuable work entitled ιερος λογος see the Bibliotheca Gr.
of Fabricius, vol. I. p. 118 and 462. In the commentary also of Syrianus on
Aristotle's Metaphysics, p. 7, 71, 83, and 108, the reader will find some curious
extracts from this celebrated work; particularly in p. 83, Syrianus informs us,
"that he who consults this work, will find all the orders both of monads and numbers, without neglecting one, fully celebrated."

goric narration concerning the Gods. These sciences likewise,
contribute in the greatest degree to the physical theory, unfolding the arrangement of those principles, according to which
the universe was fabricated; the analogy which binds together
every thing in the world, as Timaeus says, makes hostile
natures friendly, and things distant familiar, and sympathiz-
ing with each other, and causes simple and primary elements,
and in short, all things to be held together by symmetry and
equality; through which the whole universe likewise is perfected, receiving in its parts appropriate figures. The mathematical science also discovers numbers adapted to all generated natures, and to their periods and restitutions to their pristine state, through which we may collect the fecundity and
barrenness of each. For Timaeus in Plato, every where indi-
cating these particulars, unfolds through mathematical names
the theory about the nature of wholes, adorns the generation
of the elements with numbers and figures, refers to these, their
powers, passive qualities and effects, and assigns as the cause
of all-various mutation, the acuteness and obtuseness of angles,
the smoothness or roughness of sides, and the multitude or
paucity of the elements.

Must we not also say that it contributes much and in an admirable manner, to the philosophy which is called political, by
measuring the times of actions, the various periods of the universe, and the numbers adapted to generations, viz. the assimilating and the causes of dissimilitude, the prolific and the perfect, and the contraries to these, those which are the suppliers
of an harmonious, and those which impart a disorderly and in-
elegant life, and in short those which are the sources of fertility and sterility? For these the speech of the Muses in the Republic of Plato unfolds, asserting that the whole *geometric
number** is the cause of better and worse generations, of the

* See the 2nd book of this work, in which this whole geometric number is
unfolded.

indissoluble permanency of unperverted manners, and of the
mutation of the best polities, into such as are irrational and
full of perturbation. Again, the mathematical science perfects
us in ethical philosophy, inserting in our manners, order, and
an elegant life, and delivering those figures, melodies, and
motions, which are adapted to virtue, and by which the Athenian guest in Plato wishes those to be perfected who are design-
ed to possess ethical virtue from their youth. It likewise places
before our view the principles of the virtues, in one way indeed in numbers, but in another in figures, and in another in
musical symphonies, and exhibits the excesses and deficiencies
of the vices, through which we are enabled to moderate and
adorn our manners. On this account also Socrates, in the
Gorgias, accusing Callicles of an inordinate and intemperate
life, says to him, "You neglect geometry, and geometric equality." But in the Republic, he discovers the interval between
tyrannic and kingly pleasure, according to a plane and solid
generation.*

* The passage alluded to by Proclus is in the 9th book of the Republic, and is
as follows: "What then, said I, shall we boldly say concerning all the pleasures,
both respecting the avaricious and the ambitious part of the soul, that such of them
as are obedient to science and reason, and, in conjunction with these, pursue and
obtain the pleasures of which the prudent part is the leader, shall obtain the
truest pleasures, as far as it is possible for them to attain true pleasure, and in
as much as they follow truth, pleasures which are properly their own; *if indeed
what is best for every one, be most properly his own?* But surely, it is most
properly, said he, his own. When then the whole soul is obedient to the philosophic part, and there is no sedition in it, then every part in other respects per-
forms its proper business, and is just, and also reaps its own pleasures, and such
as are the best, and as far as is possible, the most true. Certainly, indeed. But
when any of the others govern, it happens that it neither attains its own pleasures,
and it compels the other parts to pursue a pleasure foreign to them, and not at all
true. It does so, said he. Do not then the parts which are most remote from
philosophy and reason, most especially effectuate such things? Very much so.
And is not that which is most remote from law and order, likewise most remote
from reason? It plainly is. And have not the amorous, and the tyrannical desires
appeared to be most remote from law and order? Extremely so. And the royal
and the moderate ones, the least remote? Yes. The tyrant, then, I think, shall
be the most remote from true pleasure, and such as is most properly his own, and

Moreover, we shall learn what great utility other sciences and arts derive from the mathematics, if we consider, as Socrates says in the Philebus, that all arts require arithmetic, mensuration, and statics; all which are comprehended in the mathematical science, and are bounded by the principles which it contains. For the distributions of numbers, the variety of measures, and the difference of weights, are known by this science. To the intelligent reader, therefore, the utility of the whole of

the other shall be the least. Of necessity. And the tyrant, said I, shall lead a life the most unpleasant, and the king the most pleasant. Of great necessity. Do you know then, said I, how much more unpleasant a life the tyrant leads than the king? If you tell me, said he. As there are three pleasures, as it appears, one genuine, and two illegitimate; the tyrant in carrying the illegitimate to extremity, and flying from law and reason, dwells with slavish pleasures as his life-guards, and how far he is inferior is not easily to be told, unless it may be done in this manner. How? said he. The tyrant is somehow the third remote from the oligarchic character, for the democratic was in the middle between them. Yes. Does he not then dwell with the third image of pleasure, distant from him with reference to truth, if our former reasonings be true? Just so. But the oligarchic is the third again from the royal, if we suppose the aristocratic and the royal the same. He is the third. The tyrant then, said I, is remote from true pleasure, the third from the third. It appears so. A plain surface then, said I, may be the image of tyrannical pleasure, as to the computation of length. Certainly. But as to power, and the third augment, it is manifest by how great a distance it is remote. It is manifest, said he, to the computer at least. If now, conversely, any one shall say, the king is distant from the tyrant as to truth of pleasure, as much as is the distance of 9, and 20, and 700, shall he not, on completing the multiplication, find him leading the more pleasant life, and the tyrant the more wretched one, by this same distance."
 The following numbers are employed by Plato in this passage. He considers the royal character as analogous to unity, the oligarchic to the number 3, and the tyrannic to the number 9. As 3 therefore is triple of unity, the oligarchic is the third from the royal character; and in a similar manner the tyrant is distant from the oligarchist by the triple in number. For 9 is the triple of 3, just as 3 is the triple of 1. But 9 is a plane number, the length of which is 3, and also its breadth. And a tyrannic, says Plato, is the last image of a royal life. He also calls 3 a *power*, because unity being multiplied by it, and itself by itself, and 9 by it, there will be produced 3, 9, 27. But he calls the third augment 27, arising from the multiplication of the power 3, and producing depth or a solid number. Lastly, 27 multiplied into itself, produces 729, which may be considered as a perfect multiplication, this number being the 6th power of 3; and 6 is a perfect number. Hence, as the king is analogous to 1, he is said, by Plato, to be 729 times distant from the tyrant.

mathematics to philosophy, and other sciences and arts, will, from all that has been said, be apparent.

Some, however, endeavour to subvert the dignity of the mathematical science, by depriving it of beauty and good, because it does not make these the subjects of discussion, and others by endeavouring to evince that sensible experiments are more useful than the universal objects of its speculation, as for instance, geodesia than geometry, vulgar arithmetic than that which consists in theorems, and nautical astronomy than that which demonstrates universally. For, say they, we are not made rich by our knowledge of riches, but by the use of them; nor do we become happy by a knowledge of felicity, but by living happily. Hence we must confess that not speculative but practical mathematics contribute to human life and actions. For those who are ignorant of the reasons of things, but are experienced in particulars, excel in every respect, in what is useful to human life, those who are engaged in theory alone.

Against objections then, of this kind, we shall reply by showing the beauty of the mathematical disciplines from those arguments by which Aristotle endeavours to persuade us. For these three things are in a remarkable degree effective of beauty, in bodies and in souls, viz. order, symmetry, and the definite. Since corporeal deformity indeed, arises from material irregularity, privation of form, and the dominion of the indefinite in the composite body. But the baseness of the soul originates from its irrational part being moved in a confused and disorderly manner, and from its being discordant with reason, and not receiving from thence its proper limitation. Hence beauty has its essence in the contraries to these, viz. in order, symmetry, and that which is definite. These, however, we may survey in the most eminent degree in the mathematical science; order indeed, in the perpetual exhibition of things posterior and more various, from such as are first and more simple. For things subsequent are always suspended from those that precede them; the former having the relation of a principle, but the latter, of things consequent to the first hypotheses. But we may perceive symmetry, in the concord of the things demonstrated with each other, and the reference of all of them to intellect. For intellect is the measure of all science, from which it receives its principles, and to which it converts the learners. And the definite is seen in the perpetually stable and immutable objects of its theory. For the subjects of its knowledge, do not subsist differently at different times, like the objects of opinion and sense, but they present themselves to the view invariably the same, and are bounded by intellectual forms. If therefore these particulars are in an eminent degree effective of beauty, but the mathematical sciences are characterized by these, it is manifest that in these the beautiful subsists. Indeed, how is it possible this should not be the case with a science which is supernally illuminated by intellect, to which it tends, and to which it hastens to transfer us from the obscure information of sense?

But we ought to judge of its utility, not looking to the conveniences and necessities of human life. For thus also we must acknowledge that contemplative virtue itself is useless; since this separates itself from human concerns, to which it does not tend, nor is in short desirous of making these the objects of its knowledge. For Socrates in the Theætetus, speaking of the coryphæan philosophers, or those that philosophize in the most eminent degree, says, that through intellectual energy they are separated from all habitude to human life, and from an attention to its necessities and wants, and that they extend the reasoning power of the soul without impediment to the contemplation of real beings. The mathematical science, therefore, must be considered as desirable for its own sake, and for the contemplation it affords, and not on account of the utility it administers to human concerns. If, however, it be requisite to refer its utility to something else, it must be referred to intellectual knowledge. For it leads us to this, and prepares the eye of the soul for the knowledge of incorporeal wholes, purifying it, and removing the impediments arising from sensible objects. As therefore, we do not say that the whole of cathartic or purifying virtue is useful, or the contrary, looking to the utility of the sensible life, but regarding the advantage of the contemplative life; thus also it is fit to refer the end of the mathematical science to intellect, and the whole of wisdom. Hence, the energy about it, deserves our most serious attention, both on its own account, and on account of an intellectual life.

It is also manifest, as Aristotle says, that this science is desirable of itself to its votaries, because, though no reward was proposed to its investigators, yet, in a short time, the mathematical theory has received such an abundant increase. Besides, all men who have in the smallest degree experienced its utility, are willingly employed in its pursuit, and are desirous of being at leisure for this purpose, omitting every other concern. Hence, those who despise the knowledge of the mathematics, have not tasted of the pleasures they contain. The mathematical science, therefore, is not to be despised, because its theoretic part does not contribute to human utility; for its ultimate progressions, and such as energize in conjunction with matter, consider as their end an advantage of this kind; but on the contrary we should admire its immateriality, and the good which it contains in itself alone. For in short, when men were entirely disengaged from the care of necessary concerns, they converted themselves to the investigation of the mathematical disciplines; and this indeed, with the greatest propriety. For things by which we are nourished, and which are connascent with sensible objects, first employed the attention of mankind; but afterwards, those concerns which liberate the soul from a life of sense, and procure its recollection of real being. After this manner, therefore, we are engaged in the pursuit of necessaries prior to that of things honourable on their own account, and of things connascent with sense, prior to such as are apprehended by intellectual energy. For the life of the human soul, is naturally adapted to proceed from the imperfect to perfection. And thus much in answer to those who despise the mathematical science.

Again, with respect to the name mathematics, it appears to me, says Proclus, that such an appellation of the science which is conversant with the objects of the reasoning power, was not like many names invented by casual persons, but, as it is also said to have been, by the Pythagoreans. For they perceived that the whole of what is called mathesis, is reminiscence,* not externally inserted in souls, in the same manner as phantasms from sensible objects are impressed in the imagination, nor adventitious like the knowledge resulting from opinion, but excited indeed from things apparent, and inwardly exerted from the reasoning power converted to itself. They likewise saw that though reminiscence might be shown from many particulars, yet it was evinced in a more eminent manner, as Plato also says,† from the mathematical disciplines. For if any one, says he, is led to the diagrams, he will from them easily prove that discipline is reminiscence. Hence also, Socrates in the Meno shows from this mode of arguing, that to *learn* is nothing else than for the soul to *recollect* the productive principles which she contains. But this is, because that which recollects, is the discursive energy of reason, which is essentialized in the principles of the mathematics, and which causally comprehends the mathematical sciences in itself, though it

---

* i.e. The recovery of lost knowledge, on the hypothesis that the soul is truly immortal, and therefore had an existence prior to that of the present life.

† In the Meno.

may not energize according to them. It contains, therefore, all of them essentially and occultly: but it unfolds each of them into light, when it is freed from the impediments originating from sense. For the senses connect the soul with divisible objects, imaginations fill her with figured motions, and appetites draw her down to a passive life. But every thing divisible is an impediment to our conversion to ourselves, every thing figured, obscures that knowledge which is unaccompanied with figure, and every thing passive, is an obstacle to impassive energy. When therefore, we have removed all these from the discursive power of reason, then we shall be able to know by it, the productive principles which it contains, then we shall become scientific in energy, and exert our essential knowledge. But while we are bound, and have the eye of the soul closed, we shall never obtain the perfection adapted to our nature. Mathesis, therefore, is the reminiscence of the eternal productive principles inherent in the soul; and the mathematical science is on this account the knowledge which contributes to our recollection of these principles. Hence the employment of this science is evident from its name. For it is motive of knowledge, excites intelligence, purifies the discursive energy of reason, unfolds the forms which we essentially contain, removes the oblivion and ignorance, which we derive from the regions of sense, and dissolves the bonds through which we are held in captivity by the irrational nature.

The subserviency also of mathematics to philosophy, is elegantly illustrated by Theo of Smyrna, who compares the tradition of it, to initiation into the mysteries, and shows that these disciplines correspond to the purification previously necessary to this initiation. But what he says* on this subject, is as follows: "Again, it may be said that philosophy is the initiation into, and tradition of real and true mysteries. But of

* In Mathemat. p. 18.

initiation there are five parts. That which has the precedency indeed, and is the first, is purification. For the mysteries are not imparted to all that are willing to be initiated, but some persons are excluded by the voice of the cryer; such as those whose hands are not pure, and whose speech is inarticulate. It is also necessary that those who are not excluded from initiation, should first undergo a certain purification. But the second thing after purification, is the tradition of the mystery. The third thing is denominated (εποπτεια or) inspection.†
And the fourth which is the end of inspection, is binding the head, and placing on it crowns; so that he who is initiated, is now able to deliver to others, the mysteries which he has received, whether it be the mystery of a torch-bearer, or of the interpretation of the sacred ceremonies, or of some other priesthood. But the fifth thing which results from these is the felicity arising from being dear to divinity, and the associate of the Gods. Conformably to these things likewise, is the tradition of political doctrines. And in the first place, a certain purification is requisite, such as that of the exercise from youth in appropriate disciplines. For Empedocles says, "it is necessary to be purified from defilement by drawing from five fountains in a vessel of unmingled brass." But Plato says that purification is to be derived from five disciplines; and these are, arithmetic, geometry, stereometry, music, and astronomy. The

---

† The word τελετη or *initiation*, say Hermeas, in his MS. Commentary on the Phædrus of Plato, "was so denominated from rendering the soul perfect. The soul, therefore, was once perfect. But here it is divided, and is not able to energize wholly by itself." He adds: "But it is necessary to know that *telete, muesis*, and *epopteia*, τελετη, μυησις, and εποπτεια, differ from each other. *Telete*, therefore, is analogous to that which is preparatory to purifications. But *muesis* which is so called from closing the eyes, is more divine. For to close the eyes in initiation is no longer to receive by sense those divine mysteries, but with the pure soul itself. And *epopteia*, is to be established in, and become a spectator of the mysteries." See more on this very interesting subject, in the second edition of my *Dissertation on the Eleusinian and Bacchic Mysteries*, in Nos. XV. and XVI. of THE PAMPHLETEER.

tradition, however, of philosophical, logical, political, and physical theorems, is similar to initiation. But Plato denominates the occupation about intelligibles, true beings, and ideas, *epopteia* or inspection. And the ability from what has been learnt of leading others to the same theory, must be considered as analogous to binding the head, and being crowned. But the fifth and most perfect thing, is the felicity produced from these, and according to Plato, an assimilation as much as possible to God."

Such then is the utility arising from the proper study of the mathematical sciences, among which theoretic arithmetic, as is shown in the first chapter of this work, is preeminent, and the leader of the rest. I trust, therefore, that the liberal part of my readers, and whose views are consequently neither directed to the gratification of appetite, nor an immoderate accumulation of wealth, will gratefully accept the present work, as another disinterested effort of a man who has laboured beyond any other in modern times to benefit his countrymen, by the dissemination of the most exalted knowledge; though he has received nothing in return from the literary censors of the age, but gross misrepresentation and virulent abuse, whatever the hatred of envy could administer to the purposes of detraction, or the cunning of malignant sophistry could pervert. But as he has elsewhere observed, he consoles himself amidst all the defamation which he has received, or may yet experience, with the consciousness of the integrity of his intention, and with the firm hope that at all times what he has written for the benefit of others will meet with the approbation of the wise and good. For he perfectly accords with Seneca, "that if a man wishes to be happy, he should first consider that he must *despise* and be *despised*."*—In particular he trusts this work will be the means of benefiting two young gentlemen of this country,

---

* Si vis beatus esse, cogita hoc primum *contemnere* et *contemni*.

WILLIAM DAY and WILLIAM GEORGE MEREDITH,
the relatives of his much esteemed and honoured friends,
WILLIAM and GEORGE MEREDITH, Esqs. the first of
these youths being the nephew of both, and the second, the
son of the latter of his friends. From the fair hopes which
their great proficiency in learning have hitherto raised in all
that know them, there is every reason to expect that they will
eventually be no less an ornament to their country than an
honour to the family to which they belong. And he requests
they will permit him thus to dedicate this work to them, both
as a testimony of gratitude to their above mentioned relations,
and an indication of his great personal regard for them, and
his sanguine expectations of their future renown.

With respect to the work itself, in the first and second
books, and the additional notes, I have incorporated whatever
appeared to me to be most important in the arithmetical writings of Nicomachus, Theo, Jamblichus, and Boetius,* these
being the only ancient authors extant in print, that have professedly written on THEORETIC ARITHMETIC. Indeed, I have
nearly given the whole of the last mentioned author, both
because he has written more clearly on this subject than the
others, and because, as Fabricius rightly conjectures, he appears to have availed himself of a greater arithmetical work of

* With respect to these celebrated men, the exact period in which Theo and
Nicomachus lived, is uncertain. And all the information that can at present be
obtained concerning them is, that Theo flourished, as the learned Bullialdus judi-
ciously conjectures, between the age of Tiberius Cæsar, and the times of Antoninus
Pius. He wrote An Exposition of such things in the Mathematics as are useful
to the reading of Plato; and that part of this work which relates to Arithmetic
and Music, is all that is published at present, though what he wrote on Astronomy
is extant in some libraries in manuscript, as we learn from the accurate Fabricius.
But Nicomachus who was a Pythagorean philosopher of Gerasa, a city bordering
on Bostra in Arabia, was, according to Fabricius, somewhat posterior to the age of
Antoninus Pius, as he mentions Ptolemy the astronomer who lived under the reign
of that Emperor. This great man was eminently skilled in the mathematical disciplines, and particularly in theoretic arithmetic, so that his extraordinary attain-

Nicomachus, which has not been transmitted to the present time. The third book was added by me, in order to show how the Pythagoreans philosophized about numbers, and to unfold as much as possible their mystical and theological arithmetic; conceiving that such an addition was wanting to the completion of the theory of numbers. The reader will also find some things entirely new. And if it should any where happen that I have ascribed to my own invention what has been discovered by others, I trust the reader will attribute it to my having been much more conversant with ancient than with modern writers on this, as well as on other subjects, and not from any intention of defrauding others of their equitable claims.

In the last place, I am desirous of adding, for the sake of the liberal reader, the following extract from the Introduction to my translation of Aristotle's Metaphysics. It relates to the contemplative, or intellectual energy, the employment of the highest part of our nature.

Aristotle denominates the metaphysical science, at one time *wisdom,* at another time *the first philosophy,* and at another *theology;* signifying by each of these appellations, that it does not rank among those arts and sciences which are conversant

ments in this science became proverbial. Hence, the author of the dialogue among the works of Lucian which is inscribed Philopatris, p. 468, says, χαι γαρ αριθμεεις ως Νιχομαχος ο Γερασηνος, "You numerate like Nicomachus of Gerasa." And Iamblichus in the Commentary on his Arithmetic, p. 3, says, "I find that Nicomachus has delivered every thing pertaining to this science of arithmetic, conformably to the doctrine of Pythagoras. For this man was great in the mathematics, and had for his preceptors men in the highest degree skilled in these disciplines. And independent of these things, he has delivered an admirable order and theory, accompanied with an accurate demonstration of scientific principles." For an account of Jamblichus, who was one of the most eminent of the genuine disciples of Plato, and who in the opinion of the Emperor Julian was indeed posterior in time to Plato, but not in genius, I refer the reader to the History of the Restoration of the Platonic Theology at the end of my Proclus on Euclid. And as to Boetius his life and works are too well known to need any discussion of them at present.

with the knowledge of things necessary, or which inquire into things subservient to the advantages and conveniences of the mortal life, but it is a knowledge and science to be pursued for its own sake, and which speculates the first principles and causes of things; for these are beings in the most eminent degree. Hence, in the sixth book of his Nicomachean Ethics, he defines wisdom to be the most accurate of sciences, the science of things most honourable, that is, principles, and the summit of all disciplines. With the multitude, indeed, merged in sense, whatever does not contribute to the good of the merely animal life, is considered as a thing of no value; and hence, by the better part of them it is regarded with indifference, and by the greater number with contempt. It is vain to talk to such as these of a good purely intellectual, which is independent of chance and fortune, which is desirable for its own sake, and which confers the most pure and permanent felicity on its possessor; for, what passion can it gratify? What sense can it charm? Ignorant of the mighty difference between things necessary and such as are eminently good, they mistake means for ends, pursue the flying mockeries of being, for such are all sensible natures, and idly attempt to grasp the phantoms of felicity.

The conceptions of the experimental philosopher who expects to find Truth in the labyrinths of matter, are, in this respect, not much more elevated than those of the vulgar: for he is ignorant that Truth is the most splendid of all things, that she is the constant companion of Divinity, and proceeds together with him through the universe; that the shining traces of her feet are only conspicuous in *form;* and that in the dark windings of *matter* she left nothing but a most obscure and fleeting resemblance of herself. This delusive phantom, however, the man of modern science ardently explores, unconscious that he is running in profound darkness and infinite perplexity, and that he is hastening after an object which eludes all detection, and mocks all pursuit.

It is well said indeed by Aristotle, that wisdom is the science of principles and causes, since he who knows these, knows also the effects of which they are the source. Such a one knows particulars so far as they are comprehended in universals, and this knowledge is superior to that which is partial, and co-ordinated to a partial object: for, does not every thing energise in a becoming manner, when it energises according to its own power and nature? As, for instance, does not nature, in conformity to the order of its essence, energise naturally, and intellect intellectually? For, this being admitted, it follows that knowledge subsists according to the nature of that which knows, and not according to the nature of that which is known. Particulars, therefore, when they are beheld enveloped in their causes, are then known in the most excellent manner; and this is the peculiarity of intellectual perception, and resembles, if it be lawful so to speak, the knowledge of Divinity himself. For, the most exalted conception we can form of his knowledge is this, that he knows all things in such a manner as is accommodated to his nature, viz. divisible things indivisibly, things multiplied uniformly, things generated according to an eternal intelligence, and totally whatever is partial. Hence, he knows sensibles without possessing sense, and, without being present to things in place, knows them prior to all local presence, and imparts to every thing that which every thing is capable of receiving. The unstable essence, therefore, of apparent natures is not known by him in an unstable, but in a definite manner; nor does he know that which is subject to all-various mutations dubiously, but in a manner perpetually the same; for, by knowing himself, he knows every thing of which he is the cause, possessing a knowledge transcendantly more accurate than that which is coordinate to the objects of knowledge. Hence, in order to know sensible natures, he is not indigent of sense, or opinion, or science; for it is himself that produces all these, and that, in the unfathomable depths of the intellection of himself, comprehends an united knowledge of them, according to cause, and in one simplicity of perception.

Wisdom, therefore, considered as a causal knowledge of particulars resembles the knowledge of Divinity, and consequently is most honorable and most excellent. And hence, the wise man, from resembling, must be the friend of Divinity. Beautifully, therefore, is it observed by Aristotle, "That the man who energises according to intellect, and is mentally disposed in the best manner, is also it would seem most dear to divinity. For if any attention is paid by the Gods to human affairs, as it appears there is, it is also reasonable to suppose that they will be delighted with that which is most excellent, and most allied to themselves; but this is intellect; and likewise that they will remunerate those who especially love and honour this, as taking care of that which is dear to themselves, and acting rightly and well.*

The contemplative or intellectual energy indeed, when it is possessed in the highest perfection of which our nature is capable, raises its possessor above the condition of humanity. "For a life according to intellect," says the Stagirite, "is more excellent than that which falls to the lot of man; for he does not thus live, so far as he is man, but so far as he contains something divine. And as much as this divine part of him differs from the composite, so much also does this energy differ from that of the other virtues. If, therefore, intellect compared with man is divine, the life also which is according to intellect will be divine with respect to human life. It is, how-

* See my translation of the Nicomachean Ethics, Book 10, p. 598.

ever, requisite that we should not follow the exhortations of those who say that man should be wise in human, and a mortal in mortal concerns, but we should endeavour as much as possible to immortalize ourselves, and to do every thing which may contribute to a life according to our most excellent part. For this, though it is small in bulk, yet far transcends all the other parts in power and dignity." After this, he shows that intellect is the true man, from its being that which is most powerful, principal, and excellent in our nature; "so that," says he, "it would be absurd not to choose that which is our proper life, but that which belongs to something different from ourselves."

Ridiculus, therefore, as well as grovelling are those conceptions which lead men to value knowledge so far only as it contributes to the necessities, the comforts, and the refinements of the merely human life; and partial and unscientific is that definition of virtue, which makes its highest energies to be those of morality: for moral virtue is more human, but intellectual more divine. The former is preparatory to felicity; but the latter, when perfect, is accompanied with perfect beatitude. Virtuous, therefore, is the man who relieves the corporeal wants of others, who wipes away the tear of sorrow, and gives agony repose; but more virtuous he, who, by disseminating wisdom, expels ignorance from the soul, and thus benefits the immortal part of man. For it may indeed be truly said, that he who has not even a knowledge of common things is a brute among men; that he who has an accurate knowledge of human concerns alone, is a man among brutes; but, that he who knows all that can be known by intellectual energy, is a God among men. *

* Agreeably to this, Aristotle observes in his Politics, "that if there is some one, or more than one, who greatly surpasses in virtue, though not sufficiently numerous to make the complement of a city, so that the virute of all the rest, or their

Wisely, therefore, does Plato assert that the philosopher ought not to descend below species, and that he should be solely employed in the contemplation of *wholes* and *universals*. For he who descends below these, descends into Cimmerian realms, and Hades itself, wanders among spectres devoid of mind, and exposes himself to the danger of beholding the real Gorgon, or the dire face of Matter, and of thus becoming petrified by a satiety of stupid passions.

The life of the man who, possessing true wisdom, energises according to the theoretic virtue, is admirably described by Plato in his Theætetus as follows:

"*Socrates.* Let us speak, since it is agreeable to you, about the coryphæi. For why should any one speak of those who are conversant with philosophy in a depraved manner? In the first place, then, the coryphæi from their youth neither know the way to the forum, nor where the court of justice or senate-house is situated, or any other common place of assembly belonging to the city. They neither hear nor see the laws or decrees, whether promulgated or written. And, as to the ardent endeavours of their companions to obtain magistracies, the associations of these, their banquets and wanton feastings accompanied with pipers,—these they do not even dream of accomplishing. But whether any thing in the city has happened well or ill, or what evil has befallen any one from his progenitors, whether male or female, of these they are more ignorant than, as it is said, of how many measures called choes the sea contains. And besides this, such a one is even ignorant

political power, should be too inferior to be compared with theirs, if there are more than one; or if but one, with his only; these are no longer to be considered as a part of the city. For it would be doing them injustice to place them on a level with those, who are so inferior to them in virtue and political power; *since it is fit to consider such a one as a God amongst men.* Hence law is not for such persons as these; for they are themselves a law. And it would be ridiculous in any one to endeavour to subject them to the laws."

that he is ignorant* of all these particulars: for he does not abstain from them for the sake of renown, but, in reality, his body only dwells and is conversant in the city; but his dianoetic part (or scientifically-reasoning power) considering all these as trifling and of no value, he is borne away, according to Pindar, on all sides, geometrizing about things beneath and upon the earth, astronomizing above the heavens,† and perfectly investigating all the nature of the beings which every whole contains, but by no means applying himself to anything which is near.

"*Theodorus.* How is this, Socrates?

"*Socrates.* Just, O Theodorus, as a certain elegant and graceful Thracian maid-servant is reported to have said to Thales, when while astronomizing he fell into a well, that he was very desirous of knowing what the heavens contained, but that he was ignorant of what was before him, and close to his feet. In the same manner all such as are conversant in philosophy may be derided. For, in reality, a character of this kind is not only ignorant of what his neighbour does, but he scarcely knows whether he is a man, or some other animal. *But what man is, and what a nature of this kind ought principally to do or suffer, this he makes the object of his inquiry, and earnestly investigates.*‡ Do you understand, Theodorus, or not?

"*Theodorus.* I do: and you are certainly right.

---

* The multitude are ignorant that they are ignorant with respect to objects of all others the most splendid and real; but the coryphæan philosopher is ignorant that he is ignorant with respect to objects most unsubstantial and obscure. The former ignorance is the consequence of a defect, but the latter of a transcendency of gnostic energy.

† i.e. Contemplating those divine forms in the intellect of the artificer of the universe, which are the paradigms of all that the heavens contain.

‡ When intellectual men, therefore, are compared with such as are solely busied in the investigation of sensible particulars, who are alone delighted with objects of

"Socrates. For, in reality, my friend, when a man of this kind is compelled to speak (as I said before) either privately with any one, or publicly in a court of justice, or any where else, about things before his feet, and in his view, he excites laughter, not only in Thracian maid servants, but in the other vulgar, since through his unskilfulness he falls into wells, and every kind of ambiguity. Dire deformity too, causes him to be considered as a rustic: for, when he is in the company of slanderers, he has nothing to say reproachful, as he knows no evil of any one, *because he has not made individuals the objects of his attention.* Hence, not having any thing to say, he appears to be ridiculous. But, when he is in company with those that praise and boast of others, as he is not only silent, but openly laughs, he is considered as delirious: for, when he hears encomiums given to a tyrant or a king, he thinks he hears some swine-herd, or shepherd, or herdsman proclaimed happy, because he milks abundantly; at the same time he thinks that they feed and milk the animal under their command, in a more morose and insidious manner; and that it is necessary that a character of this kind should be no less rustic and undisciplined through his occupation than shepherds, the one being inclosed in walls, and the other by a sheep-cot on a mountain. But when he hears any one proclaiming that he possesses ten thousand acres of land, or a still greater number, as if he possessed things wonderful in multitude, it appears to him that he hears of a very trifling thing, in consequence of being accustomed to survey the whole earth. As often, too, as any one celebrates the nobility of his family, evincing that he has seven wealthy grandfathers, he thinks that this is en-

---

sense, and who do not even dream that these objects rather resemble the delusions of sleep than the realities of vigilant perception, we may exclaim in Homeric language,

> The race of these superior far to those,
> As he that thunders to the stream that flows.

tirely the praise of a dull mind, and which looks to a thing of
a trifling nature; through want of discipline being incapable
of always surveying the universe, and of inferring by a reasoning process, that every man has had innumerable myriads of
grandfathers and progenitors, among which there has often
been an innumerable multitude of rich and poor, kings and
slaves, Barbarians and Grecians. But when any one, celebra-
ting his progenitors, enumerates five-and-twenty of them, and
refers their origin to Hercules, the son of Amphitryon, it appears to him a thing unworthy to be mentioned. For, as it is
entirely owing to fortune that any one is able to enumerate
five-and-twenty progenitors from Hercules, he would laugh,
even if any one could enumerate fifty from the same origin;
considering such as unable to reason, and liberate themselves
from the arrogance of an insane soul. But, in every thing of
this kind, the coryphæus we are describing will be ridiculed
by the vulgar, partly because he will be considered by them
as arrogant, and partly because he is ignorant of, and dubious
about, things before his feet.

"*Theodorus.* You speak, Socrates, of things which certainly take place.

"*Socrates.* But when any one, my friend, draws him on
high, and is willing that he should abandon the consideration
of whether I injure you, or you me, for the speculation of justice and injustice, what each of them is, and in what they differ from all other things, or from each other; or that, dismiss-
ing the inquiry whether a king is happy who possesses abundance of gold, he should ascend to the contemplation of a
kingdom, and universally of human felicity and misery, of
what kind they are to any one, and after what manner it is
proper for human nature to acquire this thing and fly from
that;—about all these particulars when that little sharp soul,
so conversant with law, is required to give a reason, then he in

his turn is affected worse than the coryphæus; for he becomes giddy, through being suspended from a lofty place of survey, and being unaccustomed to look so high. He is also terrified, is filled with uncertainty, and speaks in a barbaric manner; so that he does not indeed excite laughter in the Thracian vulgar, nor in any other undisciplined person (for they do not perceive his condition,) but in all those whose education has been contrary to that of slaves. And such, Theodorus, is the condition of each; the one, whom we call a philosopher, being in reality nourished in truth and leisure; and who, though he ought not to be blamed, yet appears to be stupid and of no value, when he engages in servile offices; since he neither knows how to bind together bundles of coverlids, nor to make sauce for banquets, nor compose flattering speeches. But the other of these characters is able to accomplish all these servile offices with celerity and ease, but knows not how to clothe himself in a liberal manner, nor how in harmonious language properly to celebrate the true life of the Gods and blessed men."

THEORETIC ARITHMETIC

BOOK ONE

CHAPTER I.

On the priority of Arithmetic to the other mathematical disciplines.

ARITHMETIC is to be learned the first of the mathematical sciences, because it has the relation of a principle and mother to all the rest. For it is prior to all of them, not only because the fabricator of the universe employed this as the first paradigm of his distributed intellection, and constituted all things according to number; but the priority of arithmetic is also evinced by this, whenever that which is prior by nature is subverted, that which is posterior is at the same time subverted; but when that which is posterior perishes, that which is prior suffers no essential mutation of its former condition. Thus if you take away animal, the nature of man is immediately destroyed; but by taking away man, animal will not perish. And on the contrary, those things are always posterior which together with themselves introduce something else; but those have a priority of subsistence, which when they are enunciated, cointroduce with themselves nothing of a posterior nature. Thus if you speak of man, you will at the same time introduce animal; for man is an animal. But if you speak of

1

animal, you will not at the same time introduce the species man; for animal is not the same as man. The same thing is seen to take place in geometry and arithmetic. For if you take away numbers, whence will triangle or quadrangle, or whatever else is the subject of geometry subsist? All which are denominative of numbers. But if you take away triangle and quadrangle, and the whole of geometry is subverted, three and four, and the appellations of other numbers will not parish. Again, when we speak of any geometrical figure, it is at the same time connected with some numerical appellation; but when we speak of numbers, we do not at the same time introduce geometrical figure.

The priority likewise of numbers to music may from hence be especially demonstrated, that not only those things which subsist by themselves are naturally prior to those which are referred to something else; but musical modulation itself is stamped with numerical appellations. And the same thing may take place in this, which has been already noticed in geometry. For diatessaron, diapente, and diapason, are denominated by the antecedent names of numbers. The proportion likewise of sounds to each other is found in numbers alone. For the sound which subsists in the symphony diapason, is in a duple ratio. The modulation diatessaron consists in the ratio of 4 to 3. And that which is called the symphony diapente is conjoined by the ratio of 3 to 2. That which in numbers is sesquioctave, is a tone in music. And in short, the priority of arithmetic to music will be indubitably demonstrated in the course of this work. But since geometry and music are prior to astronomy, it follows that astronomy is in a still greater degree posterior to arithmetic. For in this science, the circle, the sphere, the center, parallel circles and the axis are considered, all which pertain to the geometric discipline. Hence also, the senior power of geometry may from this be shown, that all motion is after rest, and that permanency is always naturally prior to mobility. But astronomy is the doctrine of moveable, and geometry of immoveable natures. The motion of the stars likewise is celebrated as being accompanied with harmonic modulations. Whence also it appears that the power of music precedes in antiquity the course of the stars. And it cannot be doubted that arithmetic naturally surpasses astronomy, since it appears to be more ancient than geometry and music which are prior to it. For by numbers we collect the rising and setting of the stars, the swiftness and slowness of the planets, and the eclipses and manifold variations of the moon.

CHAPTER II.

On the definition of number and the monad.

THALES* defined number conformably to the doctrine of the Egyptians by whom he was instructed, to be a collection of monads. But Pythagoras defined it to be the extension and energy of the spermatic reasons contained in the monad. Or otherwise, to be that which prior to all things subsists in a divine intellect, by which and from which all things are co-ordinated, and remain connumerated in an indissoluble order. Others, however, of his followers defined it to be a progression from unity through the magnitude of it. But Eudoxus the Pythagorean says, that number is definite multitude, in which definition he distinguishes the species from the genus. The followers of Hippasus who were called *Acousmatici* said that number is the first paradigm of the fabrication of the world;

* Vid. Iamblich. in Nicomach. Arithmet. p. 11.

and again, that it is the judicial instrument of the god who is
the demiurgus of the universe. But Philolaus says that number is the most excellent and self-begotten bond of the eternal
duration of mundane natures.

But the monad is in discrete quantity that which is the least,
or it is the first and common part of discrete quantity, or the
principle of it. According to Thymaridas indeed it is bounding quantity; since the beginning and end of every thing is
called a bound. In certain things however, as in the circle and
the sphere, the middle is called the bound. But those who are
more modern, define the monad to be that according to
which every thing that exists is called one.* To this definition however, the words, "however collected it may be," are
wanting. The followers of Chrysippus assert confusedly, that
the monad is one multitude: for the monad alone is opposed
to multitude. But certain of the Pythagoreans said that the
monad is the confine of number and parts; for from it as
from a seed and an eternal root, ratios are contrarily increased
and diminished; some through a division to infinity being
always diminished by a greater number; but others being increased to infinity, are again augmented. Some likewise have
defined the monad to be the form of forms, as comprehending
in capacity or power, (i. e. causally) all the reasons which are
in number. But it is considered after this manner, in consequence of wholly remaining in the reason of itself; as is likewise the case with such other things as subsist through the
monad.

The monad† therefore is the principle and element of numbers, which while multitude is diminished by subtraction, is
itself deprived of every number, and remains stable and firm;

---

* This is Euclid's definition of the monad, in the 7th book of his Elements.

† Vid. Theon. Smyrn. Mathemat. p. 23.

since it is not possible for division to proceed beyond the monad. For if we divide *the one* which is in sensibles into parts, again *the one* becomes multitude and many; and by a subtraction of each of the parts we end in one. And if we again divide this one into parts, the parts will become multitude; and by an ablation of each of the parts, we shall at length arrive at unity. So that *the one* so far as one is impartible and indivisible. For another number indeed when divided is diminished, and is divided into parts less than itself. Thus for instance, 6 may be divided into 3 and 3, or into 4 and 2, or into 5 and 1. But *the one* in sensibles, if it is divided indeed, as body it is diminished, and by section is divided into parts less than itself, but as number it is increased; for instead of *the one* it becomes many. So that according to this *the one* is impartible. For nothing (in sensibles) which is divided, is divided into parts greater than itself; but that which is divided into parts greater than the whole, and into parts equal to the whole, is divided as number. Thus if *the one* which is in sensibles, be divided into six equal parts, as number indeed, it will be divided into parts equal to the whole, viz. into 1. 1. 1. 1. 1. 1. and also into parts greater than the whole, viz. into 4 and 2; for 4 and 2 as numbers are more than one. Hence the monad as number is indivisible. But it is called the monad, either from remaining immutable, and not departing from its own nature; for as often as the monad is multiplied into itself, it remains the monad; since once one is one; and if we multiply the monad to infinity, it still continues to be the monad. Or it is called the monad, because it is separated, and remains by itself alone apart from the remaining multitude of numbers.*

* Archytas and Philolaus, as we are informed by Theo, called indiscriminately *the one*, the monad, and the monad, *the one*. But according to the best of the Platonists, Proclus, Damascius, & in divine natures *the monad* is that which contains *distinct*, but at the same time *profoundly-united* multitude; and *the one* is the summit of *the many*, so that *the one* is more simple than the monad. Observe

Since therefore number is the connective bond of all things, it is necessary that it should abide in its proper essence, with a perpetually invariable sameness of subsistence; and that it should be compounded, but not of things of a different nature. For what could conjoin the essence of number, since its paradigm joined all things. But it seems to be a composite from itself. Moreover, nothing appears to be composed from similars; nor yet from things which are conjoined by no analogy, and which are essentially separated from each other. Hence it is evident, since number is conjoined, that it is neither conjoined from similars, nor from things which mutually adhere by no analogy. Hence the primary natures of which number consists, are the even and the odd, which by a certain divine power, though they are dissimilar and contrary, yet flow from one source, and unite in one composition and modulation.

CHAPTER III.

On the division of numbers, and the various definitions of the even and the odd.

THE first division of number therefore is into the even and the odd. And the even number indeed is that which may be divided into two equal parts, without the intervention of unity in the middle. But the odd number is that which cannot be divided into equal parts, without unity intervening in the mid-

---

too, that in the sensible universe, the first monad is the world itself, which comprehends in itself all the multitude of which it is the cause (in conjunction with the cause of all). The second monad is the inerratic sphere. In the third place, the spheres of the planets succeed, each of which is also a monad, comprehending an appropriate multitude. And in the fourth and last place are the spheres of the elements, which are in a similar manner monads. All these monads likewise, are denominated ολοτητις, *wholenesses*, and have perpetual subsistence.

dle. And these indeed are the common and known definitions of the even and the odd. But the definition of them according to the Pythagoric discipline is as follows: The even number is that which under the same division may be divided into the greatest and the least; the greatest in space, and the least in quantity, according to the contrary passions of these two genera. But the odd number is that to which this cannot happen, but the natural division of it is into two unequal parts. Thus for instance, if any given even number is divided, there is not any section greater than half, so far as pertains to the space of division, but so far as pertains to quantity, there is no division less than that which is into two parts. Thus, if the even number 8, is divided into 4 and 4, there will be no other division, which will produce greater parts, viz. in which both the parts will be greater. But also there will be no other division which will divide the whole number into a less quantity; for no division is less than a section into two parts. For when a whole is separated by a triple division, the sum of the space is diminished, but the number of the division is increased. As discrete quantity however, beginning from one term, receives an infinite increase of progression, but continued quantity may be diminished infinitely, the contrary to this takes place in the division of the even number; for here the division is greater in space, but least in quantity. In other words, the portions of continued quantity are greatest, but the discrete quantity is the least possible.

According to a more ancient mode likewise, there is another definition of the even number, which is as follows: The even number is that which may be divided into two equal, and into two unequal parts; yet so that in neither division, either parity will be mingled with imparity, or imparity with parity; except the binary number alone, the principle of parity, which does not receive an unequal section, because it consists of two unities. Thus for instance, an even number as 10 may be divided into 5 and 5 which are two equals; and it may also be divided into unequal parts, as into 3 and 7. It is however, with this condition, that when one part of the division is even, the other also is found to be even; and if one part is odd, the other part will be odd also, as is evident in the same number 10. For when it is divided into 5 and 5, or into 3 and 7, both the parts in each division are odd.* But if it, or any other even number, is divided into equal parts, as 8 into 4 and 4, and also into unequal parts, as the same 8 into 5 and 3, in the former division both the parts are even, and in the latter both are odd. Nor can it ever be possible, that when one part of the division is even, the other will be found to be odd; or that when one part is odd, the other will be even. But the odd number is that which in every division is always divided into unequal parts, so as always to exhibit both species of number. Nor is the one species ever without the other; but one belongs to parity, and the other to imparity. Thus if 7 is divided into 3 and 4, or into 5 and 2, the one portion is even, and the other odd. And the same thing is found to take place in all odd numbers. Nor in the division of the odd number can these two species, which naturally constitute the power and essence of number, be without each other. It may also be said, that the odd number is that which by unity differs from the even, either by increase, or diminution. And also that the even number is that which by unity differs from the odd, either by increase or diminution. For if unity is taken away or added to the even number, it becomes odd; or if the same thing is done to the odd number, it immediately becomes even.

Some of the ancients also said that the monad is the first of odd numbers. For the even is contrary to the odd; but the

---

* But if it is divided into 6 and 4, each of the parts of the division is even.

monad is either even or odd. It cannot however be even; for it cannot be divided into equal parts, nor in short does it admit of any division. The monad therefore is odd. If also the even is added to the even, the whole becomes even; but if the monad is added to an even number, it makes the whole to be odd. And hence the monad is not even, but odd. Aristotle however, in his treatise called Pythagoric says, that the one or unity participates of both these natures; for being added to the odd it makes the even, and to the even the odd; which it would not be able to effect if it did not participate of both these natures. And hence the one is called evenly-odd. Archytas likewise is of the same opinion. The monad therefore is the first idea of the odd number, just as the Pythagoreans adapt the odd number to that which is definite and orderly in the world. But the indefinite duad is the first idea of the even number; and hence the Pythagoreans attribute the even number to that which is indefinite, unknown, and inordinate in the world. Hence also the duad is called indefinite, because it is not definite like the monad. The terms, however, which follow these in a continued series from unity, are increased by an equal excess; for each of them surpasses the former number by the monad. But being increased, their ratios to each other are diminished. Thus in the numbers 1, 2, 3, 4, 5, 6, the ratio of 2 to 1 is double; but of 3 to 2 sesquialter; of 4 to 3 sesquitertain; of 5 to 4 sesquiquartan; and of 6 to 5 sesquiquintan. This last ratio, however, is less than the sesquiquartan, the sesquiquartan is less than the sesquitertian, the sesquitertian than the sesquialter, and the sesquialter than the double. And the like takes place in the remaining numbers. The odd and the even numbers also surveyed about unity alternately succeed each other.*

* Vid. Theo. Smyrn. Mathemat. p. 29, &.

CHAPTER IV.

On the predominance of the monad.

EVERY number also is the half of the sum of the two numbers placed about it, in a natural series. It is likewise the half of the sum of the numbers situated above these two; and also of the sum of the numbers situated above these last two, and so on till the progression is stopped by the monad or unity. Thus about the number 5, the numbers 6 and 4 are immediately placed, the former above, and the latter below it. These therefore, if they are added together make 10, of which 5 is the half. But the numbers which are next situated about 6 and 4, are 3 and 7. And of these also when added together 5 is the half. Again, the sum of the numbers placed about 3 and 7 is likewise the double of 5; for these are 8 and 2. And the like will take place in all the numbers in a natural series, till we arrive at the boundary of the monad. For the monad alone has not two terms situated about it, and on this account it is the half of the number alone which is placed next to it. Hence, it is evident that the monad is the first of all the numbers that are in a natural series, and also that it is deservedly acknowledged to be the source of all multitude, however extended it may be.

CHAPTER V.

The division of the even number.—And on the evenly-even number, and its properties.

OF the even number however there are three species. For one species is that which is called the evenly-even, but another is denominated the evenly-odd, and the third is the oddly-odd. And the species indeed which are contrary, and obtain the place· of extremes are the evenly-even, and the evenly-odd. But the species which is a certain medium, and participates of each of the extremes, is the number which is called oddly-odd.

Again, the evenly-even number is that which may be divided into two equal parts, and each of these parts into two other equal parts, and each of these may be divided in a similar manner, and the division of the parts may be continued till it is naturally terminated by indivisible unity. Thus the number 64 has for its half 32, but the half of this is 16, the half of 16 is 8, the half of 8 is 4, of 4, two, and the half of 2 is 1, which naturally does not admit of division.

To this number it happens that whatever may be its part is found to be evenly-even both in denomination and quantity. And it seems that this number was called evenly-even, because all its parts are found to be evenly-even both in name and quantity. We shall however hereafter show how this number has even parts both in quantity and appellation.

But the generation of these numbers is as follows: All numbers in a duple ratio from unity, will always be found to be evenly-even; and it is not possible that they should be produced in any other way. Thus for instance, the numbers in a duple ratio from unity are 1. 2. 4. 8. 16. 32. 64. 128. 256. 512. and so on ad infinitum; for they are all evenly-even, and the ratio of their progression is duple.

It is remarkable in this series, that if the number of terms is even, the two middle terms correspond to each other, and this also will be the case with the terms above these, and so on till each term meets with the extremities. Thus for instance, let there be given a series of evenly-even numbers from 1 to 128. In this series therefore, because the number of terms is even, one medium cannot be found. Hence there are two media 8 and 16, which mutually correspond to each other. For of the last term 128, 8 is the sixteenth part, and 16 is the eighth part. Again, the terms above these will be found to correspond to each other. For 32 is the fourth part of 128, and 4 is the thirty-second part of it. Of the terms likewise which are above these, 64 is the second part of 128, and 2 is the sixty-fourth part of it: 128 also is once 128, and 1 is the one hundred and twenty-eighth part of 128. But if the number of terms is odd, one medium only can be found, from the nature of the odd, and this corresponds to itself. For if this series be given 1. 2. 4. 8. 16. 32. 64, there will be one medium only which is 8, and this is the eighth part of 64, and thus is converted to itself both in denomination and quantity. After the same manner also as above, the terms, which are about it, confer on each other mutual appellations according to their proper quantities. For 4 is the sixteenth part of 64, and 16 is the fourth part of it. And again, above these terms, 32 is the second part of 64, and 2 is the thirty-second part of it. 1 also is the sixty-fourth part of 64, and 64 is once 64. Hence as we have said, all the parts of this series are found to be evenly-even both in appellation and quantity.

This also is admirable that in any number of terms in this series, the sum of all the terms but the last, is equal to the last term less by one. Thus when the number of terms is 3, the sum of 1 and 2 is 3 which is less than 4 by 1. In four terms, likewise, the sum of 1, 2 and 4 is 7 which is less than 8 by 1. In five terms $1+2+4+8=15$, which is less than 16 by 1; and so in any other finite number of terms. The first progeny of numbers also preserves and guards this property; for unity is less than the following number 2 by unity alone. And hence, it is by no means wonderful that the sum of the other

terms should accord with its proper principle.* We shall likewise find this property to be of the greatest advantage in ascertaining those numbers which are called superfluous, diminished,† and perfect.

This also must not be passed over in silence, that in this
series when the number of terms is even, the rectangle under
the extremes is equal to the rectangle under the two means;
for when the series is even the media are two. Thus in that
disposition of evenly-even numbers in which the last term is
128, the two means are 8 and 16, which multiplied by each
other produce 128, equal to 1×128. The numbers likewise
which are above these, if they are multiplied, will produce the
same number. For 4×32 is equal to 1×128. But if the number of terms is odd, one middle term is found, and this multiplied into itself will be equal to the product of the two extremes. Thus in that series of terms, in which the extreme is
64, one middle term alone is found, and this is 8, which multiplied into itself is equal to 1×64. The terms also which are
above this medium will, when multiplied into each other,
give the same product; for $4 \times 16 = 64$. Thus also 32 multiplied
by 2 and 1 multiplied by 64, produce the same number without any variation.

---

* It occurred to me that a similar property might be found in the series whose
terms are in a triple, quadruple, quintuple &c. ratio. And I discovered that if
in the series whose terms are in a triple ratio, each of the terms is doubled, the sum
of all the terms but the last will be equal to the last term less by 1. Thus in the
series 1. 3. 9. 27. 81. 243. 729, &c. if each term is doubled, the series will be 2.
6. 18. 54. 162. 486, &c. And $2+6=8$, which is less than 9 by 1. Again, $2+6+$
$18=26$, which is less than 27 by 1. And $2+6+18+54=80$, which is less than 81
by 1. And so in other instances. But in a series whose terms are in a quadruple
ratio, each of the terms must be tripled. In a quintuple series, the terms must be
made quadruple; in a sextuple, quintuple, and the same property will take place.

† It is evident that each of the terms in the duple series is diminished or defective, for the sum of its parts is less than the whole. And from what we have
shown, this is evident a fortiori in the triple, quadruple &c. series.

CHAPTER VI.

On the evenly-odd number, and its properties.

The evenly-odd number however is that which is itself indeed allotted the nature and essence of parity, but is opposed in a contrary division to the nature of the evenly-even number. For it will be shown that it is divided in a very dissimilar way. For because it is even, it receives a section into equal parts, but the parts of it immediately become indivisible. And such are the numbers, 6. 10. 14. 18. 22 and others similar to these. For in dividing these numbers into equal parts, we are immediately stopt by the odd number which cannot be divided equally.

But it happens to these numbers that all their parts have denominations contrary to the quantities of the parts that are denominated; nor can it ever be possible that any part of an evenly-odd number should receive a denomination and quantity of the same kind. For always, if the denomination is even, the quantity of the part will be odd. Thus for instance, in the number 18 the half of it, which term half is the appellation of parity, is 9, which is odd in quantity. But its third part, which is an uneven denomination, is 6, which is even in quantity. Again, by conversion, the sixth part which is an even denomination is 3, but the ternary is odd. And the ninth part, which is an uneven appellation, is 2 which is an even number. And the same thing will be found to take place in all other evenly-odd numbers. Nor can it ever be possible that the name and number of any part are of the same kind.

These numbers are produced by disposing from unity all the numbers that differ from each other by 2, viz. all the odd numbers in a natural series. For if each of these is multiplied by 2, all the evenly-odd numbers will be generated. Let there be given then the following odd numbers from unity in a natural order, 1. 3. 5. 7. 9. 11. 13. 15. 17. 19. These, if each of them is multiplied by 2, will form the series 2. 6. 10. 14. 18. 22. 26. 30. 34. 38. And each of these if divided will only receive one section, a second division being excluded by the intervention of imparity.

These numbers also differ from each other by 4: and this arises from the mode of their generation. For the odd numbers which are the foundation of them, exceed each other by 2; and because each of these is multiplied by 2, the progression receives a four-fold increase.

But these species of numbers, the evenly-even, and the evenly-odd, are said to be contrary, because in the evenly-odd number, the greater extremity alone receives division,* and the less term is in this alone liberated from section; and because in the form of the evenly-even number, the product of the extremes is equal to the product of the means, as far as to the two media, if the number of terms is even; but if the number of terms is odd, the square of the medium is equal to the product of the extremes. In the evenly-odd number however, if the number of terms is odd and there is therefore only one middle term, this term will be the half of the sum of the terms placed about it. It will also be the half of the sum of the terms placed above these; and this will be the case as far as to the extremes of all the terms. Thus in the series of evenly-odd numbers 2. 6. 10., the middle term 6 is the half of 10+2. And if there are two media, the sum of these will be equal to the sum of the terms placed above them. Thus in the series 2. 6. 10. 14, the sum of the media 6+10 is equal to 2+14 the sum of the extremes.

* Viz. In the evenly-even number, it is the least part alone, i.e. unity which receives no division; but on the contrary in the evenly-odd numbers, the greater extremity alone receives division, i.e. the whole number. Thus 10 can be divided into two equal parts, but in these parts the division stops; so that in this number the section is stopped in the greatest part, while on the contrary, in the evenly-even number, it is stopped in the least part, unity.

CHAPTER VII.

On the unevenly-even number, and its properties, etc.

THE unevenly-even number is composed from both the evenly-even, and the evenly-odd number, and is a medium between both. But this number is such as may be divided into equal parts, and each of these into other equal parts, and sometimes the parts of these parts may again be divided, but this equable division does not proceed as far as to unity. And of this kind are the numbers 24 and 28. For each of these may be divided into two equal parts, and also the parts of these parts, and again the parts of these, but the division does not extend as far as to unity. Hence, because this number receives more than one division, it resembles the evenly-even, and is separated from the evenly--odd number. But because the section does not proceed as far as to unity, it associates with the evenly-odd, but is separated from the evenly-even number.

It happens however to this number, that it possesses that which both the above-mentioned numbers have not, and obtains that which both of them receive. And it as that indeed which both do not possess; for in the evenly-odd number, the major term alone is divided into two equal parts; but in the evenly-even number on the contrary, the minor term alone is deprived of this division. In the unevenly-even number however, neither the major term alone admits of this section, nor the minor alone is deprived of such a division; for the parts also are divided, and the section does not arrive as far as to unity, but prior to unity a term is found which cannot be divided. It also obtains what both the others receive; for some of its parts are of the same quantity and denomination, according to a similitude of the evenly-even number; but other parts of it receive a denomination contrary to their proper quantity agreeably to the form of the evenly-odd number. Thus in the number 24, the quantity of the part is even, being denominated from the even number. For the fourth part of it is 6, the second part is 12, the sixth part is 4, and the twelfth part is 2, which appellations of parts are not discordant from parity of quantity. The parts however 8, 3, and 1 do not correspond in denomination to the quantities; for 8 is the third part, 3 is the eighth part, and 1 is the twentyfourth part. Hence in this instance, when the denominations are even, the quantities are found to be odd, and when the quantities are even, the denominations are odd.

But these numbers are produced in such a way as to designate their essence and nature even in their very generation; for they are the progeny of the evenly-even, and the evenly-odd numbers. For the evenly-odd are produced, as we have shown from the series of odd numbers; but the evenly-even from the duple progression. Let all the numbers therefore, that are naturally odd, be disposed in order, and under these all the numbers in a duple progression beginning from 4 as follows:

| 3 | 5 | 7 | 9 | 11 | 13 | 15 | 17 | 19 | etc. |
| 4 | 8 | 16 | 32 | 64 | 128 | 256 | 512 | 1024 | etc. |

If therefore the first number in one series, is multiplied by the first in the other, viz. if 3 is multiplied by 4, or if the same first is multiplied by the second number in the second series, i.e. if 3 is multiplied by 8, or the first by the third, i.e. 3 by 16, and so on as far as to the last term; or if the second term in the first series is multiplied by the first, or second or third, or in short, by any term in the second series; or the third term in the first series, by any term in the second, and so of the fourth, fifth etc. terms in the first series, all the numbers thus produced will be unevenly-even. Thus $3 \times 4 = 12$, $5 \times 4 = 20$, $7 \times 4 = 28$, and so on. Again, $3 \times 8 = 24$, $5 \times 8 = 40$, $7 \times 8 = 56$.

And after this manner, if all the numbers in the duple series are multiplied by those in the upper series, the products will be found to be unevenly-even numbers.

This also is admirable in this species of numbers, that if the disposition and description of them according to breadth is regarded, the property of the evenly-odd numbers will present itself to the view, but the property of the evenly-even, if the disposition of them is regarded according to length. For according to breadth, the two extremes are equal to the two media, or if there is but one medium, the double of it is equal to the extremes. But according to length, the property of the evenly-even number will be discovered; for here the product of the extremes is equal to that of the two media, or if there is but one medium the square of it is equal to the product of the extremes. The description of them however, according to length and breadth, is as follows; The products arising from the multiplication of evenly-even numbers in an orderly series by 3, are to be placed in the first row. Again, the products arising from the multiplication of the same evenly-even numbers by 5, are to be placed in the second row. Those arising from the multiplication by 7, are to be placed in the third row, and so of the rest.

3	5	7	9 etc.	Odd numbers.
4	8	16	32 etc.	Evenly-even numbers.

Length.

	12	24	48	96
	20	40	80	160

Breadth,   Breadth,

	28	56	112	224
	36	72	144	288

Length.

Here in the breadth, if three terms are taken, as for instance

12, 20, and 28, the sum of the extremes is double the middle term; for $12+28=40$. Thus also $20+36=56$ equal twice 28. But where there are two media, the sum of the extremes will be equal to the sum of the means. Thus $12+36=48=20+28$. Thus also $24+72=96=40+56$; and so of the other parts of the breadth. This however takes place according to the form of the evenly-odd number, in which, as we have before observed, this property is found. Again, if we direct our attention to the length, where two terms have one medium, the product of the extremes is equal to the square of the medium or middle term; for $12\times48=576=24\times24$. Again, $24\times96=2304=48\times48$. But where two terms include two media, the product of the extremes will be found to be equal to the product of the means. Thus $12\times96=1152=24\times48$. And this is according to an imitation of and alliance with the evenly-even number, from the participation of which these numbers acquire this property. The same thing also takes place in the other rows of the length. Hence it is manifest that this number is produced from the two former numbers, because it invariably retains their properties.

CHAPTER VIII.

On the odd number, and its division.

The odd number also is that which is separated from the nature and essence of the even number; since the latter can be divided into two equal parts, but the former is prevented from this equality of division by the intervention of unity. In a similar manner also it has three subdivisions; one of these, being the number which is called first and incomposite; another, that which is second and incomposite; and the third, that which subsists as a medium between these, and naturally derives something from both through its alliance to each; which is of itself indeed second and composite, but with reference to others is found to be first and incomposite.

CHAPTER IX.

On the first and incomposite number.

AND the first and incomposite number indeed, is that which has no other part except that which is denominated from the whole quantity of the number; so that the part itself is no other than unity. And such are the numbers 3. 5. 7. 11. 13. 17. 19. 23. 29. 31. In each of these numbers therefore, no other part can be found except that which is denominated from them, and this, as we have before observed, is unity alone. For in 3 there is only one part, i.e. a third, which is denominated from 3, and this third part is unity. After the same manner in 5 there is only one part which is a fifth, and this is unity. And the same consequence will be found to take place in the rest. This number however, is called first and incomposite, because no other number measures it than unity, which is the mother of all number. And this is owing to its not being composed from any other numbers, and to its being generated from unities alone multiplied into themselves.* For thrice one is three, five times one is five, seven times one is seven, and so of the rest. But these being multiplied into themselves produce other numbers like themselves. Being allotted also a primary essence, they will be found to be as it were certain elements of all the numbers generated from them; because they are incomposite, and formed by a simple generation; and all the

* viz. From unities when added together forming a number, and this number being multiplied by unity.

numbers proceeding from them are resolved into them, but they are neither produced from others, nor resolved into other numbers.

CHAPTER X.

On the second and composite number.

THE second and composite number, is indeed itself odd, because it is formed by the same property of the odd number, but it retains in itself no principal essence; is composed from other numbers; and has parts which are denominated both from itself and a foreign word; but the part alone which is denominated from itself, will always in these numbers be found to be unity. The parts however, which are denominated from a foreign word, are sometimes many, and sometimes only one. Of this kind are the numbers 9. 15. 21. 25. 27. 33. 39. Each of these therefore has parts denominated from itself, viz. its proper unities. Thus 9 has a ninth part which is 1; 15 has a fifteenth part, which is also 1; and the like takes place in the rest. But they have also a part denominated from a foreign word. Thus 9 has a third part which is 3; and 15 has a third part which is 5, and also a fifth part, 3. Thus too, 21 has a third part, i.e. 7, and a seventh part which is 3; and there is the same consequence in all the rest. This number however, is called second, because it is not only measured by unity, but also by another number, by the conjunction of which it is formed. Nor does it contain anything in itself of a principal nature; for it is generated from other numbers; 9 indeed from 3; 15 from 3 and 5; 21 from 3 and 7; and the rest after the same manner. But it is called composite, because it may be resolved into those numbers from which it is said to be composed, viz. into those which measure a composite number.

Nothing however which can be dissolved is incomposite, but is by every necessity a composite.

CHAPTER XI.

On that number which is of itself second and composite, but with reference to another first and incomposite.

THESE numbers therefore, i.e. the first and incomposite and the second and composite being separated from each other by a natural diversity, another number presents itself to the view in the middle of these, which is indeed itself composite and second, receives the measure of another, and is therefore capable of a part with a foreign appellation, but when it is compared with another number of the same kind, is conjoined with it by no common measure; nor will these numbers have equivocal parts. Numbers of this description, are such as 9 and 25; for these have no common measure, except unity, which is the common measure of all numbers. They likewise have no equivocal parts. For that which in 9 is the third part is not in 25, and that which in 25 is the fifth part is not in 9. Hence both these numbers are naturally second and composite, but when compared with each other, they are rendered first and incomposite, because each has no other measure than unity, which is denominated from each; for in 9 it is the ninth, and in 25, the twenty-fifth part.

CHAPTER XII.

On the generation of the first and incomposite, of the second and composite numbers, and of that number which is of itself second and composite, but with reference to another first and incomposite.

THE generation however and origin of these numbers is obtained by the following method, which Eratosthenes denominates a sieve; because all the odd numbers being placed in the middle by the art which we shall shortly unfold, those numbers which are of the first, or second, or third kind are distinguished. For let all the odd numbers in an orderly series be disposed from 3, to any extent whatever, viz. 3. 5. 7. 9. 11. 13. 15. 17. 19. 21. 23. 25. 27. 29. 31. 33. 35. 37. 39. 41. 43. 45. 47. 49. These therefore, being thus disposed, it must be considered what is the first number of the series which 3 will measure. And it will be found, that two numbers being omitted, it will measure that number which immediately follows them, viz. it will measure 9. If also after 9 two others are omitted, it will measure the following number 15. Again, if beginning from 15 two numbers are omitted, it will measure the following number 21. And thus it will be found ad infinitum, that the first number 3, by omitting two numbers will measure all the following numbers posterior to itself, according to the quantity of the orderly series of odd numbers. But in order to find the numbers of which 5 the second odd number is the measure, four terms must be omitted, and the number that immediately follows will be measured by 5. Thus by omitting the four odd numbers 7. 9. 11. 13, the next term will be 15, which 5 measures according to the quantity of the first odd number 3; for the fifth part of 15 is 3. But if after this, the four following numbers are omitted, viz. 17. 19. 21. 23. the number five will measure by its plurality the next number 25. And if after this four numbers are omitted, the same constancy of order being preserved, 5 will measure 35 which is the next following number. And this is the infinite procession.

If again, it is inquired what the third number is which may be measured, six terms must be omitted, and that which is the seventh term in order is to be measured by the quantity of the first number i.e. by three. And after this six other terms being omitted, the number which immediately occurs will be measured by the third number, and will have for its quotient the second number. Thus after 7, omitting six numbers, the number 21 which immediately occurs will be measured by 3; and after 21, six numbers being omitted, the next number 35 will be measured by 7 five times. But if again other six terms are omitted, the number which next occurs viz. 49, will be measured by the same 7 seven times, which is the quantity of the third term. And this established order will proceed to the most extended number of terms. Hence, they will receive a vicissitude of measuring; just as they are naturally constituted odd numbers in an orderly series. But they will be measured by the intermission of terms according to an even number, beginning from an intermission of two terms. Thus the first odd number will measure the odd numbers that follow after an omission of two terms; the second, those that follow after an omission of four terms; the third, when 6, the fourth, when 8, and the fifth when 10 terms are omitted, will measure the numbers that follow in an orderly series. And so of the rest ad infinitum. This will also be effected if the terms double their places, and numbers are omitted conformably to the duplication. Thus 3 is the first term and one, for every first is one. If therefore this multiplies its own place twice, it will produce twice one. And since twice one is two, two terms must be omitted. Again, if the second term which is 5 doubles its place, it will produce 4, and four terms must be omitted. If 7 likewise, which is the third term, doubles its place, it will produce 6; and therefore six terms are to be omitted in an orderly series. The fourth term also, if it doubles its place, will produce 8, and 8 terms must be omitted. And the like will be found to take place in all the other terms. The series however will give the mode of measuring according to the order of collocation. For the first term numbers according to the first, i.e. according to itself, the first term which it numerates; but it numbers the second, which it numerates, by the second, the third, by the third; and the fourth by the fourth. When the second however begins to measure, it measures the first which it numerates according to the first; but it measures the second which it numerates by itself, i.e. by the second term; and the third by the third; and so of the rest. Thus 3 measures 9 by 3; 15 by 5; 21 by 7; 27 by 9, and so on. But 5 measures 15 by 3; 25 by 5; 35 by 7; 45 by 9, and so of the rest. If therefore we direct our attention to the other terms, either those that measure others, or that are themselves measured by others, we shall find that there cannot be at one and the same time a common measure of all of them, nor that all of them at the same time measure any other number; but it will appear that some of them may be measured by another number, so as only to be numbered by one term; others, so as to be numbered by many terms; and some, so as to have no other measure than unity. Hence, those that receive no measure besides unity, are said to be first and incomposite numbers; but those that receive a certain measure besides unity, or are allotted the appellation of a foreign part, these are said to be second and composite numbers.

The third species however, which is of itself second and composite, but when one number is compared to the other is first and incomposite, is obtained by the following method: The squares of the first and incomposite numbers, when compared to each other will be found to have no common measure. Thus the square of 3 is 9, and the square of 5 is 25. These therefore have no common measure. Again, the square of 5 is 25, and of 7 is 49: and these compared to each other will be found to be incommensurable. For there is no common measure of these except unity which is the generator and mother of all these.

CHAPTER XIII.
On the method of discovering the commensurability, or incommensurability of these numbers.

The art however of discovering whether such numbers are commensurable by some number besides unity, or whether each of them is measured by unity alone, is as follows: Two unequal numbers being given, it will be requisite to take the less from the greater, and if that which remains is still greater to take from it again the less, but if it is less to take it from the remaining greater number. And this must be done till unity at last prevents any farther subtraction, or till some *odd* number necessarily effects this, if both the proposed numbers are odd; and this number which remains will be the common measure of both. Thus for instance, let there be two numbers 9 and 29, of which it is proposed to investigate the common measure. From the greater let the less be taken, and there will remain 20. From this therefore let the less be again taken, and 11 will remain. From this again take 9, and 2 will remain. Let 2 then be taken from 9, and 7 will remain. From 7 let 2 be taken, and there will remain 5. Again, from 5 let 2 be taken, and 3 will remain. And farther still, if 2 be taken from 3, there will remain 1. And in the last place, if 1 be taken from 2, the subtraction will terminate in unity, which will alone be the measure of the two numbers 9 and 29. These numbers therefore, are called with reference to each other prime numbers.

Let it, however, be proposed to investigate the common measure of two other numbers 21 and 9, that it may be ascer-

THE SIEVE OF ERATOSTHENES.

Primary and In-composite Numbers.	Odd Numbers.	The series of Odd Numbers which are measured by 3.	The series of Odd Numbers which are measured by 5.	The series of Odd Numbers which are measured by 7.
	3			
5	5			
7	7			
	9	9		
11	11			
13	13			
	15	15	15	
17	17			
19	19			
	21	21		21
23	23			
	25		25	
	27	27		
29	29			
31	31			
	33	33		
	35		35	35
37	37			
	39	39		
41	41			
43	43			
	45	45	45	
47	47			
	49			49
	51	51		
53	53			
	55		55	
	57	57		
59	59			
61	61			
	63	63		63
	65		65	
67	67			
	69	69		
71	71			
73	73			
	75	75	75	
	77			77

Eratosthenes appears very properly to have called the above invention a sieve; for in it the composite are separated from the incomposite numbers, just as in a sieve, the pure is separated from the impure, and that which is subtile from that which is dense and gross.

The Sieve of Eratosthenes by which it is ascertained what numbers are primary, and what are composite.

Here the first number is measured by 3 according to itself, the second by 3 according to 5, the third by 3 according to 7, and so of the rest.

Here the first number is measured by 5 according to 3, the second by 5 according to itself, the third by 5 according to 7, and so on.

Here 7 measures the first number according to 3, the second according to 5, the third according to itself, and so of the rest.

tained of what kind they are when compared with each other. Again therefore, from the greater number 21 let the less number 9 be taken, and 12 will remain. From 12 let 9 be taken, and there will remain 3. But if 3 be taken from 9, 6 will remain; from which if 3 be taken, 3 will be the remainder. And from this 3 cannot be taken so as to leave any remainder. Hence these numbers are commensurable, and 3 is their common measure.

CHAPTER XIV.

Another division of the even number according to the perfect, deficient, and superperfect, or superabundant.

AGAIN, of even numbers a second division is as follows. Of these, some are superperfect, and others are deficient, according to each habitude of inequality. For all inequality is considered either in greater or less terms. But the superperfect numbers are such as by an immoderate plenitude, exceed, as it were, by the numerosity of their parts, the measure of their proper body. On the contrary, the deficient numbers being as it were, oppressed by poverty, are less than the sum of their parts. And the superperfect numbers indeed, are such as 12 and 24; for these will be found to be more than the aggregate of their parts. For the half of 12 is 6; the third part is 4; the fourth part is 3; the sixth part is 2; and the twelfth part is 1. And the aggregate of all these parts is 16, which surpasses the multitude of its whole body. Again, of the number 24, the half is 12; the third 8; the fourth 6; the sixth 4; the eighth 3; the twelfth 2; and the twenty-fourth 1; the aggregate of all which is 36. And it is evident in this instance also, that the sum of the parts is greater than, and overflows as it were, its proper body. And this number indeed, because the parts surpass the sum of the whole number, is called superabundant. On the contrary, that number is called deficient, the parts of which are surpassed by the multitude of the whole; and such are the numbers 8 and 14. For the half of 8 is 4; the fourth is 2; and the eighth is 1; the aggregate of all which is 7; a sum less than the whole number. Again, the half of 14 is 7; the seventh is 2; and the fourteenth is 1; the aggregate of which is 10; a sum less than the whole term. Such therefore are these numbers, the former of which in consequence of being surpassed by its parts, resembles one born with a multitude of hands in a manner different from the common order of nature, such as the hundred-handed giant Briareus, or one whose body is formed from the junction of three bodies, such as the triple Gerion, or any other production of nature which has been deemed monstrous by the multiplication of its parts. But the latter of these numbers resembles one who is born with a deficiency of some necessary part, as the one-eyed Cyclops, or with the want of some other member.

Between these however, as between things equally immoderate, the number which is called perfect is alloted the temperament of a middle limit, and is in this respect the emulator of virtue; for it is neither extended by a superfluous progression, nor remitted by a contracted diminution; but obtaining the limit of a medium, and being equal to its parts, it is neither overflowing through abundance, nor deficient through poverty. Of this kind are the numbers 6 and 28. For the half of 6 is 3; the third is 2; and the sixth is 1, which if reduced into one sum, the whole body of the number will be found to be equal to its parts. Again, the half of 28 is 14; the seventh is 4; the fourth is 7; the fourteenth is 2; and the twenty-eighth is 1; the aggregate of which is 28.

Nor must we omit to observe, that all the multiples of a perfect number are superabundant, but on the contrary all the submultiples deficient. Thus, for instance, 3 the subduple of 6 is a deficient, but 12 the double of 6 is superabundant. Thus also 2 which is subtriple of 6 is a deficient, but 18 which is the triple of it is a superabundant number. And the like will take place in other multiples, and submultiples. Hence also it is evident that a perfect number is a geometric medium between the superabundant and the deficient number. Thus in the three numbers 3. 6. 12, 6 is the geometrical mean between 3 and 12; for as 3 is to 6, so is 6 to 12. Thus, too, 28 is the geometric mean between 14 and 56, the former of which is a deficient, and the latter a superabundant number.

Perfect numbers therefore, are beautiful images of the virtues which are certain media between excess and defect, and are not summits, as by some of the ancients they were supposed to be. And evil indeed is opposed to evil, but both are opposed to one good. Good however, is never opposed to good, but to two evils at one and the same time. Thus timidity is opposed to audacity, to both which the want of true courage is common; but both timidity and audacity are opposed to fortitude. Craft also is opposed to fatuity, to both which the want of intellect is common; and both these are opposed to prudence. Thus too profusion is opposed to avarice, to both which illiberality is common; and both these are opposed to liberality. And in a similar manner in the other virtues; by all which it is evident that perfect numbers have a great similitude to the virtues. But they also resemble the virtues on another account; for they are rarely found, as being few, and they are generated in a very constant order. On the contrary, an infinite multitude of superabundant and diminished numbers may be found, nor are they disposed in any orderly series, nor generated from any certain end; and hence they have a great similitude to the vices, which are numerous, inordinate, and indefinite.

CHAPTER XV.

On the generation of the perfect number, and its similitude to virtue.

ON account of the paucity, therefore, of perfect numbers, there is only one between 1 and 10, viz. 6; one only between 10 and 100, viz. 28; between 100 and 1,000 only one, 496; and between 1,000 and 10,000 the only perfect number is 8,128. These numbers likewise, are always terminated by the two even numbers 6 and 8;* as is evident in those already adduced.

But the generation of them is fixed and firm, and can only be effected in one way. For evenly-even numbers being disposed in an orderly series from unity, the first must be added to the second, and if a first and incomposite number is produced by that addition, this number must be multiplied by the second of the evenly-even numbers, and the product will be a perfect number. If, however, a first and incomposite number is not produced by the addition, but a composite and second number, this must be passed by, and the number which follows must be added. And if this aggregate is not found to be a first and incomposite number, another must be added, and this must be done till a first number is found. When therefore this is found, it must be multiplied into the last of the added evenly-even numbers, and the product will be a perfect number. Thus for instance, in the evenly-even series of numbers 1. 2. 4. 8. 16. 32. 64. 128, if 1 is added to 2 the sum is 3, and because 3 is a first and incomposite number, this multiplied by 2 will produce the perfect number 6. But 28 the next per-

---

* Boetius asserts, that perfect numbers always *alternately* end in 6 and 8; but this is only true of the four first, and not of the rest.

fect number is produced as follows: from the addition of 1, 2 and 4 arises 7, which is a first and incomposite number, and this being multiplied by 4 the last of the evenly-even numbers, the perfect number 28 is produced. Since therefore these two perfect numbers 6 and 28 are found, others must be investigated after the same manner. Thus, in order to find the next perfect number, add 1, 2, 4, and 8 together; but the sum of these is 15. This however is a second and composite number; for it has a third and a fifth part, besides a fifteenth part, unity, which is denominated from itself. This therefore must be passed by, and the next evenly-even number, viz. 16, must be added to it, and the sum will be 31, which is a first and incomposite number. Let this then be multiplied by 16 the last of the evenly-even numbers, and the product will be 496 the next perfect number after 28. The monad therefore is in power though not in energy itself a perfect number. For if it is first assumed in the order of numbers, it will be found to be primary and incomposite, and if multiplied by itself, the same unity is produced. But this is equal to its parts in power alone. Hence the monad is perfect by its own proper virtue, is first and incomposite, and preserves itself unchanged when multiplied by itself.

The way however in which perfect numbers are generated, will immediately become manifest by the following table.

Evenly-even numbers	1	2	4	8	16	32	64	128	256	512	1024	2048	4096
Odd numbers produced by the addition of the evenly-even numbers	1	3	7	15	31	63	127	255	511	1023	2047	4095	8191
Perfect numbers . . .	1	6	28	*	496	*	8128	*	*	*	*	*	33550336

The asterisks in this table signify that the odd numbers above them produced by the addition of the evenly-even numbers, are composite, and therefore unfit to form perfect numbers.

CHAPTER XVI.

On relative quantity, and the species of greater and less inequality.

THE first division of relative quantity is twofold: for whatever is measured by comparison with another quantity, is either equal or unequal. And that indeed is equal which when compared to something else is neither less nor greater. This part however, of relative quantity, viz. equality, is naturally indivisible: for it cannot be said that one portion of equality is different from another. For all equality in its proper measurement preserves one measure. The quantity too which is compared, has not an appellation different from that to which it is compared. For as a friend is the friend of a friend, and a neighbour is the neighbour of a neighbour, so the equal is said to be equal to the equal. But of unequal quantity there is a twofold division: for that which is unequal may be cut into the greater and the less, which have a denomination contrary to each other. For the greater is greater than the less, and the less is less than the greater. Hence both have not the same appellations as was observed to be the case with equal quantity, but they are distinguished by different names, in the same manner as those of teacher and learner, or of any other relatives which are compared to contraries that are differently denominated.

Of greater inequality however, there are five parts. For one part is that which is called multiple; another is superparticular; a third superpartient; a fourth multiple-superparticular; and a fifth multiple-superpartient. To these five parts, therefore, of greater inequality, other five parts of less inequality are opposed, just as the greater is always opposed to the less. These species also of less inequality have the same appellations as those of greater inequality, with the addition of the preposition *sub*. For they are denominated submultiple, subsuperparticular, subsuperpartient, multiple-subsuperparticular, and multiple-subsuperpartient.

CHAPTER XVII.

On multiple inequality, its species, and the generation of them.

Again, the multiple is the first part of greater inequality, being more ancient than all the others, and naturally more excellent, as we shall shortly demonstrate. This number however is such, that when compared with another, it contains the number with which it is compared more than once.

This multiple inequality also is first seen in the natural series of number. For all the numbers that follow unity have the relation of multiples to it. Thus 2 with relation to unity is duple; 3 is triple; 4 quadruple; and thus proceeding in order, all multiple quantities are produced.

The inequality however, which is contra-distinguished to this, is called submultiple, and this also is the first species of less quantity. But this number is such that when compared with another, it measures the sum of the greater number more than once. If therefore, the less number measures the greater only twice, it is called subduple: but if three times, subtriple: if four times, subquadruple; and so on ad infinitum. And they are always denominated with the addition of the preposition *sub*.

Since, however, multiplicity and submultiplicity are naturally infinite, the proper generations of the species also admit of infinite speculation. For if numbers are arranged in a natural series, and the several even numbers are selected in a

consequent order, these even numbers will be double of all
the even and odd numbers from unity, that follow each
other, and this ad infinitum. For let this natural series of
numbers be given, viz. 1. 2. 3. 4. 5. 6. 7. 8. 9. 10. 11. 12. 13.
14. 15. 16. 17. 18. 19. 20. If therefore, in this series, the first
even number is assumed, i.e. 2, it will be the double of the
first, i.e. of unity. But if the following even number 4 is
assumed, it will be the double of the second, i.e. of 2. If the
third even number 6 is assumed, it will be the double of the
third number in the natural series, i.e. of 3. But if the fourth
even number is assumed, i.e. 8, it will be the double of the
fourth number 4. And the same thing will take place without any impediment in the rest of the series ad infinitum.

Triple numbers also are produced, if in the same natural
series two terms are always omitted, and those posterior to the
two are compared to the natural number, 3 being excepted,
which as it is triple of unity passes over 2 alone. After 1 and
2 therefore, 3 follows which is triple of 1. Again, 6 is immediately after 4 and 5, and is triple of the second number 2. The
number 9 follows 7 and 8, and is triple of the third number 3.
And the like will take place ad infinitum.

But the generation of quadruple numbers begins by the
omission of 3 terms. Thus after 1. 2. and 3, follows 4, which
is quadruple of the first term 1. Again, by omitting 5, 6, and
7, the number 8, which is the fourth following term, is quadruple of the second term 2. And after 8, by omitting the three
terms 9, 10, and 11, the following number 12, is quadruple of
the third term 3. This also must necessarily be the case in a
progression to infinity: and if the addition always increases
by the omission of one term, different multiple numbers will
present themselves to the view in admirable order. For by the
omission of four terms a quintuple multiple, of five a sextuple,
of six a septuple, of seven an octuple, and so on, will be pro-

duced, the name of the multiple being always one more than that of the terms which are omitted.

And all the double terms indeed are always even. But of the triple terms, one is always found to be odd, and another even. Again, the quadruple terms always preserve an even quantity; and they are formed from the fourth number, one of the prior even numbers being omitted in order; first the even number 2; then 6 being omitted, 8 follows as the next quadruple term; and after 8, the quadruple number 12 follows, the even number 10 being omitted. And so on in the rest. But the quintuple resembles the triple multiple; for in this the even and odd terms have an alternate arrangement.

CHAPTER XVIII.

On the superparticular number, its species, and the generation of them, etc.

WHEN one number contains the whole of another in itself, and some part of it besides, it is called superparticular. And if the part of the less which it contains is the half, it is called sesquialter; if the third part, sesquitertian; if the fourth, sesquiquartan; if the fifth, sesquiquintan. And the like names being employed to infinity, the form of superparticular numbers will also proceed infinitely. And the greater numbers, indeed, are thus denominated. But of the less, the wholes of which are contained in the greater, and a certain part of them besides; one is called subsesquialter; another subsesquitertian; another subsesquiquartan; another subsesquiquintan; and so on according to the rule and multitude of the greater numbers. The greater numbers also are called leaders, but the less attendants.

Of superparticular numbers likewise, the multitude is infinite; because the progression of their species is boundless.

For the sesquialter has for its leaders all the numbers that are naturally* triple after 3; but for its attendants, all the numbers that are naturally even after 2. For let the series of natural, of triple, and of double numbers be described in three rows as follows:

1	2	3	4	5	6	7	8	9	10
3	6	9	12	15	18	21	24	27	30
2	4	6	8	10	12	14	16	18	20

The first row therefore contains the series of natural numbers; the second the triple; and the third, the double of them. Hence, if 3 is compared to 2, or 6 to 4, or 9 to 6, or if all the superior triple are opposed to all the inferior double numbers, sesquialter ratio will be produced. For 3 contains in itself 2, and 1 the half of two. Six also contains in itself 4, and 2 the half of 4. And 9 contains in itself 6, and the half of 6 which is 3. And in a similar manner in the rest.

It is likewise requisite to show the method of discovering the sesquitertian, or second species of the superparticular number. And the definition indeed of this comparison is as follows: the sesquitertian is that which when compared to the less number, contains it once, and a third part of it besides. But these numbers are found, if all the terms in a continued series from 4 being made quadruple, are compared with all the numbers that are made triple from 3. And the leaders in this case will be quadruple; but the attendants triple. For let there be a series of numbers in a natural order, and under these a quadruple, and under the quadruple a triple series. Let the first triple therefore, be placed under the first quadruple number; the second under the second; the third under the

* By numbers naturally triple, the triples of the natural series 1. 2. 3. 4. 5, &c. must be understood. And in a similar manner numbers naturally duple, quadruple, &c. are such as are duple, quadruple, &c. of that series.

third; and let all the triples be arranged under all the quadruples after the same manner, as follows:

1	2	3	4	5	6	7	8
4	8	12	16	20	24	28	32
3	6	9	12	15	18	21	24

Hence, if the first number is compared with the first, a sesquitertian ratio will be formed. For 4 contains the whole of 3 in itself, and a third part of 3 besides, i.e. 1. In a similar manner 8 contains the whole of 6, and a third part of 2. And the same consequence will take place in the rest ad infinitum. It must also be observed, that 3, 6, 9, 12, etc. are attendants, and 4, 8, 12, 16, etc. leaders; and that the ratio of the former to the latter is subsesquitertian, but of the latter to the former sesquitertian.

This also is admirable and most profound in the orders of these numbers, that the first leader and the first attendant are conjoined to each other without the intervention of any other number. But between the second leader, and the second attendant, one number intervenes. Between those in the third rank, two numbers intervene. Between those in the fourth, three. And the intervening numbers are always less by one than the rank of the numbers themselves. But it is necessary that this should take place in sesquialter, sesquitertian, or other superparticular parts. Thus when 4 is compared to 3, no number intervenes; for 4 succeeds immediately to 3. But when 8 is compared to 6, which forms the second sesquitertian ratio, one number intervenes; for 7 comes between 6 and 8. Again, when 12 is compared to 9, which forms the third sesquitertian ratio, two numbers intervene, viz. 10 and 11. After the same manner, between those in the fourth order, three numbers intervene; between those in the fifth, four numbers; and so on ad infinitum.

CHAPTER XIX.

*That the multiple is more ancient than the other species of in-
equality.*

To demonstrate this, let there be first a series of numbers in
a natural order as far as to 10. In the second row let the duple
order be arranged. In the third row, the triple order. In the
fourth, the quadruple; and so on as far as to the decuple order.
For thus we shall know how the species of the multiple precedes the superparticular, superpartient, and all the other species of inequality. We shall also at the same time perceive
other things, which are exquisitely subtile, most useful in a
scientific point of view, and which afford a most delightful
exercise to the mind.

*This Table is called Pythagorean, from Pythagoras, who is said
to be the author of it.*

Length.

1	2	3	4	5	6	7	8	9	10
2	4	6	8	10	12	14	16	18	20
3	6	9	12	15	18	21	24	27	30
4	8	12	16	20	24	28	32	36	40
5	10	15	20	25	30	35	40	45	50
6	12	18	24	30	36	42	48	54	60
7	14	21	28	35	42	49	56	63	70
8	16	24	32	40	48	56	64	72	80
9	18	27	36	45	54	63	72	81	90
10	20	30	40	50	60	70	80	90	100

Breadth. (left)   Breadth. (right)

Length.

If therefore the two first sides which form an angle of the
above table are considered, and each of which proceeds from
1 to 10, and if the inferior orders which begin from the angle

4, and terminate in 20, are compared to these, the double, i.e. the first species of multiplicity will be exhibited. Hence, the first will surpass the first by unity alone, as 2 surpasses 1. The second will exceed the second by 2, as 4 exceeds 2. The third will exceed the third by 3, as 6 exceeds 3 by 3. The fourth will surpass the fourth by 4, and in this way 8 surpasses 4. And after a similar manner in the rest. But if the third angle is considered, which begins from 9, and which extends both in length and breadth as far as to the number 30, and if this is compared with the first length and breadth, the triple species of multiplicity will present itself to the view, so that the comparison will take place through the black angle. And these numbers will surpass each other according to the natural progression of the even number. For the first number will surpass the first by 2, as 3 surpasses 1. The second surpasses the second by 4, as 6 surpasses 2. The third surpasses the third by 6, as 9 surpasses 3. And after the same mode of progression the rest are increased. If again, the boundary of the fourth angle is considered, which is distinguished by the quantity of the number 16, and which terminates its length and breadth in the number 40, here also a similar comparison being made with the preceding, will unfold the quadruple species of multiplicity. Hence, the first will surpass the first by 3, as 4 surpasses unity. The second will surpass the second by 6, as 8 surpasses 2. The third will exceed the third by 9, as 12 exceeds 3. And after a similar manner in all the following numbers. If the remaining angles likewise are considered, the same thing will take place through all the species of multiplicity, as far as to the decuple species.

If however, in this description, the superparticular species are required, they may be found by the following method. For if we direct our attention to the second angle, the beginning of which is 4, and above which is 2, and if the row in which 4 is, is compared with the row immediately under it, sesquialter ratio will be unfolded. Thus 3 to 2, or 6 to 4, or 9 to 6, or 12 to 8, is a sesquialter ratio. And in a similar manner in the rest. Nevertheless, one number here exceeds another by the same quantity as in the naturally double species. For the first surpasses the first, i.e. 3 surpasses 2 by 1. The second surpasses the second by 2. The third surpasses the third by 3, and so on. But if the fourth order is compared to the third, as 4 to 3, 8 to 6, 12 to 9, etc. in all these the sesquitertian ratio will present itself to the view.

This too is divine in the table, that all the angular numbers are squares. But a square number in short, is that which is produced by the multiplication of a number into itself. Thus in this table, one multiplied by itself is one, and this is in power or capacity a square. Also, twice 2 is 4, thrice 3 is 9, four times 4 is 16; and so of the rest. But the numbers which are placed about the angular numbers, are longilateral. These, however, are such as are produced by the multiplication of two numbers that differ from each other by unity. Thus 2 and 6 are situated about 4; but 2 is produced by the multiplication of 1 by 2, and 2 differs by 1 from 1. But 6 is produced by the multiplication of 2 by 3; and these differ from each other by unity. Again, 6 and 12 are situated about 9: and 12 is formed from 3 multiplied by 4, and 6 from 2 by 3. All which are produced from sides that differ from each other by unity. And in a similar manner in the other angular numbers, the numbers which are situated about them will be found to be longilateral.

Again, from the aggregate of two longilateral numbers, and twice the square which they surround, a square number will be formed. Thus 2+6 added to twice 4 is equal to 16. Thus, too, 6+12 added to twice 9 is equal to 36. And so of the rest.

A square number also will be formed from the aggregate of two proximate square numbers together with the double of the intermediate longilateral number. Thus in the following series,

1. 2. 4. 6. 9. 12. 16. 20. 25. 30. 36. 42. 49.

in which between two proximate squares there is a longilateral number, if 4 is added to 1 and to twice 2 the sum will be 9. Thus, too, 4 added to 9, added to twice 6, is equal to 25. And thus also, 9 added to 16, added to twice 12, is equal to 49. And so of the rest. From this aggregation likewise, it is evident that the squares thus formed are odd numbers; but those arising from the former aggregation are even numbers. For 9, 25, 49, etc. are odd, and 16, 36, 64, etc. are even numbers.

Moreover, of the monads or unities at the four corners of the table, the first and the third are squares, viz. 1 and 100; but the other corners have the two other monads 10 and 10. Farther still, the product arising from the multiplication of the two squares 1 and 100, is equal to that of the two other monads multiplied into each other, viz. is equal to 10×10. These squares too, cut the table into two equal triangles. They also become, as it were, the diameter of the figure; and hence they are called diametral.

CHAPTER XX.

On the third species of inequality, which is called superpartient:—Its species, and the generation of them.

AFTER the two first habitudes therefore, the multiple and the superparticular, and those habitudes which are under them, viz. the submultiple and the subsuperparticular, the third species of inequality presents itself to the view, which we have already denominated superpartient. But this takes place when one number on being compared to another contains the whole of it in itself, and certain parts of it besides, such as two, three, or four parts, or any other that may arise from the comparison. This habitude also begins from two third parts: for if one number besides containing the whole, contained two halves of the other, the ratio would be duple instead of superpartient. And if the greater, besides containing the whole, has only two third parts of the less, the greater will surpass the less by odd numbers. For if it contained the whole and two fourths of it, the ratio would necessarily be superparticular; since two fourths are the same as half, and the comparison will be sesquial-ter. But if it contained two sixths, again the ratio is superparticular; for two sixths are the same as a third part. And this in the comparison will produce the form of the sesquitertian habitude. After these, the attendants arise which are called subsuperpartient. These, however, are such as are contained in another number, and two, three, four, or any other parts of them besides. If, therefore, a number containing another number in itself, has also two parts of it, it is called superbipartient; if three, supertripartient; if four, superquadripartient, and so on ad infinitum.

But the order of them is natural, as often as all the even and odd numbers naturally constituted, are disposed from 3; and under these others are adapted, which are all odd numbers beginning from 5. These, therefore, being thus disposed, if the first is compared to the first, the second to the second, the third to the third, and the rest to the rest, a superpartient habitude will be produced; as is evident from the following arrangement:

$$3 \quad 4 \quad 5 \quad 6 \quad 7 \quad 8 \quad 9 \quad 10$$
$$5 \quad 7 \quad 9 \quad 11 \quad 13 \quad 15 \quad 17 \quad 19$$

If, therefore, the comparison of 5 to 3 is considered, it will be that superpartient which is called superbipartient; for 5 contains in itself the whole of 3, and two parts of it besides, viz. 2. But if 7 is compared to 4, the ratio will be supertripartient; for 7 contains in itself the whole of 4, and three parts of it be-

sides. And in the following numbers, all the species of superpartient ratio will be found in an orderly progression.

The manner however in which each of them is produced
ad infinitum, is as follows: If each of the terms that form the
superbipartient habitude is doubled, superbipartient ratio will
always be generated. Thus by doubling 3 and 5, 6 and 10 will
be produced, and these numbers will form a superbipartient
ratio. And if these again are doubled, the same order of ratio
will arise. By thus proceeding also ad infinitum, the states of
the former habitude will not be changed.

Again, in order to find supertripartient habitudes, the first
supertripartients 7 and 4 must be tripled, and numbers of this
kind will be generated. And if those that are produced from
these are also tripled, the same ratio will be formed.

Thus, too, in order to produce superquadripartient habitudes
ad infinitum, the first roots of them, i.e. 9 and 5, must be multiplied by 4, and the products of this multiplication must be
also quadruplicated, and the same ratio will present itself to
the view. The other species likewise will be generated by
causing the roots always to increase by one multiplication. But
the numbers in the above table are called roots, because all the
before-mentioned habitudes are derived from them. In the
superbipartient ratio also, because the greater contains the less,
and two thirds of the less, the habitude is called superbipar-
tient-tertian. Thus, too, the supertripartient ratio is denominated supertripartient-quartan, because the greater contains
the less, and three fourths of it besides. Thus again, the superquadripartient is denominated superquadripartient-quintan.
And after a similar manner in the rest. Hence the ratio which
is called superbipartient, may also be called superbitertian.
That which is denominated supertripartient, may also be called supertriquartan. And that which has the appellation of

superquadripartient, may likewise be denominated superquad-
riquintan. And names maybe produced ad infinitum according to the same similitude.

CHAPTER XXI.

On the multiple superparticular and superpartient ratio.

THESE, therefore, are the simple and first species of relative
quantity. There are, however, two other species which are
composed from these as from certain principles. And these
are, the multiple superparticular, and multiple superpartient;
and the attendants of these the submultiple superparticular,
and the submultiple superpartient. For in these, as in the before-mentioned ratios, the less numbers and their species are
denominated with the addition of the preposition *sub*. But the
definition of them is as follows: Multiple superparticular ratio
is produced, when one number being compared to another,
contains it more than once, and one part of it besides; viz. it
contains either the double, or triple, or quadruple, or some
other multiple of it, and a certain part of it besides, as the half,
third, fourth, or some other part. Hence this ratio consists
both of multiple and superparticular. The number, therefore,
which contains another number twice, and the half of it besides, is called duple sesquialter. That which contains the
double and a third, is duple sesquitertian. But that which contains the double and a fourth, is duple sesquiquartan, and so
on. If also, one number contains the whole of another thrice,
and its half, third, or fourth part, it is called triple sesquialter,
triple sesquitertian, triple sesquiquartan, and after the same
manner in the rest. And as often as it contains the whole of
the less number in itself, it is denominated by the species of
multiple number; but from the part of the compared number
which it contains, it will be denominated according to a super-

particular comparison and habitude. Examples of these are as follow: Duple sesquialter ratio is such as that of 5 to 2; for 5 contains 2 twice, and the half of it, which is 1. But duple sesquitertian ratio, is such as that of 7 to 3. Duple sesquiquartan ratio is such as that of 9 to 4. And duple sesquiquintan, such as that of 11 to 5.

These ratios too will always be produced, if the numbers which are naturally even and odd, being disposed in order from 2, the odd numbers beginning from 5 are compared to them; viz. if the first is compared to the first, the second to the second, the third to the third, and so on, as in the following table:

2	3	4	5	6	7	8	9	10	11	12
5	7	9	11	13	15	17	19	21	23	25

But if even numbers being disposed from 2 are compared to those which, beginning from 5, surpass each other by 5, duple sesquialter ratios will be produced, as will be evident from the following diagram.

2	4	6	8	10	12
5	10	15	20	25	30

If the series begins from 3, and the numbers that follow surpass each other by 3, and if those that begin from 7, and exceed each other by 7, are compared to them, duple sesquitertian ratios will be formed, as below:

3	6	9	12	15	18	21
7	14	21	28	35	42	49

If also the quadruplicates of the natural numbers 1, 2, 3, 4, etc. beginning from 4 are disposed in order, and numbers beginning from 9, and surpassing each other by 9, are compared to them, duple sesquiquartan ratios will be produced, as is evident from the following diagram:

$$4 \quad 8 \quad 12 \quad 16 \quad 20 \quad 24$$
$$9 \quad 18 \quad 27 \quad 36 \quad 45 \quad 54$$

But the species of this number which is triple sesquialter, is generated, if even numbers are disposed in order from 2, and a series of numbers beginning from 7, and surpassing each other by 7, are compared to them, as in the following diagram:

$$2 \quad 4 \quad 6 \quad 8 \quad 10 \quad 12 \quad 14$$
$$7 \quad 14 \quad 21 \quad 28 \quad 35 \quad 42 \quad 49$$

And if to the triples of the natural numbers beginning from 3, a series of numbers beginning from 10 and exceeding each other by 10, are compared, the species which is triple sesquitertian will be produced, as below:

$$3 \quad 6 \quad 9 \quad 12 \quad 15 \quad 18 \quad 21$$
$$10 \quad 20 \quad 30 \quad 40 \quad 50 \quad 60 \quad 70$$

By directing our attention however, to the Pythagorean table in chapter 19, we may perceive examples of all these species. For all the rows after the first will produce when compared to the first, all the species of multiple ratio. The numbers in the third row when compared to those in the second, will exhibit a species of superparticular ratio. Those in the fifth row compared to those in the third, present to the view a species of superpartient ratio. But multiple superparticular ratio will be produced when those in the fifth row, or those in the 7th or 9th are compared to those in the second. And thus, if the table is extended *ad infinitum,* infinite species of this ratio will be produced. It is likewise manifest that the attendants of these ratios are always expressed with the preposition sub; as for instance, subduple sesquialter, subduple sesquitertian, subduple sesquiquartan; and after the same manner in all the rest.

Multiple superpartient ratio however is, when one number on being compared to another, contains the whole of it more than once, and two, three, or some other number of parts, according to the species of the superpartient number. Here too, from the cause before mentioned, there will not be two halves, nor two fourths, nor two sixths; but there will be two thirds, or two fifths, or two sevenths. Nor will it be difficult according to the examples before adduced, to discover these numbers also. These are denominated according to their proper parts, duple superbipartient, or duple supertripartient, or duple superquadripartient, and so on. And again, they are called triple superbipartient, triple supertripartient, triple superquadripartient, and the like. Thus 8, compared to 3, produces a duple superbipartient ratio. This is also the case with 16 compared to 6; and with all those numbers that beginning from 8, and surpassing each other by 8, are compared to those that begin from 3, and surpass each other by 3. It will likewise be easy to find other parts of these numbers according to the before mentioned mode. Here too, the less numbers are not denominated without the preposition sub, as subduple superbipartient, subduple supertripartient. And after a similar manner in the rest.

CHAPTER XXII.

A demonstration that all ineqality proceeds from equality.

IT now remains for us to deliver a certain profound discipline, which especially pertains to all the power of nature and integrity of things. For it is highly advantageous in this science, not to be ignorant that the nature of good is definite, but that of evil indefinite. That the more indefinite the nature of evil is, the worse it is; and that it is goodness alone, which by

the impression of itself, defines and bounds that which is of itself indefinite. Hence in the human soul, there is a certain
vestige of divine goodness, which moderates the inequality of
its motions. This vestige is the rational power, by which we
restrain the inordinate tendencies of desire, and the efferves-
cence of anger, both which partake of the nature of inequality.
This however will be evident, if we demonstrate that all the
species of inequality originate from equality; so that obtaining as it were, the power of a mother and a root, she pours
forth with primordial exuberance, all the species and orders of
inequality. Let there be three equal terms, therefore, i.e. three
unities, or three of the number 2, or of 3, or of 4, or of any
other number. For that which takes place in one three terms,
will happen in the rest. From the three rules therefore, that
will be given, it will be seen, that in the first place multiples
will be produced, first duple, then triple, then quadruple, and
so on. Again, if the multiples are converted, from these superparticulars will arise. And from such as are duple indeed, the
sesquialter; from such as are triple, the sesquitertian; from the
quadruple, the sesquiquartan; and the rest after the same manner. But from the conversion of superparticulars, it is necessary, that superpartient ratios should be produced; so that the
superbipartient will originate from the sesquialter; the supertripartient from the sesquitertian; and the superquadripartient
from the sesquiquartan. From the former superparticulars
however, remaining in a direct position, and not being converted, multiple superparticulars will arise; but multiple superpartients will be produced, from the position of the former superpartients remaining unchanged.

The three rules however, are as follows: The first number
must be made equal to the first; but the second, to the first
and second; and the third, to the first, to twice the second,
and the third. When this is effected therefore, in equal terms,

the numbers produced from these will be duple. And if the same thing is done with these duples, triple numbers will be generated. From the triple, quadruple numbers will arise. And thus *ad infinitum,* all the multiple forms of number will be unfolded. Let there be, therefore, three equal terms, viz. 1. 1. 1. Let the first therefore be placed equal to the first, i.e. to 1. But let the second be equal to the first and the second, viz. to 2. And the third, to the first, to twice the second, and to the third, viz. to 4. And the order of the terms will be woven together in a duple ratio, as below.

$$\begin{array}{ccc} 1 & 1 & 1 \\ 1 & 2 & 4 \end{array}$$

Again, let the same thing be done with the duple numbers. And let the first be equal to the first, viz. to 1. But let the second be equal to the first and second, viz. to 1 and 2, which make 3. And let the third be equal to the first, to twice the second, and to the third, which together make 9; and this form will be unfolded, viz.

$$\begin{array}{ccc} 1 & 2 & 4 \\ 1 & 3 & 9 \end{array}$$

viz. the terms produced will be in a triple ratio.

Farther still, if the same thing is done with the triple numbers, quadruple terms will be immediately produced. For let the first be equal to the first, i.e. to 1. Let the second be equal to the first and second, i.e. to 4. And let the third be equal to the first, to twice the second, and to the third, viz. to 16, as below:

$$\begin{array}{ccc} 1 & 3 & 9 \\ 1 & 4 & 16 \end{array}$$

And in the rest, these three rules must be used according to this form.

If, however, the multiples which are produced from the equal terms are disposed in a converse order, and the same rules are employed, sesquialter ratio will be generated from the double terms; sesquitertian from the triple; sesquiquartan from the quadruple, etc. For let there be three double terms which are generated from equals, and let that which is the last be placed as the first, viz.

$$4 \quad 2 \quad 1$$

Let the first therefore be made equal to the first, i.e. to 4. But let the second be equal to the first and second, viz. to 6. And let the third be equal to the first, to twice the second, and to the third, viz. to 9.

$$4 \quad 2 \quad 1$$
$$4 \quad 6 \quad 9$$

And it is evident, that sesquialter ratio will be produced from the double terms.

Again, let the former triple terms be disposed in a converse order, viz. 9. 3. 1. Let the first therefore be equal to the first, i.e. to 9. But let the second be equal to the first and second, i.e. to 12. And the third to the first, to twice the second, and the third, viz. to 16.

$$9 \quad 3 \quad 1$$
$$9 \quad 12 \quad 16$$

And thus the second species of the superparticular number, i.e. the sesquitertian is generated.

By the same process also with the quadruple numbers, the sesquiquartan ratio will be immediately produced, as is evident from the subject description:

$$16 \quad 4 \quad 1$$
$$16 \quad 20 \quad 25$$

And if the same thing is done with all the parts multiplied *ad infinitum,* the order of superparticularity will be appropriately discovered.

If, likewise, the superparticulars which were formed by conversion, are themselves converted according to these rules, superpartient ratios will be immediately produced. And from the sesquialter indeed, the superbipartient, but from the sesquitertian, the supertripartient ratio will be generated. The rest also will be produced according to the common species of denomination without any innovation of order. Let the superparticulars, therefore, be disposed as follows:

$$9 \quad 6 \quad 4$$

Let the first therefore be equal to the first, i.e. to 9. But the second, to the first and second, i.e. to 15. And the third, to the first, to twice the second, and to the third.

$$9 \quad 6 \quad 4$$
$$9 \quad 15 \quad 25$$

And superbipartient ratio will, as is evident, be produced.

But if after the same manner the sesquitertian ratio is changed, the superpartient order will present itself to the view. Let the converted sesquitertian terms therefore be:

$$16 \quad 12 \quad 9$$

Let the first therefore be equal to the first, i.e. to 16. But the second to the first and second, i.e. to 28. And the third, to the first, to twice the second, and to the third, i.e. to 49. And the ratio, as is evident, will be supertripartient:

$$16 \quad 12 \quad 9$$
$$16 \quad 28 \quad 49$$

Again, by converting after the same manner the sesquiquartan, the superquadripartient ratio will immediately be generated, as is evident from the subject description:

$$25 \quad 20 \quad 16$$
$$25 \quad 45 \quad 81$$

It now remains therefore, to show how from superparticular and superpartient, multiple superparticular, and multiple superpartient ratios are produced. Of these, however, we shall only make two descriptions. For from the sesquialter in a direct, and not in a converted position, duple superparticular ratio will be generated. Let the direct sesquialter terms therefore be:

$$4 \quad 6 \quad 9$$

And then according to the former mode, let the first be equal to the first, i.e. to 4. But let the second be equal to the first and second, i.e. to 10. And the third, to the first, to twice the second, and to the third, i.e. to 25:

$$4 \quad 6 \quad 9$$
$$4 \quad 10 \quad 25$$

And duple sesquialter ratios will be produced.

But from the sesquitertian ratio, the terms not being transposed, the duple sesquitertian will be produced, as is evident from the subject description:

$$9 \quad 12 \quad 16$$
$$9 \quad 21 \quad 49$$

If, however, we direct our attention to superparticular ratios, and dispose the terms of them according to the former rules, we shall find multiple superpartients produced in an orderly series. For by proceeding according to the rules in this formula of the superpartient, viz. in 9. 15. 25. the duple superbipartient ratios 9. 24. 64. will be generated. But from the supertripartient ratios 16. 28. 49. the duple supertripartient will be produced, viz. 16. 44. 121.

And thus multiple superparticulars, or multiple superpartients arise from superparticular, or superpartient ratios. Hence it is evident that equality is the principle of all inequalities; since all unequals are generated from it.

BOOK TWO

CHAPTER I.

How all inequality may be reduced to equality.

N the former book we have shown how the whole essence of inequality proceeds from equality as the principle of its nature. From those things however which are elements, all things are principally composed, and by analysis are resolved into the same. Thus because letters are the elements of speech, the conjunction of syllables proceeds from them, and are again terminated in the same as in bounding extremes. Sound also obtains the same power in music. And every one knows that four elementary bodies constitute the world. But an ultimate analysis is again effected into these four elements. Hence, because we see that all the species of inequality proceed from the bounding nature of equality, it is requisite that inequality should be again resolved by us into equality, as into a certain element of its proper genus. This, however, is again effected by a triple rule; and the art of analyzation is as follows: Three terms being given, which are unequal indeed, but proportionally constituted, viz. so that the middle may have the same ratio to the first term, which the last term has to the middle, in every ratio of inequality, either in multiple, or superparticular, or superpartient ratios, or in those which are generated from these, i.e. in multiple superparticulars, or multiple superpartients;—three terms therefore being given with these conditions, one and the same indubitable method must be observed. For the first term must be placed as the first. The second term must be that which remains from the subtraction of the first from the middle term. But the third term must be obtained by subtracting the first term from the third, and also twice the second term that remained from the former subtraction; for then the remainder will be the third term. By this process the proportion will be reduced; so that if the proportion is quadruple, it will first be reduced to a triple, then to a duple proportion, and last of all to equality. We shall only demonstrate that this will be the case in multiple proportion, as it will be easy to apply the same process to the other species of inequality also.

Let there be three terms therefore quadruple of each other, viz. 8. 32. 128. From the middle term, therefore, 32, let the first term 8 be taken, and 24 will remain. Let 8 then be placed as the first, and 24 as the second term. But from the third term 128, take away the first term 8, and twice the remaining second, i.e. twice 24, and 72 will remain. Hence, the three terms will be 8. 24. 72; and the quadruple will be reduced to a triple proportion.

Again, by the same process with these three terms, the triple will be reduced to a duple proportion. For, let the first be equal to the first, i.e. to 8. And from the second take away the first, and 16 will remain. But from the third 72, take away the first, i.e. 8, and twice the remaining second, i.e. 16, and 32 will remain. So that the three terms will be 8. 16. 32; and the habitude will be reduced to a duple proportion.

By the same process however with these terms, they will be

reduced to equality. For let the first be equal to the first, i.e. to 8. And from 16 subtract 8, and 8 will remain. But from the third term 32, take away the first 8, and twice the remaining second, i.e. twice 8, and 8 will remain. So that the three terms will become by reduction, 8. 8. 8.

The other species of inequality also, will, by the same process be brought to equality. Hence, it may be indubitably asserted, that as unity is the principle and element of quantity that subsists by itself, so equality is the mother of relative quantity.

CHAPTER II.

On discovering in each number, how many numbers of the same ratio may precede—description of them and an exposition of the description.

In this affair however, there is a certain profound and admirable speculation, and as Nicomachus says, εννοιοφατον θεωρημα, or, *a theorem replete with intellectual conception,* useful for the purpose of understanding the Platonic generation of the soul in the Timaeus, and the intervals of the harmonic discipline. For in the Timaeus we are ordered to produce and extend three or four sesquialter, or a certain number of sesquitertian ratios, and sesquiquartan comparisons. But lest this, which is always indeed attended with the greatest labour, should frequently be done without advantage, it is now requisite to investigate how many superparticulars every multiple has for its attendants. For all multiples will be the leaders of as many proportions similar to themselves, as they themselves are distant from unity. But similar proportions are those which are of the same ratio and denomination. The meaning however, of multiples, being the leaders of proportions similar to themselves, is as follows: The multiplicity of the duple, as we have before observed, always produces sesquialter ratios; and the triple is the leader of sesquitertian; but the quadruple of sesquiquartan ratios.

The first duple, therefore, will only have one sesquialter; the second will have two; the third three; the fourth four; and according to this order, there will be the same progression *ad infintium.* Nor can it ever be possible, that the equable location from unity, should either surpass or fall short of the number of the proportions. The first duple, therefore, is the binary number, i.e. 2, which receives one sesquialter alone, i.e. 3. For 2 when compared to 3, produces a sesquialter ratio. The number 3, however, because it has not a half, cannot be compared to any other number in a sesquialter ratio. But 4 is the second double. This therefore is the leader of two sesqui-alter numbers. For 6 compared to it is sesquialter; and to 6 because it has a half, 9 is sesquialter. Hence, there are two sesquialters, to 4 indeed 6, but to 6, 9. But 9, because it wants a half, is excluded from this comparison. The third double is 8. This therefore is the leader of three sesquialters. For the number 12 is compared to it in this ratio; but to 12 18; and again to 18, 27. But 27 wants a half. The same thing will also necessarily happen in other numbers, as is evident in the following table:

1	2	4	8	16	32
	3	6	12	24	48
		9	18	36	72
			27	54	105
				81	162
					243

For this always occurs by a certain divine, and no human ordination, that the last sesquialter number is among sesquialters as much distant from its leader, as its leader is among doubles from unity. Thus 9 is the second sesquialter from 4; and 4 is the second double from 1. Thus too, 27 is the third sesquialter from 8; and 8 is the third double from 1. And so of the rest. This last sesquialter likewise, is always incapable of being divided into two equal parts.

The same thing also takes place in triple numbers; for from them sesquitertians are generated. Thus, because 3 is the first triple number, it has one sesquitertian, i.e. 4; of which a third part cannot be found, and therefore it is deprived of a sesqui-tertian number. But the second triple number which is 9, has for a sesquitertian number 12. And 12 because it has a third part, has also a sesquitertian 16, which is excluded from a third part. The number 27, however, because it is the third triple, has for a sesquitertian 36; and this again is compared in the same ratio to 48; and 48 has also for a sesquitertian, 64. But 64 has no sesquitertian, because it has no third part. And thus it will be found in all triple numbers, that the last number of the same ratio has, preceding it, as many numbers, as the first of them is distant from unity; and that it is incapable of being divided into three equal parts:

1	3	9	27	81	243
	4	12	36	108	324
		16	48	144	432
			64	192	576
				256	768
					1024

The description of quadruple numbers is according to the following scheme, which will be immediately obvious to those who understand what has been already delivered. And the same thing will take place in all the other multiples.

1	4	16	64	256	1024
	5	20	80	320	1280
		25	100	400	1600
			125	500	2000
				625	2500
					3125

Hence also it is evident, as was before shown, that multiples precede all superparticulars, since they produce duple sesquialters, triple sesquitertian, etc.; and all the multiples generate all the superparticulars in an orderly series. This likewise is admirable in these numbers, that where, as in the first scheme, the first row consists of numbers that are double, those in the second and following rows will also be double. But if those in the first row are triple, as in the second scheme, those in the following rows will also be triple. And if they are quadruple in the first row, as in the third scheme, those in the other rows will be quadruple; and so of the other multiples ad infinitum. All the angular numbers likewise are necessarily multiples. And of the double series indeed, the angular numbers will be triple; but of the triple, quadruple; of the quadruple, quintuple. And thus all things will accord with themselves, according to one invariable order.

CHAPTER III.

The method of finding the superparticular intervals from which the multiple interval is produced.

IF, therefore, the two first superparticular species are conjoined, the first species of multiplicity arises. For every duple ratio is composed from the sesquialter and sesquitertian; and all sesquialter and sesquitertian ratios from a duple ratio. For 3 is sesquialter of 2; but 4 is sesquitertian of 3; and 4 is the double of 2.

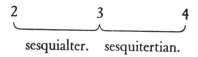

And thus the sesquialter and the sesquitertian compose one duple ratio. In short, if there are two numbers, one of which is the double of the other, between the two, one such medium may be found, which is sesquialter to the one extreme, but sesquitertian to the other. Thus if 4 is placed between 6 and 3, i.e. between a double and a half, when compared to 3, it contains a sesquitertian, but to 6 a sesquialter ratio.

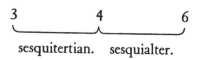

Rightly therefore, is it said that the duple ratio is conjoined from the sesquialter and the sesquitertian, and that these two species of superparticular ratio, generate the duple ratio, i.e. the first species of the multiple.

Again, from the first species of the multiple, and from the first superparticular, i.e. the sesquialter, the second species of the multiple, i.e. the triple number is formed. For 12 is the double of 6; but 18 is sesquialter to 12, and is the triple of 6.

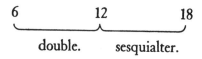

If also between the same numbers 6 and 18, 9 is placed as a

medium, it will be sesquialter to 6, and subduple to 18; and 18 is triple of 6.

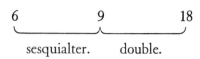

From the duple and sesquialter therefore, triple ratio arises; and into them is again by analysis recalled. But if the triple number, which is the second species of the multiple, is adapted to the second species of the superparticular, i.e. to the sesquitertian, the form of the quadruple will be immediately produced, and will be again dissolved by a natural separation into the same parts, according to the mode which has been before demonstrated.

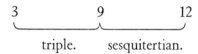

But from the quadruple and the sesquiquartan, the quintuple ratio will immediately be formed.

4	16	20
quadruple.	sesquiquartan.	

And from the quintuple and the sesquiquintan, the sextuple ratio will arise.

5	25	30
quintuple.	sesquiquintan.	

And thus, according to this progression, all the species of multiplicity, without any variation of established order, will be produced.

CHAPTER IV.

On the quantity subsisting by itself, which is considered in geometrical figures, etc.

And thus much may suffice at present, respecting relative quantity. In what follows, we shall discuss certain particulars pertaining to that quantity which subsists by itself, and is not referred to any thing else, which may be profitable to what we shall afterwards again unfold about relative quantity. For the speculation of mathesis loves in a certain respect to be conversant with alternate demonstration. Our business however, at present, is with the numbers which subsist in geometrical figures, and their spaces and dimensions, viz. with linear, triangular, or square numbers, and with others which superficies alone unfolds, as also with those that are formed by an unequal composition of sides. We have likewise to discuss solid numbers, viz. such as are cubical, spherical, and pyramidal, and such as have the form of tiles or beams, or wedges; all which indeed, properly pertain to the geometric speculation. But as the science of geometry is produced from arithmetic, as from a certain root and mother, so likewise we find the seeds of its figures in the first numbers.

Unity therefore, or the monad, which is in arithmetic what a point is in geometry, is the principle of interval and length; but itself is neither capacious of interval nor of length; just as a point is the principle of a line and of interval, but is itself neither interval nor line. For a point placed on a point, does not produce any interval. Between things also that are equal there is no interval. Thus, if three sixes are placed after this manner, 6. 6. 6. as is the first to the second, so is the second to the third; but between the first and second, or the second

and third, nothing intervenes; for no intervals of space disjoin
6 and 6. Thus also unity multiplied into itself, generates
nothing but itself. For that which is without interval does
not possess the power of generating interval. But every number multiplied into itself, produces another number greater
than itself, because intervals when multiplied, distend themselves by a greater length of space. That, however, which is
without interval, has not the power of generating more than it
is itself. From this principle, therefore, i.e. from unity, the
first extension into length proceeds, and which unfolds itself
into all numbers from the duad; because the first interval is a
line; but two intervals are length and breadth, i.e. a superficies; and three intervals, are length, breadth, and depth, i.e.
a solid. But besides these, no other intervals can be found; so
that the six species of motion subsist conformably to the natures and number of the intervals. For one interval contains in
itself two motions. Thus in length there is before and behind;
in breadth, the right and the left; and in depth, upward and
downward. But it is necessary that every solid body should
have length, breadth, and depth; and that whatever contains
these three dimensions in itself, should be a solid. Since therefore, a line surpasses a point by one dimension, viz. by length,
but a superficies surpasses it by two dimensions, i.e. by length
and breadth, and a solid surpasses it by three dimensions, i.e.
by length, breadth, and depth, it is evident that a point itself is
without any corporeal magnitude, or dimension of interval; is
the principle of all intervals; and is naturally incapable of being divided. Hence a point is the principle of the first interval,
yet is not itself interval; and is the summit of a line, but is not
yet a line. Thus too a line is the principle of a superficies, but
is not itself a superficies; and is the summit of the second interval, yet retains no vestige of the second interval. And thus
also a superficies is the principle of a solid, but is itself neither

distended by a triple dimension, nor consolidated by any crass-itude.

Thus also in numbers, unity indeed is not itself a linear num-ber, yet it is the principle of number extended into length. And linear number being itself void of all breadth, is the ori-gin of number distended into breadth. Superficial number likewise, is itself deprived of all solidity, yet being added to depth is the summit of a numerical solid. This however we shall render more manifest by examples. But linear number begins from 2; and the series of such numbers is formed by the continual addition of unity; as in the following example:

11. 111. 1111. 11111.

CHAPTER V.

On plane rectilinear figures.—That the triangle is the principle of them. And on the distribution of triangles, their sides, and generation.

A PLANE superficies however, is found in numbers to have its beginning from 3, and with the addition of breadth the an-gles are dilated in the multitude of numbers that follow each other in a natural order. Hence the first plane superficies in numbers is a triangle; the second is a square; the third, a pen-tagon; the fourth, a hexagon; the fifth, a heptagon; the sixth, an octagon; and the rest after the same manner increase their angles, in the plane description of figures, according to the order of the natural numbers.

But these begin from the number 3, because the ternary alone is the principle of breadth and superficies. The same thing also, is more evidently found to take place in geometry. For two right lines do not contain space. And in every multangular figure, whether it be square, pentagon, or hexagon, etc. lines drawn from the middle of it through the several angles, will divide it into as many triangles, as the figure has angles; as is evident in the following diagrams:

If the triangular figure however, is divided after this manner, it will not be resolved into any other than itself; for it will be divided into three triangles, as is evident from the following diagram:

Hence this figure is the principle of breadth, so that all other superficies are resolved into this; but because it is not itself derived from other principles, and does not assume its beginning from any other breadth, it is resolved into itself. But that the same thing takes place also in numbers, will be shown in the course of this treatise.

The first of all triangular numbers therefore, is that which is formed from unity. But this is first in capacity or power, and not in energy. For if it is the mother of all numbers, whatever is found in those numbers that proceed from it, must necessarily be contained in it by a certain natural power. The first triangular number however in energy is 3; and this has for its side the binary, or as it is called by the Greeks, the duad. But the second triangle in energy is 6; and this has for its side the ternary. The third triangle is 10, the side of which is 4. The fourth is 15; and the side of it is 5; and so on ad infinitum, as in the following diagrams:

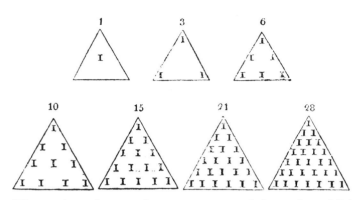

These triangular numbers are generated from the addition
of the natural series of numbers; viz. from the addition of the
series 1. 2. 3. 4. 5. 6. 7. 8. 9, etc. If unity therefore is assumed,
it will be the first triangle in capacity. 1+2=3 will be the
second triangle in order, but the first in energy. 1+2+3=6
will be the third triangle. 1+2+3+4=10 will be the fourth,
and so of the rest. As many units likewise, as there are in the
last number which is added to the rest, so many will the triangle which is produced contain in its side. Thus 3 which is
the first triangle in energy, is generated by adding 2 to 1; and
therefore it has two units in its side. Thus too, 6 is produced
by the addition of 3 as the last number; and it has three units in
its side. And the like will be found to take place in the rest.

This also deserves to be remarked, that in a continued series
of triangular numbers, two even and two odd numbers alternately present themselves to the view. For 1 and 3 which are
the two first triangles, are odd; but 6 and 10, the two following triangles, are even. Again, 15 and 21 are odd; but 28 and
36 are even; and so of the rest.

If there be a series likewise of triangular numbers, omitting
unity, and a series of numbers in a natural order, the several
triangles separately taken will correspond in proportion to the
numbers of the natural order continually assumed. So that the

first and second of the one, will correspond to the first and second of the other; but the third and fourth of the one, to the second and third of the other; and the fifth and sixth of the one, to the third and fourth of the other; and so on. Thus let there be a series of numbers in the natural order, viz. 1. 2. 3. 4. 5. 6. 7. 8. 9. And under it a series of triangles, viz. 3. 6. 10. 15. 21. 28. 36. 45. Then as 1 is to 2, so is 3 to 6. And as 2 is to 3, so is 10 to 15. Likewise as 3 is to 4, so is 21 to 228; and so of the rest.

Triangular numbers also are obtained after the following manner. For in the natural series of numbers from unity, by first omitting one term, then two terms, afterwards three, then four, and so on, triangles will be formed in a continued series:

The series of natural numbers } 1 2 3 4 5 6 7 8 9 10 11 12 13 14 15 16 17 18 19 20 21 22 23 24 25 26 27 28

The series of trian-gles } 1   3   6   10   15   21   28

Here it is evident, that between the first and second triangle, in the natural order of numbers, one number intervenes; between the second and third triangle, two numbers; between the third and fourth, three; and so on in the rest.

CHAPTER VI.

On square numbers, their sides, and generation.

A SQUARE number is that which does itself indeed unfold breadth, yet not in three angles, as the preceding number, but four. It likewise is extended by an equal dimension of sides. But such numbers are as follows:

```
                                    1  1  1  1
                        1  1  1     1  1  1  1
              1  1      1  1  1     1  1  1  1
     1        1  1      1  1  1     1  1  1  1
   _____    _____   _____   _____
```

But in these numbers also the sides increase according to the natural series of numbers. For the first square in power and capacity, i.e. unity, has 1 for its side. But the second square, which is the first in energy, ie. 4, has 2 for its side. And the third, which is 9, and is the second square in energy, has 3 for its side. And after the same manner all the rest proceed.

Such numbers however, are generated from the series of natural numbers, not indeed after the same manner as triangles, but by the continual omission of one number, in the addition of the terms to each other. For in the natural series of numbers from unity, 1. 2. 3. 4. 5. 6. 7. 8. 9. 10. 11, etc. 1 is the first square in power. Then $1+3=4$, the second square. $1+3+5=9$, the third square. $1+3+5+7=16$, the fourth square. And thus by continually omitting one term, and adding the rest, the whole series of squares will be produced.

In these numbers likewise, there is this subtilty of nature, and immutable order, that each square retains as many units in its side as there are numbers by the aggregation of which it is formed. Thus in the first square, because it is produced from 1, the side is 1. In the second square, i.e. 4, because it is generated from 1 and 3, which are two terms, the side is 2. In 9 because it is generated from three numbers, the side is 3. And so of the rest.

CHAPTER VII.

On pentagons, their sides, and generation.

A PENTAGON is a number which being expressed by its units, exhibits the form of a quinquangular figure; and which when thus described, has five angles, and five equal sides. But pentagonal numbers are such as the following, viz. 1. 5. 12. 22. 35. 51. 70. Their sides also increase after the same manner. For in every pentagon, the units that form its side, correspond in number to the class of the pentagon. Thus 1 which is the first pentagon in power, has 1 for its side. But 5 which is the second pentagon has 2 for its side. The third pentagon which is 12, has 3 for its side. The fourth which is 22, has 4. And so on, according to the progression of the series of natural numbers:

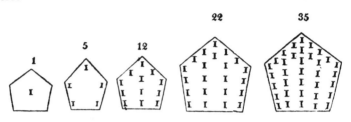

But these numbers which being extended into breadth unfold five angles, are also generated from the addition of the natural series of numbers, so that two terms being continually omitted, and the posterior added to the prior, the several pentagons are formed, as below:

The series of natural numbers, two being continually omitted.	1	4	7	10	13	16	19	22	25	28	31	34
The series of pentagons.	1	5	12	22	35	51	70	92	117	145	176	210

Pentagons also are produced from squares and triangles, after the following manner. The second square added to the first triangle, will produce the second pentagon. The third square added to the second triangle, will produce the third pentagon. The fourth square added to the third triangle, will produce the fourth pentagon. And so on; each square being added to a triangle of a class immediately antecedent to it. Thus for instance, the second square 4 being added to the first triangle 1, produces the second pentagon 5. Thus too, the third square 9 added to the second triangle 3, forms the third pentagon 12. And so of the rest.

CHAPTER VIII.

On hexagons and heptagons, and the generation of them. A general method of discovering the generation of all figures, etc.

THE sides of hexagons and heptagons increase after the following manner. In the generation of triangular numbers, those terms were added together which followed each other in a natural order, and surpassed each other by unity alone. But the generation of squares was from numbers which were added together, one term being omitted, and which surpassed each other by 2. In the generation of pentagons two terms were omitted, and the number by the addition of which they were formed, surpassed each other by 3. Thus also in the generation of the hexagon, three terms being omitted, those are added together that surpass each other by 4; and these terms indeed, will be the roots and foundations, from the aggregation of which all hexagons will be produced. These roots therefore are the numbers 1. 5. 9. 13. 17. 21, etc. and from the addition of these, hexagons will be formed, viz. 1. 6. 15. 28. 45. 66, etc.

But in the generation of heptagons, four terms being omitted, those are to be added that surpass each other by 5; and these numbers, as was before observed, will be the roots and foundations of them:

1. 6. 11. 16. 21.

The heptagons formed from the addition of these are, 1. 7. 18. 34. 55.

The forms of an octagon of an enneagon, or figures of eight and of nine angles, are generated according to the same order, so that the first numbers, or roots of them, are distant from each other conformably to an equal progression. For in the generation of octagons five terms are omitted; but in that of enneagons, six terms. And in short, the number of omissions continually increasing by 1, the series of plane numbers will be formed by the addition of the remaining terms.

CHAPTER IX.

On the figurate numbers that are produced from figurate numbers; and that the triangular number is the principle of all the rest.—A speculation pertaining to the description of figurate numbers.

PLANE numbers thus subsisting, let us in the next place investigate what is consequent to their subsistence. All the squares which are disposed under triangles in a natural arrangement are generated from triangular numbers. Thus the square 4 is formed from the addition of 1 and 3, i.e. from two triangular numbers. Thus too, 9 is formed from 3 and 6; and both of these are triangles. But 16 is from the triangles 6 and 10; and 25 is from the triangles 10 and 15. And the same thing in the following order of squares will be found to take place perpetually without any variation. But pentagons are generated from the aggregation of squares and triangles. Thus the pentagon 5 is generated from the addition of the square 4 and the triangle 1. Thus too the pentagon 12 is formed from the aggregation of the square 9, and the triangle 3. The pentagon

22 is formed from the square 16, and the triangle 6; and the pentagon 35, from the square 25, and the triangle 10. And in a similar manner all other pentagons are formed.

If also we direct our attention to hexagons, we shall find that they are generated from the aggregation of triangles and pentagons. Thus the hexagon 6 is formed from the addition of the pentagon 5, and the first triangle in power 1. Thus too, the hexagon 15 is generated from the aggregation of the pentagon 12, and the triangle 3. Again, the hexagon 28, is formed from the pentagon 22, and the triangle 6. And in a similar manner the rest are formed.

Thus too in heptagons. For the heptagon 7 is generated from the hexagon 6, and the triangle 1. The heptagon 18, from the hexagon 15, and the triangle 3. And the heptagon 34, from the hexagon 28, and the triangle 6. And this will be found to take place in all multangular numbers. It is evident therefore that the triangular number is the principle of all figurate numbers.

All these, however, if they are composed with each other, i.e. triangles with squares, or squares with pentagons, or pentagons with hexagons, or these again with heptagons, will indubitably surpass each other by triangles. For if the triangle 3 is compared to the square 4, or the square 4 to the pentagon 5, or 5 to the hexagon 6, or 6 to the heptagon 7, they will surpass each other by the first triangle, i.e. by unity alone. But if 6 is compared to 9, or 9 to 12, or 12 to 15, or 15 to 18, they will surpass each other by the second triangle, i.e. by 3. Again, if 10 is compared to 16, or 16 to 22, or 22 to 28, or 28 to 34, they will surpass each other by the third triangle, i.e. by 6. And this will be the case with all other figurate numbers; for all of them will surpass each other by triangles. Hence, it is perfectly evident that the triangle is the principle and element of all forms.

CHAPTER X.

On solid numbers.—On the pyramid, that it is the principle of all solid figures, in the same manner as the triangle, of plane figures; and on its species.

HENCE, however, the way becomes easier to the contemplation of solid figures. For by foreknowing what the power of quantity naturally effects in the plane figures of numbers, there will be no impediment in the transition to solid numbers. For as we add to the length of numbers another interval, i.e. superficies, in order that breadth may be exhibited, so now by adding to breadth that which is called depth, the solid body of number will receive its completion.

It appears, however, that as in plane figures the triangular number is the first, so in solids that which is called the pyramid, is the principle of depth. For it is necessary to find the primordials of all the established figures in numbers. But one kind of pyramid is that which raises itself into altitude from a triangular base. Another kind is that which raises itself from a square base; another, from a pentagonal base; and others, from other multangular bases; as may be seen in the following diagrams:

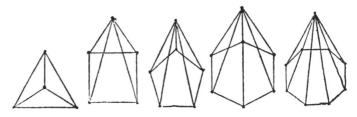

These pyramids also are denominated from their bases; so that the first is called a triangular; the second, a square; the third, a pentagonal; the fourth, an hexagonal pyramid; and so of the rest.

CHAPTER XI.

The generation of solid numbers.

As linear numbers are those which proceeding from unity extend to infinity, such as 1. 2. 3. 4. 5. 6, etc. and as superficial numbers are formed from the addition of these, in a similar manner solid are generated from the junction of superficial numbers. Thus, triangular pyramids are formed from the addition of triangular numbers; square pyramids from the addition of squares; pentagonal, from the addition of pentagons; and so of the rest.

The first triangle therefore, in power or capacity, is unity, and unity is also the first pyramid. But the second triangle is 3; and this added to 1 the first triangle, forms the second pyramid 4. If to these the third triangle 6 is added, the third pyramid 10 will be generated. And if to these, the fourth triangle 10 is added, the fourth pyramid 20 will be formed. In all the rest likewise, there will be the same mode of conjunction.

Triangles.
1 3 6 10 15 21 28 36 45 55
Pyramids from Triangles.
1 4 10 20 35 56 84 120 165 220

In this conjunction therefore, it is necessary that the last of the conjoined numbers should always be as it were the base of the pyramid. For it is found to be broader than all the rest; and all the numbers that are conjoined prior to it are necessarily less, till we arrive at unity, which in a certain respect obtains the place of a point and a vertex.

The pyramids also which are from the square, are generated by the addition of squares to each other, as will be evident from an inspection of the following schemes.

Squares.

1 4 9 16 25 36 49 64 81 100

Pyramids from Squares.

1 5 14 30 55 91 140 204 285 385

And after the same manner all the forms that proceed from the other multangles are produced. For every multangular form proceeds ad infinitum from unity, by the addition of unity to a figure of its own kind. Hence it necessarily appears, that triangular forms are the principles of the other figures; because every pyramid from whatever base it may proceed; whether from a square, or pentagon, or hexagon, or heptagon, etc. is contained by triangles alone, as far as to the vertex.

CHAPTER XII.

On defective pyramids.

As the pyramid is perfect which proceeding from a certain base arrives as far as to unity, which is the first pyramid in power and capacity; so the pyramid whose altitude does not reach to unity, is called defective. Thus, if to the square 16, the square 9 is added, and to this the square 4, but unity is omitted to be added, the figure indeed is that of a pyramid, but because it does not arrive as far as to the summit, it is called defective, and has not for its summit unity, which is analogous to a point, but a superficies. Hence if the base is a square, the ultimate superficies will be a square. And if the base is a pentagon, or hexagon, or heptagon, etc. the ultimate superficies will be of the same form as the base. If however, the pyramid does not only not arrive at unity and the extremity, but not even at the first multangle in energy, which is of the same kind as the base, it is called twice defective. Thus, if a pyramid proceeding from the square 16, should terminate in 9, and not arrive at 4, it will be twice defective; and in short, as many squares as are wanting, so many times is the pyramid said to be deficient. And all pyramids will be denominated in a similar manner, from whatever multangular base they may proceed.

CHAPTER XIII.

On the numbers called cubes, wedges, and parallelopipedons

And thus much concerning the solid numbers which have the form of a pyramid, equally increasing, and proceeding from a proper multangular figure as from a root. There is however another orderly composition of solid bodies, such as cubes, wedges, and parallelopipedons, the superficies of which are opposite to each other, and though extended to infinity will never meet. Squares therefore, being disposed in an orderly series, viz. 1. 4. 9. 16. 25, etc. because these have alone length and breadth, but are without depth; if each is multiplied by its side, it will have a depth equal to its breadth or length. For the square 4 has 2 for its side, and is produced from twice two. From the multiplication therefore of the square 4 by its side 2, the form of the cube 8 is generated. And this is the first cube in energy. Thus also the square 9 multiplied by its side 3, produces the cube 27. And the square 16 multiplied by its side 4 generates the cube 64. And after a similar manner the other cubes are formed. Every cube also, which is formed by the multiplication of a square into its side, will have six superficies, the plane of each of which is equal to its forming square. It will likewise have twelve sides, each of them equal to the side of the square by which it is produced;

and eight angles, each of which is contained under three such angles as those of its producing square.

Because also every cube proceeds from equilateral squares, it is equal in all its parts. For the length is equal to the breadth, and the depth, to each of these. It is likewise necessarily equal to itself according to six parts, viz. upward, downward, on the right hand, on the left hand, behind and before.

But it is requisite that the solid which is opposite and contrary to this, should be that which has neither the length equal to the breadth, nor the depth to either of these, but has all these unequal. Solids of this kind are such as thrice four multiplied by 2, or thrice four multiplied by 5, and the like, which unequally proceed through unequal degrees of spaces. Solids of this form are called in Greek *scalenoi scalene,* but in Latin *gradati,* because they increase like steps from the less to the greater. Certain Greeks also called them *spheniscoi;* i.e. *little wedges.* By some of the Greeks likewise they were called *bomiscoi,* i.e. certain *little altars,* which in the Ionic region of Greece, as Nicomachus says, were fashioned after this manner, so that neither the depth corresponded to the breadth, nor the breadth to the length. Between cubes therefore, extending themselves in equal spaces, and those solids which increase gradually from the less to the greater, those subsist as media, which are neither equal in all their parts, nor unequal in all; and these are called parallelopipedons.

CHAPTER XIV.

On the numbers called HETEROMEKEIS, *or,* LONGER IN THE OTHER PART;—*and on oblong numbers, and the generation of them*

THE numbers which are longer in one part than in the other when they are considered according to breadth, will be found to have four angles and four sides. They are not however all equal, but are always less by unity. For neither are all the sides equal to all, nor is the breadth equal to the length; but as we have said, one part being greater, it precedes and surpasses the less part by unity alone. If therefore the series of natural numbers is disposed in order, and the second is multiplied by the first, or the second by the third, or the third by the fourth, or the fourth by the fifth, and so on, the numbers called heteromekeis will be produced:

$$1.\ 2.\ 3.\ 4.\ 5.\ 6.\ 7.$$

Hence 2×1, 2×3, 3×4, 4×5, etc. i.e. 2, 6, 12, 20, etc. will be numbers longer in one part.

If therefore the numbers that are multiplied differ only from each other by unity, the above mentioned numbers will be produced. But if they differ by any other number, as thrice seven, or thrice five, etc. and their sides do not differ by unity alone, these numbers are not called *heteromekeis,* or longer in the other part, but *oblong.* For Pythagoras, and the heirs of his wisdom, ascribed *other* or the *different* to the binary or duad alone. And this they asserted to be the principle of difference. But they said that the primaeval and unbegotten monad was the principle of a nature always the same, and which is similar to, and in concord with itself. The duad however, is primarily dissimilar to the monad, because it is first disjoined from it; and therefore is the principle of a certain difference, because it is only dissimilar by unity to that primary essence which possesses an invariable sameness of subsistence. These numbers therefore, are deservedly called *longer in the other part,* because their sides precede each other by unity alone.

This however is an argument that difference is justly constituted in the binary number, that the term *other* or *different,* is only asserted of two things, by those who are not negligent in speaking accurately. Farther still, it has been shown that the odd number derives its completion from unity alone; but the even number from the duad alone. Hence, it must be said, that, the odd number participates of the essence which possesses an invariable sameness of subsistence, because it is formed by unity; but that the even number is full of the nature of difference, because it derives its completion from the duad.

CHAPTER XV.

That squares are generated from odd numbers; but the HETEROMEKEIS *from even numbers.*

IF all the odd numbers are arranged from unity, and under these are placed the even numbers from the duad, the coacervation of the odd numbers forms squares, but the coacervation of the even numbers produces the above mentioned numbers called heteromekeis. Hence, because this is the nature of squares, that they are generated from odd numbers, which participate of the monad, i.e. of an essence invariably the same, and because they are equal in all their parts, angles being equal to angles, sides to sides, and breadth to length, it must be said that numbers of this kind participate of the immutable essence. But we must assert that those numbers which parity or evenness generates *longer in the other part,* participate of the nature of difference. For as 1 differs only from 2 by 1, so the sides of these numbers differ only from each other by unity. Let therefore all the odd numbers be disposed in order from unity, and under these all the even numbers from 2, viz.

$$1. \quad 3. \quad 5. \quad 7. \quad 9. \quad 11. \quad 13.$$
$$2. \quad 4. \quad 6. \quad 8. \quad 10. \quad 12. \quad 14.$$

The leader therefore of the odd series is unity, which is itself the efficient cause, and after a manner a certain form of imparity. Hence, in consequence of its sameness and immutable nature, when it mutiplies itself, either in breadth or depth, it still retains its own form, or if it multiplies any other number by itself, the number which it multiplies does not recede from its own quantity;—a property which cannot be found in any other number. But the duad is the leader of the even series, and is likewise the principle of all difference. For if it multiplies itself either in breadth or depth, or any other number, a number different from itself immediately produced. Squares however are produced by adding the terms in the above series of odd numbers to each other. Thus $1+3=4$, (1 being the first square in power), $1+3+5=9$, $1+3+5+7=16$, $1+3+5+7+9=25$, and so of the rest. But from the addition of the terms in the series of even numbers, the heteromekeis are produced. For the first term of the series 2 is produced from twice one. But $2+4=6$, and 6 is produced from 3 multiplied by 2. Again $2+4+6=12$, and 12 is produced from 4 multiplied by 3. And after a similar manner all the rest are produced.

CHAPTER XVI.

On the generation of the numbers called LATERCULI *or tyles, and of those denominated asseres or planks.—Their definition; and, On circular or spherical numbers.*

THE numbers called *laterculi,* which are also themselves solids, are generated after the following manner. When spaces are equally extended in length and breadth, but have a less depth, the solid produced from these is a *laterculus.* Of this kind are $3\times3\times2=18$, or $4\times4\times2=32$, or any other of a similar formation. But they are defined to be solids produced by the multiplication of equal numbers equally into a less number. The solids however called *asseres* or *planks,* are produced from equal terms multiplied equally into a greater term, such as $4 \times 4 \times 9 = 144$. But the *spheniscoi,* or *little wedges* are such as are multiplied by unequal numbers into unequal numbers. And cubes are produced from equal numbers equally through such as are equal.

Those cubes however, which are of such a kind that the extremity of their depth terminates in the same number as that from which the side of the cubic quantity began, are denominated spherical; and such are the multiplications which proceed from the numbers 5 and 6. For $5 \times 5 = 25$, the multiplication beginning from 5 and ending in 5. And again $25 \times 5 = 125$. And if this again is multiplied by 5, the extremity will be terminated by 5. Nor will there be any variation in the terminating number, though the multiplication should be continued ad infinitum. The same thing also will take place in the involutions of 6.* But these numbers are called circular or spherical, because in the same manner as a circle or sphere, they terminate in the principle from which they originated. The monad also, is in capacity or power a circle and a sphere; because in all the multiplications of itself, it terminates in itself from whence it began. If there is only one multiplication therefore, a plane is produced, and it becomes a circle; but by a second multiplication, a sphere is formed. For the second multiplication is always effective of depth.

CHAPTER XVII.

On the nature of sameness and difference, and what the numbers are which participate of these.

AND thus much may suffice at present concerning solid figures. But those who have been most skilful in investigating

* The number 5 in all the multiplications by itself has always 2 preceding the

the principles of things, and who have given a twofold division to the nature of all beings,—these assert that the essences
of all things consist of sameness and difference, the former of
which is the cause of an immutable, and the latter of a variable
mode of subsistence. These two principles likewise, pertain to
the monad and the duad, the latter of which being the first
number that departs from the monad, becomes on this account
different. And because all odd numbers are formed according
to the nature of the monad, and the numbers arising from the
addition of these are squares, hence squares are said to be
participants of sameness in a twofold respect, because they are
formed from equality, each being produced by the multiplication of a number into itself, and both angles and sides being
equal to each other, and because they are generated from the
coacervation of odd numbers. But even numbers, because
they are the forms of the binary number, and the aggregates of
these form the numbers that are *longer in the other part,* are
said, through the nature of the duad to depart from the nature of sameness, and to be participants of difference. Hence,
since the sides of squares proceeding from equality tend to
equality, the numbers that are *longer in the other part,* by the
addition of unity depart from the equality of sides, and on
this account are conjoined from sides that are dissimilar, and
in a certain respect *different* from each other. Every thing
incorporeal therefore, form its immutability participates of the
nature of *sameness,* and every thing corporeal, from its mutable and variable essence, participates of the nature of *difference.*

It must now therefore be shown, that all the species of numbers, and all habitudes, whether of relative discrete quantity,

---

final number; but 6 in the multiplications by itself, has either 1, 3, 5, 7, or 9,
preceding the final number, as is evident in the following numbers, 36, 216, 1296,
7776, 46656, 279936, 1679616, &c.

such as those of multiples, or superparticulars, etc., or of discrete quantity considered by itself, are comprehended in this twofold nature of numbers, viz. of squares, and numbers *longer in the other part.* Hence as the world consists of an immutable and mutable essence, so every number is formed from squares which partake of immutability, and from numbers *longer in the other part,* which participate of mutability. And in the first place, the numbers that are *promekeis* or oblong, must be distinguished from those that are *heteromekeis,* or *longer in the other part.* For the latter is produced by the multiplication of two numbers that differ from each other by unity, such as 6 which is produced by 2 multiplied by 3, or 12 which is produced by 4 multiplied by 3. But the oblong number is produced by the multiplication of two numbers that differ from each other by more than unity, such as thrice five, or thrice six, or four times seven. Hence, because it is more extended in length than in breadth, it is very properly called *promekes,* or *longer in the anterior part.* But squares, because their breadth is equal to their length, may aptly be denominated *of a proper length,* or *of the same breadth.* And the *heteromekeis* because they are not extended in the same length, are called *of another length,* and *longer in the other part.*

CHAPTER XVIII.

That all things consist of sameness and difference; and that the truth of this is primarily to be seen in numbers.

EVERY thing, however, which in its proper nature and essence is immoveable, is terminated and definite; since that which is changed by no variation, never ceases to be, and never can be that which it was not. The monad is a thing of this kind: and those numbers which derive their formation from the monad, are said to be definite, and to possess a sameness of subsistence. These, however, are such as increase from equal numbers, as squares, or those which unity forms, i.e. odd numbers. But the binary, and all the numbers that are *longer in the other part,* in consequence of departing from a definite essence, are said to be of a variable and infinite nature. Every number, therefore, consists of the odd and the even, which are very remote from and contrary to each other. For the former is stability; but the latter unstable variation. The former possesses the strength of an immoveable essence; but the latter is a moveable permutation. And the former is definite; but the latter is an infinite accumulation of multitude. These, however, though contrary, are after a manner mingled in friendship and alliance; and through the forming power and dominion of unity, produce one body of number. Those, therefore, who have reasoned about the world, and this common nature of things, have neither uselessly, nor improvidently made this to be the first division of the essence of the universe. And Plato, indeed, in the Timaeus, calls every thing that the world contains the progeny of sameness and difference; and asserts, that there is one thing which is always real being, and indivisible without generation, but another which is generated, or continually rising into existence, and divisible, but never truly is. But Philolaus says, it is necessary that whatever exists should be either infinite or finite; for he wished to demonstrate that all things consists of either infinites or finites, according to the similitude of number. For this is formed from the junction of the monad and duad, and from the odd and the even; which evidently belong to the same series as equality and inequality, sameness and difference, the definite and the indefinite. Hence, it is not without reason asserted, that all things that consist of contraries, are conjoined and composed by a certain harmony. For harmony is a union of many things, and the consent of discordant natures.

CHAPTER XIX.

That from the nature of the numbers which are characterized by sameness, and from the nature of those which are characterized by difference, viz. from squares, and numbers LONGER IN THE OTHER PART, *all the habitudes of proportions consist.*

LET there be now therefore disposed in an orderly series, not even and odd numbers, from which squares and numbers *longer in the other part* are produced, but the two latter species of numbers themselves. For thus we shall see a certain consent of them, in the production of the other species of number. Let there be two series, therefore, the one of squares from unity; but the other of numbers *longer in the other part* from the duad, viz.

$$1. \quad 4. \quad 9. \quad 16. \quad 25. \quad 36. \quad 49.$$
$$2. \quad 6. \quad 12. \quad 20. \quad 30. \quad 42. \quad 56.$$

If, therefore, the first term of the one series is compared with the first term of the other, the quantity of the duple will be found, which is the first species of multiplicity. But if the second term of the one is compared with the second term of the other, the habitude of the sesquialter quantity is produced. If the third is compared with the third, sesquitertian ratio is generated. If the fourth with the fourth, sesquiquartan; and if the fifth with the fifth sesquiquintan ratio. And thus proceeding *ad infinitum,* superparticular ratio will be invariably produced. In the first ratio, however, which is that of the duple, the difference between the two terms is only 1; but in the sesquialter ratio, the difference is 2. In the sesquitertian ratio, the difference is 3. In the sesquiquartan it is 4. And thus, according to the superparticular form of numbers, the difference continually increases by 1. If again, the second square is com-

pared with the first number *longer in the other part,* the third
with the second, the fourth with the third, and the fifth with
the fourth, etc. the same ratios will be produced as those above
mentioned. Here, however, the differences do not begin from
unity, but they proceed from the binary number through the
same terms *ad infinitum.* And the second term of the one
series will be double the first term of the other. The third of
the one will be sesquialter of the second of the other. The
fourth will be sesquitertian of the third; and so on according
to the concord above demonstrated.

Again, squares differ from each other by odd numbers; but
the heteromekeis by even numbers.

Odd differences.

3.	5.	7.	9.	11.	13.	
1.	4.	9.	16.	25.	36.	49.

Squares.

Even differences.

4.	6.	8.	10.	12.	14.	
2.	6.	12.	20.	30.	42.	56.

Heteromekeis.

But if the first number *longer in the other part,* is placed
between the first and second square, it is conjoined to both of
them by one ratio; for in each of the ratios, the multiplicity of
the duple is found. If also the second number *longer in the
other part,* is placed between the second and third square, the
form of the sesquialter ratio to both terms will be produced.
And if the third of these numbers is placed between the third
and fourth square, the sesquitertian ratio will be generated.
And by proceeding in this way in the rest, all the superparticular species will be found to be produced.

Again; if two of the above squares are added together, and
the number *longer in the other part* which is a medium be-

tween them, is multiplied by 2, and added to the sum of the
two squares, the aggregate will be a square number. Thus 1
+4=5, and 5 added to twice 2 is equal to 9. Thus too 4+9
=13, and 13 added to twice 6, is equal to 25; and so of the
rest. But if the process is converted, and between the two first
terms *longer in the other part,* the second square is placed,
which is in order the second, but in energy the first; and if this
square is doubled, and is added to the sum of the two other
terms, the aggregate will again be a square. Thus 2 added to
6, added to twice 4, is equal to the square 16. Thus too, if
the second and third terms *longer in the other part* are added
together, and to their sum the double of the third square is
added, viz. if to 12+6=18 the double of 9 is added, the
aggregate will be the square 36. And thus also, 12+20=32,
added to twice 16, is equal to the square 64; and so of the rest.

This too, is no less admirable, that when a number *longer in
the other part* is placed as a medium between two squares, and
a square by the above process is produced from the three terms,
the square so produced has always an odd number for its side.
Thus from 1+4 and twice 2 the square 9 is produced, the side
of which is the odd number 3. And the square 25 which is
produced from 4+9, and twice 6, has for its side the odd number 5. Thus likewise, the square 49, arising from the addition
of 9, 16, and twice 12, has for its side the odd number 7. And
the like will be found to take place in the rest.

But when one square subsists between two numbers *longer
in the other part,* all the squares produced from them will have
even numbers for their sides. Thus the square 16, produced
from the addition of 2, 6, and twice 4, has for its side the even
number 4. Thus too, the square 36, arising from the addition
of 6, 12, and twice 9, has for its side the even number 6. And
thus also the square 64, produced by the addition of 12, 20,

and twice 16, has for its side the even number 8; and so of the rest.

CHAPTER XX.

That from squares and numbers LONGER IN THE OTHER PART, *all numerical figures consist.—How numbers* LONGER IN THE OTHER PART, *are produced from squares and vice versa, the latter from the former, etc.*

NOR does it less deserve to be considered, that from these two, all figures are produced. For triangles which are the elements of all the other arithmetical forms, as we have before shown, arise from the aggregates of these. Thus from 1 which is the first square in power or capacity, and 2 which is the first number longer in the other part, the triangle 3 is formed. Thus also from 2, and 4 the second square, the triangle 6 is generated. From 4 likewise and 6, the triangle 10 arises; and so of the rest. For let squares and numbers *longer in the other part,* be arranged alternately, and let the triangles produced by the addition of them, be placed under them as follows.

Squares and heteromekeis alternately arranged.

1.	2.	4.	6.	9.	12.	16.	20.	25.	30.	36.	42.
3.	6.	10.	15.	21.	28.	36.	45.	55.	66.	78.	

Triangles.

But every square, if its side is either added to, or taken from it, becomes a number *longer in the other part.* Thus, if to the square 4 its side 2 is added, the sum is 6, and if 2 be taken from 4, the remainder is 2, and both 6 and 2 are numbers *longer in the other part.* Thus too, by adding 3 to 9, and by taking 3 from it, 12 and 6 are produced; and these are numbers *longer in the other part.* This, however, arises from the

great power of difference. For every finite and definite
power, when it departs from the nature of equality, and from
an essence which contains itself within its own bounds, either
becomes exuberant or deficient, verges to the greater, or de-
clines to the less. And, on the contrary, by taking the side of
the square from the greater, or adding it to the less number
longer in the other part, the intermediate square will be produced. Thus 6—2, or 2+2 is equal to 4.

Hence it appears in the first place, that the monad is the
principle of an essence which is properly immutable and the
same; but that the duad is the principle of difference and mutation. In the second place it appears that all odd numbers on
account of their alliance to the monad, participate of the essence which is invariably the same; but that even numbers
on account of their alliance to the duad, are mingled with
difference. Thus too, squares, because their composition and
conjunction is from odd numbers, participate of an immutable
essence; but numbers *longer in the other part,* because they
are generated from the conjunction of even numbers, are never
separated from the variety of difference.

CHAPTER XXI.

*What agreement there is in difference and in ratio, between
squares and numbers* LONGER IN THE OTHER PART, *when they
are alternately arranged.*

IF, therefore, squares and numbers *longer in the other part,*
are arranged in an alternate order, there is so great a conjunction between these, that at one time they accord in the same
ratios, but are discordant in their differences; and at another
time they are equal in their differences, but discordant in their

ratios. Let them, therefore, be alternately arranged from unity as follows: 1. 2. 4. 6. 9. 12. 16. 20. 25. 30. In this arrangement we shall find, that between 1 which is the first square in capacity, and 2, there is a duple ratio; and that between 2 and 4, the ratio is also duple. Here, therefore, a square is joined to a number *longer in the other part,* and this to the following square, in the same ratio, but not with the same differences. For the difference between 2 and 1 is unity alone, but between 4 and 2 the difference is 2. Again, if 4 is compared to 2 the ratio is duple, but if 6 is compared to 4 the ratio is sesquialter. Here then, the terms are discordant in ratios, but equal in differences. For the difference between 4 and 2 is 2, and there is the same difference between 6 and 4. In the following also, after the same manner as in the first numbers, the ratio is the same, but the differences are not the same. Thus 4 is joined to 6, and 6 to 9 by a sesquialter ratio; but 6 surpasses 4 by 2, and 9 surpasses 6 by 3. In the terms that follow likewise, at one time the ratios are the same, but the differences not the same; and at another, vice versa, the differences are the same, but the ratios are different. The squares too, and numbers longer in the other part, surpass each other in their differences according to the series of natural numbers, but with a duplication of the terms, as is evident from the following scheme.

1.	2.	4.	6.	9.	12.	16.	20.	25.	30.	36.
	1.	2.	2.	3.	3.	4.	4.	5.	5.	6.

Differences.

That the agreement and difference however, of these two species of numbers may become more apparent, let there be two series of them, in the former of which numbers *longer in the other part* come between the squares, and in the latter squares, between numbers *longer in the other part* as below:

| Unequal differences. | 1. | 2. | 2. | 3. | 3. | 4. | 4. | 5. | 5. | 6, |

| Numbers *longer in the other part,* between squares. | 1. | 2. | 4. | 6. | 9. | 12. | 16. | 20. | 25. | 30. | 36, |

| Equal differences. | 2. | 2. | 3. | 3. | 4. | 4. | 5. | 5. | 6. | 6, |

| Squares between numbers *longer in the other part.* | 2. | 4. | 6. | 9. | 12. | 16. | 20. | 25. | 30. | 36. | 42, |

In the first of these series it is evident that the numbers *longer in the other part,* accord in ratio with the squares between which they are inserted; but are discordant in differences. Thus 2 is to 1 as 4 to 2. And 6 is to 4 as 9 to 6. And 12 is to 9 as 16 to 12. And so of the rest. But the difference between 1 and 2 is 1; but between 2 and 4 is 2. The difference between 4 and 6 is 2; but between 6 and 9 is 3. The difference between 9 and 12 is 3; but between 12 and 16 is 4. And so of the rest. But in the second of these series the differences are equal; but the ratios are discordant. For 4 is not to 2 as 6 to 4. Nor is 9 to 6 as 12 to 9. Nor is 16 to 12 as 20 to 16. Hence it is evident that squares when they come between numbers *longer in the other part,* preserve an arithmetical mean; but that numbers *longer in the other part,* when they come between squares preserve a geometrical mean. Thus 4 is an arithmetical mean between 2 and 6. Thus too 9 is an arithmetical mean between 6 and 12. And this is the case with 16 between 12 and 20. And so of the rest. But in the other series 2 is a geometrical mean between 1 and 4; 6 between 4 and 9; 12 between 9 and 16. And so on.

In the first series also, the differences are unequal in quantity, but equal in denomination. Thus the difference between 1 and 2 is 1, but between 2 and 4, the difference is 2. In quantity, however, 1 and 2 are unequal, but in appellation equal. For each is the whole of the less, and the half of the greater quantity. For 1 is the whole of 1 to which it is equal, and is the half of 2. Thus also the difference 2 is the whole of 2 to which it is equal, and the half of 4. Again, 2 is the difference of 4 and 6, and 3 is the difference of 6 and 9. And these are unequal in quantity, but equal in denomination. For in each the difference is the half of the less, and the third of the greater number. For 2 is the half of 4, and the third of 6. And 3 is the half of 6, but the third of 9. After the same manner 3 is the difference between 9 and 12, and 4 is the difference between 12 and 16; and these are unequal in quantity, but equal in denomination; since each is the third part of the less, and the fourth part of the greater. And so of the rest. Hence it is evident that the differences proceed from the whole through every part. For the first and second differences are the whole and the second part. The third and fourth differences are the second and third parts. The fifth and sixth differences, are the third and fourth parts. And in a similar manner in the rest.

On the contrary, in the second series, the differences are equal in quantity, but unequal in denomination. For of the two first terms 2 and 4, the difference is 2, and this is also the difference of 4 and 6. These differences, therefore, are equal in quantity. The difference 2, however, though it is the whole of the less of the terms, is only the half of the less of the second terms. And though it is the half of the greater of the first terms, it is only the third part of the greater of the second terms. Thus also the difference between 6 and 9 is 3, and the same likewise is the difference between 9 and 12. But this difference is the second part of the less of the first, but the third part of the less of the second terms. The same also is the third part of the greater of the first, but is only the fourth part of the greater of the second terms. And so of the rest.

CHAPTER XXII.

A demonstration that squares and cubes partake of the nature of sameness.

It is a most evident sign that all squares are allied to odd numbers, because in every arrangement of them, whether in a duple or triple series of terms, from unity, they are never found but in the place of an odd number according to the natural series of numbers. And they will also be found to be in the place of odd numbers in a quadruple, quintuple, etc. series, though it is not true in these series, that they are found in these places alone. For let numbers be disposed in an orderly series, first the duple, then the triple, etc. as follows:

The places of odd numbers.	1	3		5		7	
The duple series.	1 2	4	8	16	32	64	128
The triple series.	1 3	9	27	81	243	729	2187
The quadruple series.	1 4	16	64	256	1024	4096	16384
The quintuple series.	1 5	25	125	625	3125	15625	78125
The sextuple series.	1 6	36	216	1296	7776	46656	279936

Here in the duple and triple series, it will be found that all the squares are in the places of the odd numbers. Thus 4 and 9 are in the place of 3; 16 and 81 are in the place of 5; and 64 and 729 are in the place of 7. And so of the rest. But in the quadruple series, the numbers which are in the second and fourth places (and these are the places of even numbers) viz. 4 and 64 are also squares, as well as those which are in the third, fifth, etc. places.

Cubes also, though they have three intervals, yet on account of the equal multiplication by which they are produced, par-

ticipate of an immutable essence, and are the associates of
sameness; for they are generated by the coacervation of odd,
but never by that of even numbers. For if all the odd numbers
are disposed in an orderly series from unity, viz.

$$1 \quad 3 \quad 5 \quad 7 \quad 9 \quad 11 \quad 13 \quad 15 \quad 17 \quad 19 \quad 21$$

the addition of these will form cube numbers. Thus, since 1
is the first cube in power or capacity, if the two following
numbers, i.e. 3 and 5, are added together, their sum will be the
second cube, which is 8. If the three numbers also that follow
these are added together, viz. 7. 9. 11. their sum 27 will be the
third cube. And the four following numbers, 13, 15, 17, 19
will, when added together, produce the fourth cube, viz. 64.
And so of the rest.

CHAPTER XXIII.

On proportionality, or analogy.

AND thus much may suffice concerning these particulars.
It is now requisite that we should discuss what pertains to
ratios, so far as may be necessary to a knowledge of the theoretic part of music, astronomy, and geometry, and of the philosophy of Plato and Aristotle. Proportionality, therefore, is the
collection into one, of two, or more than two ratios.* Or according to a more common definition, it is the similar habitude
of two or more ratios, though they are not constituted in the
same quantities and differences. But difference is the quantity
between numbers; and ratio is a certain habitude, and as it
were, connexion of two terms to each other; the composition

---

* Analogy is most accurately defined by Proclus on the Timæus of Plato, to be,
identity of ratio, and the most beautiful of bonds.

of which produces that which is proportional or analogous. For proportionality arises from the junction of ratios. The least proportionality, however, is found in three terms, such as 4, 2, 1. For as 4 is to 2, so is 2 to 1; the proportionality consisting of two ratios, each of which is a duple ratio. Proportionality, however, may consist in any number of terms greater than three. Thus in the four terms 8, 4, 2, 1, as 8 is to 4, so is 4 to 2, so is 2 to 1; and in all these the proportionality consists of duple ratios. This will also be the case in the five terms 16, 8, 4, 2, 1; and in the six terms 32, 16, 8, 4, 2, 1, and so on *ad infinitum*. As often, therefore, as one and the same term so communicates with two terms placed about it, as to be the antecedent to the one, and the consequent to the other, this proportionality is called continued, as in the instances above adduced. But if one term is referred to one number, and another to another number, it is necessary that the habitude should be called disjunct. Thus in the terms 1, 2, 4, 8, as 2 is to 1, so is 8 to 4, and conversely as 1 is to 2, so is 4 to 8. And alternately as 4 is to 1, so is 8 to 2.

CHAPTER XXIV.

On the proportionality which was known to the ancients, and what the proportions are which those posterior to them have added.—And on arithmetical proportionality, and its properties.

THE three middles which were known to the more ancient mathematicians, and which have been introduced into the philosophy of Pythagoras, Plato, and Aristotle, are, the arithmetical, the geometrical, and the harmonic. After which habitudes of proportions, there are three others without an appropriate appellation; but they are called the fourth, fifth, and sixth, and are opposite to those above mentioned. The philosophers however, posterior to Plato and Aristotle, on account of the perfection of the decad according to Pythagoras, added four other middles, that in these proportionalities a decad might be formed. It is indeed in conformity to this number, that the former five habitudes and comparisons, which we have discussed, are described; where to the five greater proportions, which we called leaders, we adapted other less terms which we called attendants. Hence it is evident, that in the description of the ten predicaments by Aristotle, and prior to him by Archytas (though it is considered as dubious by some, whether these predicaments were invented by Archytas), the Pythagoric decad is to be found.

Let us now, however, direct our attention to proportionalities and middles. And, in the first place, let us discuss that middle which preserves the habitudes of terms according to equality of quantity, neglecting similitude of ratio. But with these quantities that middle is conversant in which there is an equal difference of the terms from each other. What the difference of terms is, however, has been before defined. And that this middle is arithmetical, the ratio itself of numbers will evince, because its proportion consists in the quantity of number. What then is the reason that the arithmetical habitude is prior to all other proportionalities? In the first place, it is because the natural series of numbers in which there is the same difference of the terms, comprehends this middle. For the terms differ from each other by unity, by the fecundity of which the nature of number is first unfolded. In the second place, it is because, as was observed in the first chapter of the first book, arithmetic is prior both to geometry and music; the two latter cointroducing at the same time the former; and the former when subverted, subverting the two latter. The discussion, therefore, will proceed in order, if we first begin from that middle which is alone conversant with the difference of number.

That is called an arithmetical middle, therefore, when three or more terms being given, an equal and the same difference is found between all of them; in which the identity of ratio being neglected, the difference only of the terms is considered. Thus in the natural series of numbers 1. 2. 3. 4. 5. 6. 7. 8. 9. 10, the differences are equal, but there is not the same ratio and habitude. If, therefore, three terms are given, the proportionality is said to be continued. But if there are four or more terms, the middle is called disjunct. Whether, however, the terms are three or four, or any other number, there will always be the same difference of the terms, the ratios only being changed. Thus the differences of the terms 1. 2. 3. are the same, but the ratios are different. For 2 to 1 is a duple, but 3 to 2 is a sesquialter ratio. And the same thing will take place in the other terms.

If, also, an equal number of terms are omitted, the differences will be equal, but the ratios different. Thus if one term is omitted, the difference will be 2; for then the terms will be 1. 3. 5. the difference between which is 2. But the ratio of 3 to 1 is very different from that of 5 to 3. If two terms are omitted, the difference will be 3; if three terms are omitted, it will be 4; and so of the rest, both in continued and disjunct proportions. But the quality of the ratio will not be the same, though the terms are distributed by equal differences. If, however, conversely, there should be the same quality of ratio, but not the same differences, such proportionality is called geometrical, but not arithmetical.

It is the peculiarity of this middle, that in three terms, the sum of the extremes is double the mean; as in 1. 2. 3, $1+3=4=2\times2$. But if there are four terms, the sum of the extremes is equal to the sum of the two means. Thus if the terms are 1. 2. 3. 4., $1+4=2+3$.

This also is a very subtile property of this proportion, which no one of the ancients who were skilled in the mathematical disciplines discovered, except Nicomachus, that in every continued arrangement of terms, the rectangle under the extremes, is less than the square of the middle, by the product arising from one difference multiplied by the other. Thus in the three terms, 3, 5, 7, $3\times7=21$, and $5\times5=25$. And 21 is less than 25 by 4, which is equal to the difference between 3 and 5 multiplied by the difference between 5 and 7, viz. is equal to 2×2. But if there are four terms, the rectangle under the extremes is less than the rectangle under the means by the product arising from the difference between the greatest of the terms, and one of the means, multiplied by the difference between the same mean and the least term. Thus in the four terms 12. 10. 4. 2., $12\times2=24$, and $10\times4=40$, and 24 is less than 40 by 16, which is equal to the difference between 12 and 10, i.e. 2 multiplied by the difference between 10 and 2, i.e. 8; for $2\times8=16$. And it is also equal to the difference between 12 and 4. i.e. 8 multiplied by the difference between 4 and 2, i.e. 2. And so in other instances.

Another peculiarity likewise of this proportionality, which was known to those who were prior to Nicomachus is this, that in less terms a greater ratio, but in greater terms a less ratio, is necessarily found. Thus in the numbers 1. 2. 3., the ratio of the less terms, i.e. of 2 to 1 is double; but the ratio of the greater terms, i.e. of 3 to 2 is sesquialter. And a duple is greater than a sesquialter ratio. Thus too, in four terms 12. 10. 8. 6., the ratio of 8 to 6 is greater than the ratio of 12 to 10. For the ratio of 12 to 10 is sesquiquintan, but that of 8 to 6 is sesquitertian. In harmonic proportionality, on the contrary, in less terms there is a less, but in greater terms a greater ratio, as will be hereafter shown. But of these middles, viz. the arithmetical and the harmonic, the geometric proportionality is the medium; for this preserves both in greater and less terms an equality of ratio. And equality is the medium between the greater and the less.

CHAPTER XXV.

On the geometrical middle and its properties.

IT is now requisite to discuss the geometrical which follows the arithmetical middle, and which alone or principally, may be called proportionality or analogy; because both in the greater and the less terms of which it consists, there is found to be the same ratio. For here the same ratio is always preserved, and contrary to the arithmetical middle, the quantity of the number is neglected. Thus, in the duple series, 1. 2. 4. 8. 16. 32. etc. or in the triple series, 1. 3. 9. 27. 81. etc. or in any other, whether quadruple or quintuple, etc. the prior to the following number, will always be in the same ratio as the following to another number that is immediately consequent to it. Thus, if there are three terms 2. 4. 8. it will be $2:4::4:8$, and conversely $8:4::4:2$. And in four terms 2. 4. 8. 16, it will be $2:4::8:16$, and conversely $16:8::4:2$. And in a similar manner in all the rest.

The peculiarity of this middle is, that in every arrangement of the terms, the differences are in the same ratio to each other, as the terms of which they are the differences. For if the terms are double of each other, the differences also will be double; if the former are triple, the latter will be likewise triple; if the one is quadruple, the other also will be quadruple. And whatever the multiplicity of the terms may be, there will be the same multiplicity in the differences, as will be evident from an inspection of the following schemes:

Duple differences.

1.	2.	4.	8.	16.	32.	64.	128.
1.	2.	4.	8.	16.	32.	64.	128.

Duple terms.

Triple differences.

2.	6.	18.	54.	162.	486.	1458.	
1.	3.	9.	27.	81.	243.	729.	2187.

Triple terms.

Quadruple differences.

3.	12.	48.	192.	768.	3072.	12288.	
1.	4.	16.	64.	256.	1024.	4096.	16384.

Quadruple terms.

There is also another peculiarity of this middle, that where the ratios are duple, every greater term compared to the less has for its difference the less term. Thus 2 compared to 1 differs from it by 1. Thus 4 compared to 2 differs from it by 2. And thus 8 compared to 4 differs from it by 4. And so of the rest. But if the ratios are triple, the greater term differs from the less by the double of the less term. Thus 3 differs from 1 by 2 the double of 1. Thus 9 differs from 3 by 6 the double of 3. And thus 27 differs from 9 by 18 the double of 9. And in all the rest the same property will be found. If also the ratios are quadruple, the greater term will differ from the less by the triple of the less term. Thus 4 differs from 1 by 3 the triple of 1. Thus 16 differs from 4 by 12, the triple of 4. And thus 64 differs from 16 by 48, the triple of 16. And so of the rest. Thus likewise, if the ratios are quintuple, sextuple, etc. the greater term will always be found to differ from the less by the quantity of the ratio less by unity.

In continued geometrical proportionality also, the rectangle under the extremes is equal to the square of the mean. Thus in the three terms 2. 4. 8. which are in geometrical proportion, $2 \times 8 = 4 \times 4 = 16$. The same thing will also take place though there should be a greater number of terms than three, if the number of terms is odd. Thus in the five terms 16. 8. 4. 2. 1, the rectangle under the extremes, i.e. 16×1 is equal to the square of the middle term 4. Thus too in the seven terms 64. 32. 16. 8. 4. 2. 1., $64 \times 1 = 8 \times 8$. But where the terms are not continued, the rectangle under the extremes is equal to the rectangle under the means; as is evident in the terms 2. 4. 8. 16; for $2 \times 16 = 4 \times 8 = 32$. And if the terms are more than four, if only they are even, the same thing will take place. Thus in the six terms 2. 4. 8. 16. 32. 64, $2 \times 64 = 128 = 4 \times 32 = 8 \times 16$.

Another property of this middle is, that there is always an equal ratio both in the greater and the less terms. Thus in all the terms 2. 4. 8. 16. 32. 64, there is a duple ratio. This is likewise the case in the terms, 3. 9. 27. 81. 243. 729. And in a similar manner in others.

And in the last place, it is peculiar to this middle, squares and numbers *longer in the other part,* being alternately arranged, to proceed from the first multiple into all the habitudes of superparticular ratios, as will be evident from the following scheme.

		Squares and numbers longer in the other part, alternately arranged.							
1	2	4	6	9	12	16	20	25	30	37
Duple	Duple	Sesqui- alter	Sesqui- alter	Sesqui- tertian	Sesqui- tertian	Sesqui- quartan	Sesqui- quatan	Sesqui- qintan	Sesquiquintan
|	|	|	|	|	|	|	|	|	|

Hence the arithmetical middle is compared to an oligarchy, or the republic which is governed by a few, who pursue their own good, and not that of the community; because in its less terms there is a greater ratio. But the harmonic middle is said to correspond to an aristocracy, because there is a greater ratio in its greater terms. And the geometric middle is analogous to a popular government, in which the poor as well as the rich have an equal share in the administration. For in this there is an equality of ratio both in the greater and the less terms.*

CHAPTER XXVI

That plane numbers are conjoined by one medium only, but solid numbers by two media.

It is now time, however, that we should discuss certain things very useful to a knowledge of the fabrication of the world, as delivered in the Timaeus of Plato, but not obvious to every one. For all plane figures are united by one geometrical medium only; and hence in these there are only two intervals, viz. from the first to the middle, and from the middle to the third term. But cubes have two media according to a geometrical ratio; whence also solid figures are said to have three in-

---

* With respect to these three middles, the arithmetic, the geometric and the harmonic, Proclus in Tim. p. 238. observes "that they pertain to the three daughters of Themis, viz. Eunomia, Dice, and Irene. And the arithmetic middle indeed pertains to Irene or *peace,* which surpasses and is surpassed by an equal quantity, which middle we employ in our contracts during the time of peace, and through which likewise the elements are at rest. But the geometric middle pertains to Eunomia or *equitable legislation,* which also Plato denominates the judgment of Jupiter, and through which the world is adorned by geometrical analogies. And the harmonic middle pertains to Dice or Juctice, through which greater terms have a greater; but less, a less ratio."

The geometric middle also comprehends the other two. For let there be any three terms in arithmetical proportion, for instance 1. 2. 3, and let a fourth term be added which shall cause all the four to be in geometrical proportion. This fourth term will be 6. For 1:2::3:6. This analogy therefore, will comprehend both arithmetical and harmonical proportion. For 2. 3. and 6 are in harmonic, and 1. 2 and 3 in arithmetic proportion.

tervals. For there is one interval from the first to the second, another from the second to the third, and another from the third to the fourth, which is the ultimate distance. Plane figures, therefore, are very properly said to be contained by two, and solid, by three intervals. Let there be two squares, therefore, viz. 4 and 9. Of these, therefore, there can only be one medium constituted in the same ratio; and this medium is 6. For 6 is sesquialter to 4, and 9 is sesquialter to 6. This, however, takes place, because the side of the one square, multiplied by the side of the other, produces the middle term 6. For the side of 4 is 2, and of 9 is 3, and these multiplied together produce 6. Hence, in order to find the medium of two squares, their sides must be multiplied together, and the product will be the medium that is sought. But if two cubes are given, as 8 and 27, two media only can be constituted between these in the same ratio, viz. 12 and 18. For 12 to 8, and 18 to 27 are conjoined by a sesquialter ratio alone.

These two media also are found as follows: If the side of the greater cube is multiplied by the side of the less, and afterwards the product is multiplied by the less, the less of the two media will be obtained. But if the square of the side of the greater cube, is multiplied by the side of the less cube, the product will be the greater medium. Thus in the two cubes 8, and 27. The side of the greater cube is 3, and the side of the less is 2, and $3 \times 2 \times 2 = 12$, the less medium. And $3 \times 3 \times 2$ $= 18$, the greater medium. Thus too in the cubes 27 and 64. The side of the greater cube is 4, and the side of the less is 3, and $4 \times 3 \times 3 = 36$, the less medium. And $4 \times 4 \times 3 = 48$, the greater medium. Hence the less medium derives two sides from the less cube, and one side from the greater cube. And after the same manner the greater medium derives two sides from the greater cube, and one side from the less cube. Thus 12 the less medium between the cubes 8 and 27, has two sides from 8, and one side from 27; for $2\times2\times3=12$. And 18, the greater medium, has two sides from 27, and one side from 8; for $3\times3\times2=18$.

It is also universally true, that if a square multiplies a square, the product will be a square.* But if a number *longer in the other part,* multiplies a square, or *vice versa,* an oblong number, and not a square, will always be produced.† Again, if a cube multiplies a cube, the product will be a cube;‡ but if a number *longer in the other part,* multiplies a cube, or *vice versa,* the product will never be a cube.§ And this happens from a similitude to the even and the odd. For if an even multiplies an even number, the product will always be an even number.** And if an odd multiplies an odd number, an odd number will be immediately produced.†† But if an odd multiplies an even, or an even an odd number, an even number will always be produced.‡‡ This, however, will be more easily known, by consulting that part of the eighth book of the Republic of Plato, in which the Muses are introduced by the philosopher speaking of the geometric number, which is the source of better and worse generations, and which will be hereafter explained.

* Thus $4\times9=36$, which is a square number. Thus also $9\times16=144$, which is also a square number.

† Thus $2\times4=8$ an oblong number. Thus also 6 which is a number *longer in the other part,* multiplied by 9, is equal to 54, an oblong number.

‡ Thus $8\times27=216$ a cube number, the root of which is 6. Thus too, $8\times64=512$, a cube number, the root of which is 8.

§ Thus $2\times8=16$ which is not a cube. Thus also $6\times27=162$, a non-cubic number.

** Thus $6\times6=36$ an even number. Thus too, $8\times8=64$, which is an even number.

†† Thus $3\times5=15$; and $7\times9=63$, both which are odd numbers.

‡‡ Thus $5\times4=20$; and $6\times9=54$, both which are even numbers.

CHAPTER XXVII

On the harmonic middle and its properties.

THE harmonic middle is neither constituted in the same differences, nor in equal ratios; but in this, as the greatest term is to the least, so is the difference of the greatest and the middle, to the difference of the middle and the least term: as in the numbers 3. 4. 6, and 2. 3. 6. For as 6 is to 3, so is the difference between 6 and 4, i.e. 2, to the difference between 4 and 3, i.e. 1. And as 6 is to 2, so is the difference between 6 and 3, i.e. 3, to the difference between 3 and 2, i.e. 1. Hence in this middle, there is neither the same ratio of the terms, nor the same differences.

But it has a peculiarity, as we have before observed, contrary to the arithmetical middle. For in that, there is a greater ratio in the less, but a less ratio in the greater terms. On the contrary, in the harmonic middle, there is a greater ratio in the greater, but a less in the less terms. Thus in the terms 3. 4. 6. if 4 is compared to 3, the ratio is sesquitertian, but if 6 is compared to 4, the ratio is sesquialter. But sesquialter is as much greater than sesquitertian ratio, as $\frac{1}{2}$ is greater than $\frac{1}{3}$. With great propriety therefore, is geometrical proportionality said to be a medium between that in which there is a less ratio in the greater, and a greater in the less terms, and that in which there is a greater ratio in the greater, and a less in the less terms. For that is truly proportionality or analogy, which obtaining as it were the place of a medium, has equal ratios both in the greater and the less terms.

This also is a sign that geometrical proportion is a medium in a certain respect between two extremes; that in arithmetical proportion the middle term precedes the less, and is preceded by the greater, by the same part of itself, yet by one part of the less, and a different part of the greater term. Thus in the three terms, 2, 3, 4, the term 3 precedes 2, by a third part of itself, i.e. 1. and is preceded by 4 by the same part of itself. But 3 does not surpass 2 by the same part of 2, nor is surpassed by 4, by the same part of 4. For it surpasses 2 by 1, which is the half of 2, but it is surpassed by 4, by 1, which is the fourth part of 4. The ratios, however, in the harmonic middle, have a contrary mode of subsistence. For the middle term in this ratio, does not surpass the less, nor is surpassed by the greater, by the same part of itself; but it surpasses the less by the same part of the less, as is that part of the greater, by which it is surpassed by the greater. Thus in the harmonic arrangement, 2. 3. 6., the term 3 surpasses 2 by the half of 2, and the same 3 is surpassed by 6, by 3 which is the half of 6. But in the geometric proportionality, neither does the middle surpass the less term, nor is it surpassed by the greater term, by the same parts of itself, nor does it surpass the less term by the same part of the less, nor is surpassed by the greater by the same part of the greater; but by that part of itself, by which the middle surpasses the less term, by the same part of itself the greater surpasses the middle term. Thus in the three terms 4. 6. 9, the middle term 6 surpasses 4 by a third part of itself, and 9 also surpasses 6 by a third part of itself. The harmonic proportion also has another property, that if the two extremes are added together, and multiplied by the middle, the product will be double that of the extremes multiplied by each other. Thus in the terms 3. 4. 6, 3+6=9, and 9×4=36, which is the double of 3 multiplied by 6. Thus too, in the terms 2. 3. 6., 2+6=8, and 8×3=24, the double of 2×6=12.

In the harmonic proportionality likewise, the sum of the extremes is always more than double of the middle term. Thus in the numbers above adduced 6+3 is more than twice 4.

And 6+2 is more than twice 3. The extremes also multiplied by each other, exceed the square of the middle term by the product arising from the difference between one extreme and the middle, multiplied by the difference between the middle and the other extreme. Thus 3×6=18, which exceeds 16, the square of the middle term 4 by 2. And 2 is equal to the difference between 6 and 4, multiplied by the difference between 4 and 3. Thus too 2×6 exceeds 9 the square of 3, by 3. And 3 is equal to the difference between 6 and 3 multiplied by the difference between 3 and 2.

CHAPTER XXVIII

Why this middle is called harmonic, and on geometrical harmony.

THE reason, however, why this middle is called harmonic is this, that an arithmetical arrangement of terms, divides the quantities by equal differences only; but a geometrical arrangement conjoins the terms by an equal ratio. The harmonic arrangement, however, being more amply conversant with relation than the other middles, neither speculates ratio solely in the terms, nor solely in differences, but is in common conversant with both. For it shows that as the extreme terms are to each other, so is the difference between the greater and middle term, to the difference between the middle and last term. But that the consideration of what is relative, is peculiar to harmony, has been shown by us before.

The proportions also of the musical concords which are denominated symphonies, are frequently found in this middle alone. For the symphony diatessaron which is the principal, and after a manner possesses the power of an element with respect to the other symphonies, being constituted in a sesquitertian ratio, or that of 4 to 3, is found in harmonic middles of this kind. For let the terms of harmonic proportion be of such a kind as that the extremes are in a duple ratio, and again let there be other terms, the extremes of which are in a triple ratio, viz. let them be

3. 4. 6. and 2. 3. 6.

In the first arrangement, therefore, 6 is double of 3, and in the second, 6 is triple of 2. If the differences then of these are collected and compared to each other, a sesquitertian ratio will be produced, whence the symphony diatessaron is formed. For the difference between 6 and 3 is 3, and between 6 and 2 is 4, and 4 compared to 3, produces a sesquitertian ratio.

In the same middle also, the symphony diapente is formed from the sesquialter ratio. For in the first of the above arrangements, 6 to 4 is sesquialter, and in the second, 3 to 2. From each of which the symphony diapente is formed. In the next place, the symphony diapason which consists in a duple ratio, is formed in the first of these, viz. in the ratio of 6 to 3. In the second of the arrangements also, the symphonies diapente and diapason are formed, which preserve a sesquialter and a duple ratio. For of the terms 2. 3. 6., 3 to 2 is diapente, and 6 to 3 diapason. And because the extreme terms in this arrangement, which contains two symphonies, are in a triple ratio, the differences likewise of the terms will be found to be triple. For the difference between 3 and 2 is 1, and between 6 and 3, the difference is 3. But in the first of these arrangements, viz. 3. 4. 6., the greater term 6 is triple of the difference between it and the middle term, viz. is triple of 2. And again, the less term is also triple of the difference between it and the middle term, viz. 3 is triple of 1. The greatest symphony likewise which is called bis diapason, or as it were twice double, because the symphony diapason is collected from a duple ratio, is found in this harmonic middle. For in the arrangement 3. 4. 6., the middle term 4 is quadruple of 1, the difference between it and the less extreme. In the arrangement also, 2. 3. 6., the difference of the extremes 6 and 2 is quadruple of the difference between the middle and the less term; for the former difference is 4, but the latter 1. And the ratio of 4 to 1 forms the symphony bis diapason.

Some, however, call a middle of this kind harmonic, because it is allied to geometric harmony. But they denominate the cube geometric harmony. For its extension into length, breadth, and depth is such, that proceeding from equals, and arriving at equals, the whole increases equally, so as to accord with itself. The harmonic middle, however, is beheld in all cubes, which constitute geometric harmony. For every cube has 12 sides, or bounding lines, eight angles, and six superficies. But this arrangement is harmonic; for 6. 8. 12. are in harmonic proportion. For as 12 is to 6, so is the difference between 12 and 8 to the difference between 8 and 6. Again, 8 which is the medium, precedes the less term 6 by one part of itself, and is preceded by the greater term by another part of itself. But it surpasses the less term by the same part of the less, as is that part of the greater by which it is surpassed by the greater. Again, if the extremes are added together, and their sum is multiplied by the middle term, the product will be double the product arising from the multiplication of the extremes by each other. For $12+6=18$, and $18\times8=144$. But 144 is the double of $12\times6=72$.

All the musical symphonies, likewise, may be found in this arrangement. For the diatessaron, indeed, is the ratio of 8 to 6, because it is a sesquitertian ratio. But the diapente is the ratio of 12 to 8, because what is called sesquialter ratio, is found in that symphony. The diapason which is produced from a duple ratio, is found in the ratio of 12 to 6. But the diapason and at the same time, diapente, which is in a triple ratio, arises from a comparison of the difference of the extremes with the difference between the middle and the less extreme. For the difference between 12 and 6 is 6, and the difference between 8 and 6 is 2; and 6 is triple of 2. And the greater symphony which is the bis diapason, and consists in a quadruple ratio, is beheld in the comparison of 8 with the difference between 8 and 6, viz. in the comparison of 8 with 2. Hence a proportionality of this kind, is properly and appropriately called an harmonic middle.

CHAPTER XXIX

How two terms being constituted on either side, the arithmetic, geometric, and harmonic middle is alternately changed between them; and on the generation of them.

We ought, however, to show, that as when in musical pipe, the extreme holes remaining, it is usual, by changing the middle hole, and opening one and shutting another with the fingers, to cause them to emit different sounds; or as when two chords being extended on each side, the musician causes the sound of the intermediate chord to be either sharp or flat, by stretching or relaxing it; thus also, two numbers being given, we may insert between them, at one time an arithmetical, at another a geometrical, and at another an harmonic middle. We may, however, be able to change this middle, when placed between two terms that are either odd or even, so that when the middle is arithmetical, the ratio and equability of the differences only is preserved; but when it is geometrical, the conjunction of the ratios will remain firm; and if there is an harmonic comparison of the differences, it will not be discordant with the ratio of the terms. In the first place, therefore, let the extremities be the even numbers 10 and 40, between which it is required to insert all these middles. Let the arithmetical middle then be first inserted. And this will be effected, if 25 is placed between these numbers; for 10, 25, and 40, are in arithmetical proportion. Again, if between 10 and 40, the number 20 is inserted, the geometric middle, with all its properties, will be immediately produced; for as 10 is to 20, so is 20 to 40. But if 16 is inserted between 10 and 40, the harmonic middle will be produced; for as 10 is to 40, so is the difference between 16 and 10, i.e. 6, to the difference between 40 and 16, i.e. 24.

If odd numbers, however, are proposed as the two extremes, such as are 5 and 45, it will be found that 25 will constitute the arithmetical, 15 the geometrical, and 9 the harmonic middle.

It is necessary, however, to show how these middles may be found. Two terms being given, if it is required to constitute an arithmetical middle, the two extremes must be conjoined, and the sum arising from the addition of them must be divided by 2, and the quotient will be the arithmetical mean that was to be found. Thus 10+40=50, and 50 divided by 2 is equal to 25. This, therefore will be the middle term, according to arithmetical proportion. Or if the number by which the greater surpasses the less term, is divided by 2, and the quotient is added to the less term, the sum thence arising, will be the arithmetical mean required. Thus the difference between 40 and 10 is 30, and if this is divided by 2 the quotient will be 15. But if 15 is added to 10, the sum will be 25, the arithmetical mean between 10 and 40. Again, in order to find the geometrical mean, the two extremes must be multiplied together, and the square root of the product will be the required mean. Thus 10×40=400, and the square root of 400 is 20. Hence 20 will be the geometrical mean between 10 and 40. Or if the ratio which the given terms have to each other is divided by 2, the quotient will be the middle that was to be found. For 40 to 10 is a quadruple ratio. If this, therefore, is divided by 2, it will become duple, which is 20; for 20 is the double of 10. This, therefore, will be the geometrical mean, between the two given terms. But to find the harmonic middle, the difference of the terms must be multiplied into the less term; then the product must be divided by the sum of the extremes; and in the last place, the quotient must be added to the less term, and the sum will be the mean required. Thus the difference between 40 and 10 is 30; but $30 \times 10 = 300$; and 300 divided by $40 + 10 = 50$, gives for the quotient 6; and $6 + 10 = 16$, the harmonic mean between 10 and 40.

CHAPTER XXX

On the three middles which are contrary to the harmonic and geometric middles.

THE middles which we have now discussed, were invented and approved of by the more ancient mathematicians; and we have more largely unfolded them, because these are especially found in the writings of the ancients, and are most useful to a genuine knowledge of them. We shall therefore mention the other middles with brevity, because they are scarcely of any other use than that of giving completion to the duad. But these middles appear to be contrary to the former, from which they nevertheless originate. The fourth middle, however, is that which is opposite to the harmonic. For in the harmonic, as the greatest is to the least term, so is the difference between the greatest and the middle, to the difference between the middle and the least term, as in the terms 3. 4. 6; but in this fourth proportionality, three terms being given, as is the greatest to the least, so is the difference between the middle and least, to the difference between the greatest and middle terms;

as in 3. 5. 6. For as 6 is to 3, so is the difference between 5 and 3, i.e. 2, to the difference between 6 and 5. i.e. 1. But it appears that this middle is opposite, and after a manner contrary to the harmonic middle, because in the latter, as is the greatest to the least term, so is the difference of the greater to the difference of the less terms; but in the former, as is the greatest to the least term, so is the difference of the less to the difference of the greater terms. It is the peculiarity of this middle, that the rectangle under the greatest and middle terms, is double the rectangle under the middle and least terms. Thus $5 \times 6 = 30$; but $3 \times 5 = 15$. But the two other proportionalities, viz. the fifth and sixth, are contrary to the geometric proportionality, and appear to be opposite to it.

For the fifth is when in three terms, as is the middle to the less term, so is their difference to the difference between the middle and greater terms; as in the terms 2. 4. 5. For as 4 is to 2, so is the difference between 4 and 2, i.e. 2, to the difference between 5 and 4, i.e. 1. But this is contrary to geometric proportion, because there, as is the ratio of the greater to the less, i.e. to the middle, and of the middle to the least term, so is the difference of the greater to the difference of the less terms, as in 8. 4. 2. For the ratio of 8 to 4, and of 4 to 2, is the same as the ratio of 8—4, to the ratio of 4—2. But in the fifth proportionality, as is the ratio of the greater to the less term, so is the ratio of the difference of the less, to the difference of the greater terms. The peculiarity also of this proportionality is, that the rectangle under the greater term and the middle, is the double of the rectangle under the two extremes. Thus in the terms 2. 4. 5. $5 \times 4 = 20$, and 20 is the double of 5×2.

The sixth proportionality is when in three given terms, as is the greater to the middle term, so is the difference of the less, to the difference of the greatest terms; as in the terms 1. 4. 6.

For here the greatest is to the middle term in a sesquialter ratio; and the difference between 4 and 1, i.e. 3. is in the same ratio to the difference between 6 and 4, i.e. 2. For as 6:4::3:2. After the same manner also as the fifth, this proportionality is contrary to the geometrical, on account of the converse ratio of the differences of the less to the greater terms.

CHAPTER XXXI

On the four middles which the ancients posterior to those before mentioned, invented for the purpose of giving completion to the decad.

And these indeed are the six middles, three of which remained from Pythagoras as far as to Plato and Aristotle. But those that followed them inserted in their commentaries the three others, which we discussed in the preceding chapter. And the following age, as we have said, added four other middles, in order to the completion of the decad. What these are, therefore, we shall briefly relate. The first of them, which is in order the seventh, is when in three terms, as the greatest is to the last, so is the difference of the greatest and least term, to the difference of the less terms; as in the terms 6. 8. 9. For 9 to 6 is sesquialter, the difference of which is 3. But the difference of the less terms, i.e. of 8 and 6, is 2, which compared to the former 3 produces a sesquialter ratio.

Again, the second proportionality of the four, but the eighth in order is, when in three terms, as the extremes are to each other, so is their difference to the difference of the greater terms; as in 6. 7. 9. For 9 to 6 is sesquialter, and their difference is 3, which compared to the difference of the greater terms, i.e. to the difference of 9 and 7 which is 2, produces also a sesquialter ratio.

The third proportion among the four, but the ninth in order is, when three terms being given, as is the middle to the least term, so is the difference of the extremes to the difference of the less terms; as in 4. 6. 7. For 6 to 4 is sesquialter, the difference of which is 2. But 7 differs from 4 by 3, which is sesquialter to 2.

And the fourth proportion, but which is in order the tenth, is when in three terms, as is the middle to the least term, so is the difference of the extremes to the difference of the greater terms; as in 3. 5. 8. For 5 the middle term is to 3 in a super-bipartient ratio. But the difference of the extremes is 5, which to the difference of the greater terms 8 and 5, i.e. 3, is also superbipartient.*

CHAPTER XXXII

On the greatest and most perfect symphony, which is extended in three intervals;—and also on the less symphony.

IT now remains for us to speak of the greatest and most perfect harmony, which subsisting in three intervals, obtains great power in the temperaments of musical modulation, and in the speculation of natural questions. For nothing can be found more perfect than a middle of this kind, which being extended in three intervals, is allotted the nature and essence of the most perfect body. For thus we have shown that a cube, which possesses three dimensions, is a full and perfect harmony. This, however, may be discovered, if two terms being given, which have themselves increased by three intervals, viz.

---

* Jordanus Brunus has added an eleventh to these proportions; and this is when in three terms, as is the greatest to the middle term, so is the difference of the extremes to the difference of the greater terms; as in 6. 4. 3. For as 6 is to 4; so is the difference of 6 and 3, i.e. 3, to the difference of 6 and 4, i.e. 2.

by length, breadth, and depth, two middle terms of this kind are found, which having three intervals, are either produced from equals, through equals equally, or from unequals to unequals equally, or from unequals to equals equally, or after some other manner. And thus, though they preserve an harmonic ratio, yet being compared in another way, from the arithmetical middle; and to these, the geometric proportionality which is between both, cannot be wanting.

Let the following, therefore, be an instance of this arrangement, viz. 6. 8. 9. 12. That all these then are solid quantities, cannot be doubted. For 6 is produced from $1 \times 2 \times 3$; but 12 from $2 \times 2 \times 3$. Of the middle terms, however, between these, 8 is produced from $1 \times 2 \times 4$; but 9 from $1 \times 3 \times 3$. Hence all the terms are allied to each other, and are distinguished by the three dimensions of intervals. In these, therefore, the geometric proportionality is found, if 12 is compared to 8, and 9 to 6; for $12 : 8 :: 9 : 6$. And the ratio in each is sesquialter. But the arithmetical proportionality will be obtained, if 12 is compared to 9, and 9 to 6; for in each of these the difference is 3, and the sum of the extremes is the double of the mean. Hence we find in these, geometrical and arithmetical proportion. But the harmonic proportionality may also be found in these, if 12 is compared to 8, and again 8 to 6. For as 12 is to 6, so is the difference between 12 and 8, i.e. 4, to the difference between 8 and 6, i.e. 2. We may likewise here find all the musical symphonies. For 8, when compared to 6, and 9 to 12, produce a sesquitertian ratio, and at the same time the symphony diatessaron. But 6 compared to 9, and 8 to 12, produce a sesquialter ratio, and the symphony diapente. If 12 also is compared to 6, the ratio will be found to be duple, but the symphony diapason. But 8 compared to 9, forms the epogdous, which in musical modulation is called a tone. And this is the common measure of all musical sounds; for it is of all sounds the least. Hence a tone is the difference of the symphonies diatessaron and diapente;* just as the epogdous alone is the difference between the sesquitertian and sesquialter ratio.

Moreover, the less harmony is when in an arrangement of solid numbers, two proportionalities only are assumed, as the arithmetical and geometrical, or the geometrical and harmonic, or lastly, the arithmetical and harmonic; as in the terms 5. 15. 25. 45. For in these numbers, the arithmetical and geometrical proportionalities alone are found; the geometrical in 5. 15. and 45, since 5 : 15 :: 15 : 45; and the arithmetical in 5. 25. and 45, since there is the same difference between 25 and 5, as between 45 and 25. There is a less harmony also in the numbers 40. 25. 16. 10. For 40. 16 and 10 form an harmonic proportion, since as 40 is to 10, so is the difference between 40 and 16, to the difference between 16 and 10. But 40. 25. and 10 form an arithmetical proportionality, since the difference between 40 and 25, is the same as the difference between 25 and 10. And lastly, there is a less harmony in the terms 80. 40. 32. 20, which comprehend in themselves geometric and harmonic proportionalities. For 80. 40. 20. are in geometrical; but 80. 32. and 20 in harmonic proportion. The following scheme however will facilitate the comprehension of all that has been said in this chapter.

---

* For 8 to 12 which is diapente, is compounded of 8 to 9, and 9 to 12; so likewise $\frac{8}{9} = \frac{8}{8} + \frac{8}{9}$.

The greatest harmonies.	Proportionalities.	Differences and habitudes.	Tone and Symphonies.
12. 9. 8. 6.	Geome. 12. 9. 8. 6.	Sesquitertian when disjoined.	Sesquioct- ave. . . . 9. 8 Tone.
	Arithm. 12. 9. 6.	Difference 3. 3.	Sesquiter- [aron.
			tian . . . 8. 6 Diatess-
	Harmo. 12. 8. 6.	Duple. Difference 4. 2.	Sesquial- [te.
			ter . . . 9. 6 Diapen-
			Duple 12. 6.
			Triple 12. 4 Diapen-
			te Dia-
			pason.
			Quadru- [pason.
			ple . . . 12. 3 Disdia-
	Geome. 24. 18. 16. 12.	Sesquitertian when disjoined.	Sesquioct. 18. 16 Tone.
	Arithm. 24. 18. 12.	Difference 6. 6.	Sesquiter. 16. 12 Diatess.
	Harmo. 24. 16. 12.	Duple. Difference 8. 4.	Sesquialt. 18. 12 Diapen.
24. 18. 16. 12.			Duple 24. 12 Diapa.
			Triple 18. 6 Diapen. ⎱
			Diapa. ⎰
			Quadru. 12. 3 Disdia-
			[pa.

Less harmonies.	Proportionalities.	Habitudes and differences.	
45. 25. 15. 5.	Geome. 45. 15. 5.	Triple proportion.	
	Arithm. 45. 25. 5	Difference 20. 20.	
40. 25. 16. 10.	Harmo. 40. 16. 10.	Quadruple. Difference 24. 6.	
	Arithm. 40. 25. 10.	Difference 15. 15.	
80. 40. 32. 20.	Geome. 80. 40. 20.	Duple proportion.	
	Harmo. 80. 32. 20.	Quadruple. Difference 48. 12.	

CHAPTER XXXIII

On amicable numbers.

IAMBLICHUS in his treatise On the Arithmetic of Nicomachus observes p. 47. "that certain numbers were called amicable by those who assimilated the virtues and elegant habits to
numbers." He adds, "that 284 and 220 are numbers of this
kind; for the parts of each are generative of each other according to the nature of friendship, as was shown by Pythagoras.
For some one asking him what a friend was, he answered, *ano-*

ther I (ετερος εγω) which is demonstrated to take place in these numbers." And he concludes with informing us, "that he shall discuss in its proper place what is delivered by the Pythagoreans relative to this most splendid and elegant theory." Unfortunately, he has not resumed this subject in the above mentioned treatise, nor in any work of his that is extant. And the only writer I am acquainted with, who has written more fully concerning these numbers, is Ozanam, who in his Mathematical Recreations p. 15. observes of them as follows: "The two numbers 220 and 284 are called amicable, because the first 220 is equal to the sum of the aliquot parts of the latter, viz. $1+2+4+71+142=220$. And reciprocally the latter 248 is equal to the sum of the aliquot parts of the former, viz. $1+2+4+5+10+11+22+44+55+110=284$.

"To find all the amicable numbers in order, make use of the number 2, which is of such a quality, that if you take 1 from its triple 6, from its sextuple 12, and from the octodecuple of its square, viz. from 72, the remainders are the three prime numbers 5, 11 and 71; of which 5 and 11 being multiplied together, and the product 55 being multiplied by 4, the double of the number 2, this second product 220 will be the first of the two numbers we look for. And to find the other 284, we need only to multiply the third prime number 71, by 4, the same double of 2 that we used before.

"To find two other amicable numbers, instead of 2 we make use of one of its powers that possesses the same quality, such as its cube 8. For if you subtract an unit from its triple 24, from its sextuple 48, and from 1152 the octodecuple of its square 64, the remainders are the three prime numbers viz. 23, 47, 1151; of which the two first 23, 47 ought to be multiplied together, and their product 1081 ought to be multiplied by 16 the double of the cube 8, in order to have 17296 for the first of the two numbers demanded. And for the other amicable number which is 18416, we must multiply the third prime number 1151 by 16, the same double of the cube 8.

"If you still want other amicable numbers, instead of 2 or its cube 8, make use of its square cube 64; for it has the same quality, and will answer as above."

Thus far Ozanam. But the two amicable numbers produced from 64, which he has omitted in this extract are, 9363584, and 9437056. And the three prime numbers which are the remainders are 191, 383, and 73727.

CHAPTER XXXIV

*On lateral and diametrical numbers.**

As numbers have trigonic, tetragonic, and pentagonic reasons, (or productive principles) and the reasons of all other figures in power (i.e. causally) so likewise we shall find lateral and diametrical reasons, spermatically as it were presenting themselves to the view in numbers. For from these, figures are elegantly arranged. As therefore, the monad is the principle of all figures, according to a supreme and seminal reason, thus also the reason of a diameter and a side, are found in the monad or unity. Thus for instance, let there be two units, one of which we suppose to be a diameter, but the other a side; since it is necessary that the monad which is the principle of all figures, should be in power, or causally both a side and a diameter. And let the diameter be added to the side, but two sides to the diameter; since the diameter is once in power what the side is twice.† The diameter therefore will be made more, but the

* Vid. Theon. Smyrn. Mathemat. p. 67.

† For in a square figure, the square of the diagonal is twice the square of one of the sides, by 47. 1, of Euclid.

side less. And in the first monadic side and diameter indeed, the square in power of the diametrical monad, will be less by one monad, than the double of the square of the side produced by the monad. For the monads or units are in equality. But 1 is less than 2 by 1. Let us therefore add one to the side in power, i.e. to the monad. Hence the side will be two monads. And let us add to the diameter two sides, i.e. to the monad two monads. The diameter therefore will consist of three monads. And the square indeed, which is made from the side, i.e. from 2 is 4. But the square which is made from 3 is 9. Hence 9 exceeds the double of the square, which is made from 2 by 1.

Again, let us add 3 in power to the side 2. The side therefore will consist of 5 monads. But to the triad in power, let us add two sides, i.e. twice two, and the aggregate will be 7 monads. Hence, the square from the side will be 25; but the square from 7 will be 49. The square 49 therefore is less by the monad than the double of the square 25. Farther still, if to the side you add 7, the sum will be 12. And if to the diameter 7 you add twice the side 5, the square from 17, viz. 289, will exceed the double of the square from 12, i.e. the double of 144, by 1. And thus successively, an addition being similarly made, there will be an alternate analogy, the square from the diameter being sometimes less by 1, and sometimes more by 1, than the double of the square from the side. And such sides and diameters are effable.* But the diameters alternately sometimes exceed by 1 the double in power of the sides, and are sometimes less by 1 than the double of them. All the diameters therefore will become double in power of all the sides, by an alternate excess and defect, the same monad in all of them producing equality, so that the double in all of them neither exceeds, nor is deficient. For what was deficient in the

---

* Effable quanities are such as can be expressed either in whole numbers or fractions.

former diameter, exceeds in power in that which follows. These numbers therefore are as follow:

Sides.	Diameters.	The double of the squares of the sides.	The squares of the diameters.
1	1	2	1
2	3	8	9
5	7	50	49
12	17	288	289
29	41	1682	1681
70	99	9800	9801
169	239	57122	57121

The sides are composed from the addition of the preceding diameter and preceding side. Thus 29 is formed from the side 12 and the diameter 17. The diameters are composed from the preceding diameter, and the double of the preceding side. Thus 41 consists of 17 and twice 12. And 99 consists of 41 and twice 29, i.e. $=41+58$.

CHAPTER XXXV

On arithmetical and geometrical series.

In the preceding part of this work, what has been delivered is almost wholly derived from the ancients; in what follows, the observations are I believe, for the most part, if not entirely, new.

In the arithmetical series $1+2+3+4+5$, &c. when the number of terms is even and finite, the sum of the two middle terms multiplied by the number of terms, is equal to twice the sum of the series. Thus in 4 terms $3+2=5$, and $5\times4=20$, which is the double of 10, the sum of the series.

In the geometrical series $1+2+4+8+16+32$, &c. when

the number of terms is finite, the sum of the series added to unity, is equal to the double of the last term. Thus the sum of 1+2+1 is the double of 2. The sum of 1+2+4+1 is the double of 4, and so of the rest.

In the geometrical series 1+3+9+27+81, &c. the triple of the last term exceeds the double of the sum of the series by unity. Thus in two terms the triple of 3, i.e. 9, exceeds the double of the sum 1+3, i.e. 4, by 1. Thus the triple of 9, i.e. 27, exceeds the double of the sum, 1+3+9, i.e. 13 by 1, and so of the rest.

In the geometrical series 1+4+16+64+256, &c. the quadruple of the last term exceeds the triple of the sum of the series by unity.

And in the geometrical series 1+5+25+125+625, &c. the quintuple of the last term exceeds the quadruple of the sum of the series by unity.

Again, in the series 1+2+4+8+16, &c. when the number of terms is finite, the last term added to the last term less by unity, is equal to the sum of the series. Thus 2 added to 2 less by 1=1+2. 4 added to 4 less by 3=1+2+4, &c.

In the series 1+3+9+27+81, &c. if unity is subtracted from the last term, and the remainder divided by 2 is added to the last term, the sum is equal to the sum of the series. Thus 3—1=2 this divided by 2=1 and 1+3=4= the sum of the two first terms; 9—1=8 and 8 divided by 2=4, and 4+9 =13=1+3+9, &c.

In the series 1+4+16+64+256, &c. if unity is subtracted from the last term, and the remainder divided by 3 is added to the last term, the sum is equal to the sum of the series.

In the series 1+5+25+125+625, &c. if unity is subtracted from the last term, and the remainder divided by 4 is added to the last term, the sum is equal to the sum of the series.

In the geometrical fractional series $\frac{1}{1} + \frac{1}{2} + \frac{1}{4} + \frac{1}{8}$ &c.

$$\frac{1}{1} + \frac{1}{3} + \frac{1}{9} + \frac{1}{27} \text{ &c.}$$

$$\frac{1}{1} + \frac{1}{4} + \frac{1}{16} + \frac{1}{64} \text{ &c.}$$

$$\frac{1}{1} + \frac{1}{5} + \frac{1}{25} + \frac{1}{125} \text{ &c.}$$

the last term multiplied by the sum of the denominators is equal to the sum of the series, when the number of terms is finite.

Thus $\frac{1}{8} \times 1+2+4+8 = \frac{15}{8}$ the sum of $1 + \frac{1}{2} + \frac{1}{4} + \frac{1}{8}$. Thus $\frac{1}{27} \times 1+3+9+27 = \frac{40}{27}$, and so of the rest. And this will be the case whatever the ratio of the series may be.

And in the first of these series if unity be taken from the denominator of the last term, and the remainder be added to the denominator, the sum arising from this addition multiplied by the last term will be equal to the sum of the series. Thus 8—1=7 and 7+8=15, and $\frac{1}{8} \times 15 = \frac{15}{8}$, the sum of the series. In the second of these series, if unity be subtracted from the denominator of the last term, the remainder be divided by 2, and the quotient be added to the said denominator, the sum multiplied by the last term will be equal to the sum of the series. In the 3rd series after the subtraction the remainder must be divided by 3: in the 4th by 4: in the fifth by 5: in the 6th by 6, and so on.

In the series $1 + \frac{1}{3} + \frac{1}{6} + \frac{1}{10} + \frac{1}{15}$, &c. which infinitely continued is equal to 2, an infinitesimal excepted, if any finite number of terms is assured, then if the denominator of the last term be added to the denominator of the term immediately preceding it, and the sum of the two be multiplied by the last term, the product will be equal to the sum of the series. Thus in two terms $1+3 \times \frac{1}{3} = \frac{4}{3} =$ the sum of $1+\frac{1}{3}$. If there are three terms, then $3 + 6 \times \frac{1}{6} = \frac{9}{6} = 1 + \frac{1}{3} + \frac{1}{6}$. If there are four terms, then $6 + 10 \times \frac{1}{10} = \frac{16}{10} = 1 + \frac{1}{3} + \frac{1}{6} + \frac{1}{10}$, and so of the rest.

If the half of each term of this series is taken, so as to produce the series $\frac{1}{2} + \frac{1}{6} + \frac{1}{12} + \frac{1}{20} + \frac{1}{30}$, &c. then the half of the sum of the denominator of the last term, and the denominator of the term immediately preceding the last, multiplied by the last term, will be equal to the sum of the series. If the 3rd of each term is taken, the sum of the two denominators must be divided by 3. If the 4th of each term is taken, the division must be by 4; and so of the rest.

If the half of each term of the series $1 + \frac{1}{2} + \frac{1}{4} + \frac{1}{8} + \frac{1}{16}$, &c. is taken, so as to produce the series $\frac{1}{2} + \frac{1}{4} + \frac{1}{8} + \frac{1}{16} + \frac{1}{32}$, &c. and if the sum of the denominators is divided by 2, the quotient multiplied by the last term is equal to the sum of the series. Thus $\frac{2+4+8}{2} \times \frac{1}{8} = \frac{1}{2} + \frac{1}{4} + \frac{1}{8}, \frac{2+4+8+16}{2} \times \frac{1}{16} = \frac{1}{2} + \frac{1}{4} + \frac{1}{8} + \frac{1}{16}$, and so of the rest.

But if the third of each term of this series is taken, the divisor must be 3; if the 4th is taken, the divisor must be 4; if the 5th, is must be 5; if the 6th, 6; and so on.

CHAPTER XXXVI

On imperfectly amicable numbers.

IMPERFECTLY amicable numbers are such as 27, and 35, 39 and 55, 65 and 77, 51 and 91, 95 and 119, 69 and 133, 115 and 187, 87 and 247. For the parts of $27 = 3 \times 9$ are 1, 3, 9, the sum of which is 13; and the parts of $35 = 5 \times 7$ are 1, 5, 7, the sum of which is also 13.

The parts of $39 = 3 \times 13$, are 1, 3, 13, and the sum of these is 17. And this is aso the sum of 1, 5, 11, the parts of $55 = 5 \times 11$.

The parts of $65 = 13 \times 5$ are 1, 5, 13. The parts of 77 are 1, 7, 11; and the sum of each is 19.

The parts of $51=17\times8$ are 1, 3, 17. The parts of $91=13\times7$ are 1, 7, 13; and the sum of each is 21. And so of the rest.

The sums of the numbers from the multiplication of which these imperfectly amicable numbers are formed, are 12, 16, 18, 20, 24, 26, 28, 32, of which the first differs from the second by 4, the 2nd from the 3rd, and the 3rd from the 4th by 2. And again the 4th differs from the 5th by 4, the 5th from the 6th by 2, the 6th from the 7th by 2, and the 7th from the 8th by 4. Hence the differences are 2, 2, 4, 2, 2, 4, and so on ad infin.

Numbers of this kind are not noticed by writers on arithmetic that I am acquainted with. I call them imperfectly amicable numbers; because in two perfectly amicable numbers, the aggregate of the parts of the one is equal to the other; but in these the aggregate of the parts of one number is equal to the aggregate of the parts of the other, but the sum of each is less than the whole number. In perfectly amicable numbers therefore, the parts of the one embosom as it were the whole of the other; but in these, the parts of the one do not embosom the whole, but only a part of the other, because the aggregate of the parts falls short of the whole.

Hence, in numbers that are deficient, or the sum of whose parts is less than the numbers themselves, there is a great abundance of numbers, the sums of the parts of two of which are equal to each other. But in super-perfect numbers, or such the sum of whose parts exceeds the numbers of which they are the parts, the numbers are very rare that have the above mentioned property of deficient numbers. Thus between 12 and 144, there are only two numbers, the sums of the parts of which are equal to each other, and these are 80 and 104. For the sum of the parts of each is 106.

As perfectly amicable numbers also adumbrate perfect

friendship, and which consequently is founded in virtue, so
these numbers are perspicuous images of the friendship subsisting among vicious characters; such of them whose parts are
less than the whole, adumbrating the friendship between those
who fall short of the medium in which true virtue consists;
and those whose parts are greater than the whole, exhibiting
an image of the friendship of such as exceed this medium. As
likewise, of the vicious characters situated on each side of the
medium, those that exceed it are more allied to virtue, than
those that fall short of it, and being more allied to virtue are
more excellent, and being more excellent, are more rarely to be
found;—thus also in these numbers, the pairs whose parts are
less than the whole numbers, are far more numerous than those
whose parts are greater than the wholes of which they are the
parts.

CHAPTER XXXVII

On the series of unevenly-even numbers.

THE series of these numbers is as follows: 12, 20, 24, 28, 36,
40, 44, 48, 52, 56, 60, 68, 72, 76, 80, 84, 88, 92, 96, 100, 104, 108,
112, 116, 120, 124, 132, 136, 140, 144, 148, 152, 156, 160, 164,
168, 172, 176, 180, 184, 188, 192, 196, 200, 204, 208, 212, 216,
220, 224, 228, 232, 236, 240, 244, 248, 252, 260, &c.

In this series, it is observable in the first place, that the difference between the terms is every where either 8 or 4. Thus
the difference between 12 and 20 is 8; but between 20 and 24,
and 24 and 28 is 4. Again, the difference between 28 and 36
is 8; but between 36 and 40, 40 and 44, 44 and 48, 48 and
52, 52 and 56, 56 and 60, is 4. And again the difference between 60 and 68 is 8; but between 68 and 72 is 4, and so on,
till we arrive at 124 and 132, the difference between which is 8.

In the second place, it is observable, that the difference between 12 and 20 is 8; between 20 and 36 is 16; between 36 and 68 is 32; between 68 and 132 is 64, and so on, which differences are in a duple ratio.

In the third place, if the number which exceeds its preceding number by 8, is added to the number immediately preceding that which is so exceeded, the sum will be the following number, immediately preceding that which exceeds by 8. Thus $36+24=60$, the number immediately preceding 68. Thus too $68+56=124$, which immediately precedes 132. And $132+120=252$. And so of the rest. From all which it is evident, that the series of unevenly-even numbers ad infinitum may be easily obtained.

CHAPTER XXXVIII

On the aggregate of the parts of the terms of different series.

THE sum of the parts of each term of the duple series, 2, 4, 8, 16, 32, 64, &c. is equal to the whole of the term less by unity. Thus the part of 2 is 1; the parts of 4 are 2 and 1, the sum of which is 3; the parts of 8 are 4, 2, and 1, the aggregate of which is 7; and the parts of 16 are 8, 4, 2, 1, the sum of which is 15. And so of the rest.

But each of the terms of the triple series 3, 9, 27, 81, 243, &c. exceeds the double of the sum of its parts by unity. Thus the only part of 3 is 1; and 3 exceeds 2 by 1. The parts of 9 are 3 and 1; and 9 exceeds the double of the aggregate of these, i.e. 8 by 1. Thus too 27 exceeds the double of 13, the aggregate of its parts 9, 3 and 1 by 1. Thus also, 81 exceeds the double of 40 the sum of its parts, 27, 9, 3, and 1, by 1. And thus 243 exceeds twice 121, the aggregate of its parts, 81, 27, 9, 3 and 1 by 1. And so of the rest.

In the quintuple series, 5, 25, 125, 625, &c. it will be found that each term of the series exceeds the quadruple of the sum of its parts, by unity.

In the septuple series, each term exceeds the sextuple of the sum of its parts, by unity.

In the noncuple series, each term exceeds the octuple of the sum of its parts, by unity. And thus in all series formed by the multiplication of odd numbers, each term will exceed the sum arising from the multiplication of its parts by the odd number, by unity.

If to each term of the series	1	2	4	8	16	32	64	128	256
6 is added, viz.	6	6	6	6	6	6	6	6	6
the sums will be	7	8	10	14	22	38	70	134	262

And if to the series	1	3	9	27	81	243	729	2187	6561
be added	3	6	6	6	6	6	6	6	6
the sums will be	4	9	15	33	87	249	735	2193	6567, &c.

In which it is remarkable, that the aggregates of the parts of the five sums 8, 10, 14, 22, 38, are 7, 8, 10, 14, 32; and of the parts of the five sums 9, 15, 33, 87, 249, are 4, 9, 15, 33, 87. The aggregates also of the parts of the sums 134, 262, are 70, 134; but this will not be the case with the sums beyond 262, if the terms of the duple series are continued, and 6 is added to them. Nor will it be the case with the sums of the triple series beyond 249.

CHAPTER XXXIX

On the series of terms arising from the multiplication of even-ly-even numbers, by the sums produced by the addition of

*them; (see Chap. 15, Book I) in which series perfect num-
bers also are contained.*

This series consists of the terms 1, 6, 28, 120, 496, 2016,
8128, 32640, 130816, &c. the aggregate of which series is the
expression $\dfrac{1}{1-6+8;}$ for this when expanded gives the series
1+6+28+120+496, &c. in which all the prefect numbers
likewise are contained.

If therefore to the series 6, 28, 496, 8128, 130816, 2096128,
33550336, 536854528, &c. viz. if to the terms of the above series,
omitting every other term after 28, and beginning from 6, the
numbers 2, 4, 16, 64, 256, &c. are added as below:

2	4	16	64	256	1024	4096	16384
	6	28	496	8128	130816	2096128	33550336	536854528
1	8	32	512	8192	131072	2097152	33554432	536870912

then, the first sum will be equal to the 3rd power of 2, the
second to the 5th power of 2, the third to the 9th, the fourth to
the 13th, the fifth to the 17th, the sixth to the 21st, the seventh
to the 25th, the eighth to the 29th, and so on, there being
always an interval after the first and second sums of 4 powers.
But the expression $\dfrac{1-8-96}{1-16}$ when evolved, gives the series
1+8+32+512+8192+131072, &c. ad infin. And the ex-
pression $\dfrac{1-2-4}{1-4}$ gives the series 1+2+4+16+64+256, &c.
ad infin. But this latter subtracted from the former, viz.
$\dfrac{1-8-96}{1-16} - \dfrac{1-2-4}{1-4}$ gives $\dfrac{6-92+320}{1-20+64}$ which when evolved, is the series 6+28+496+8128+130816, &c.

The terms which being multiplied by numbers in a duple
ratio produce the series, 1, 6, 28, 496, 8128, &c. are 1, 3, 7, 31,

127, 511, 2047, 8191, &c. And the series equal to the last term of these numbers is $1+2+4+24+96+384$, &c. For $1=1$, $1+2=3$, $1+2+4=7$, $1+2+4+24=31$; and so of the rest. In which series it is remarkable, that each term after the first three terms, viz after 1, 2, 4, is the $\frac{1}{4}$ of the following term. Thus 24 is the $\frac{1}{4}$ of 96; 96 is the $\frac{1}{4}$ of 384; and 384 is the $\frac{1}{4}$ of 1536; and so on.

After the first three terms likewise, if each term is multiplied by 4, and 3 is added to the product, the sum will be the following term. Thus $31\times4=124$, and $124+3=127$. Thus too, $127\times4=508$, and $508+3=511$. And again, $511\times4=2044$, and $2044+3=2047$. And so of the rest.

It is also remarkable, that the sum of the divisors consisting of 2 and its powers, is always equal with the addition of unity, to the last quotient of the division. Thus $2+1=3$, the quotient in the division of 6. Thus too, $2+4+1=7$, the last quotient in the division of 28. And $2+4+8+16+1=31$, the quotient of 496. And so of the rest.

It is likewise possible to find an expression which when evolved will give the series $1+3+7+31+127$, &c. For this expression will be $\dfrac{1-2-4+8}{1-5+4}$.

As perfect numbers are resolved into their component parts through a division by 2 and its powers, so that the sums arising from these as divisors, and from the quotients, together with unity, are respectively equal to the perfect numbers themselves, thus also the sum arising from a similar division of any term in the series $6+28+496+8128+130816+2096128$, &c. that is not a perfect number, will be equal to that term, though such division will not resolve it into all its parts.

But that the reader may more clearly apprehend my meaning, and be fully convinced of the truth of this assertion, the following instances are subjoined of a distribution of ten terms

of this series into their parts by these divisors; among which
terms, four are perfect numbers:

(1).		(2).		(3).	
2)6	3	2)28	14	2)496	465
——	2	——	7	——	2
3	1	2)14	4	2)248	4
	——	——	2	——	8
	6	7	1	2)124	16
			——	——	1
			28	2)62	——
				——	496
				31	
				——	
				465	

(4).		(5).		(6).	
2)8128	8001	2)130816	130305	2)2096128	2094081
——	2	——	2	——	2
2)4064	4	2)65408	4	2)1048064	4
——	8	——	8	——	8
2)2032	16	2)32704	16	2)524032	16
——	32	——	32	——	32
2)1016	64	2)16352	64	2)262016	64
——	1	——	128	——	128
2)508	——	2)8176	256	2)131008	256
——	8128	——	1	——	512
2)254		2)4088	——	2)65504	1024
——		——	130816	——	1
127		2)2044		2)32752	——
——		——		——	2096128
8001		2)1022		2)16376	
		——		——	
		511		2)8188	
		——		——	
		130305		2)4094	
				——	
				2047	
				——	
				2094081	

(7).		(8).	
2)33550336	33542145	2)536854528	536821761
	2		2
2)16775168	4	2)268427264	4
	8		8
2)8387584	16	2)134213632	16
	32		32
2)4193792	64	2)67106816	64
	128		128
2)2096896	256	2)33553408	256
	512		512
2)1048448	1024	2)16776704	1024
	2048		2048
2)524224	4096	2)8388352	4096
	1		8192
2)262112		2)4194176	16384
	33550336		1
2)131056		2)2097088	
			536854528
2)65528		2)1048544	
2)32764		2)524272	
2)16382		2)262136	
8191		2)131068	
33542145		2)65534	
		32767	
		536821761	

(9).

2)8589869056	8589737985
	2
2)4294934528	4
	8
2)2147467264	16
	32
2)1073733632	64
	128
2)536866816	256
	512
2)268433408	1024
	2048
2)134216704	4096
	8192
2)67108352	16384
	32768
2)33554176	65536
	1
2)16777088	
	8589869056
2)8388544	
2)4194272	
2)2097136	
2)1048568	
2)524284	
2)262142	
131071	
8589737985	

(10).

2)137438691328	137438167041
	2
2)68719345664	4
	8
2)34359672832	16
	32
2)17179836416	64
	128
2)8589918208	256
	512
2)4294959104	1024
	2048
2)2147479552	4096
	8192
2)1073739776	16384
	32768
2)536869888	65536
	131072
2)268434944	262144
	1
2)134217472	
	137438691328
2)67108736	
2)33554368	
2)16777184	
2)8388592	
2)4194296	
2)2097148	
2)1048574	
524287	
137438167041	

Here it is evident in the first instance, that 3, 2, and 1, are all the possible parts of 6. For 3 is the half, 2 the third, and 1 the sixth part of 6. And it is likewise manifest that 14, 7, 4, 2, and 1, are all the parts of 28. Thus too, in the division of 496 into its parts, 465 is the sum of the parts that are the quotients arising from the division by 2 and its powers. And as the half of 496 is 248, it is the same thing to divide 248 by 2, as to divide 496 by 4. For the same reason it is the same thing to divide 124, the half of 248, by 2, as to divide 496 by 8. And to divide 62, the half of 124, by 2, as to divide 496 by 16. Hence the divisors of 496 are 2, 4, 8, 16, and the sum of these added to 1 and to 465, is 496. In a similar manner in the fourth instance, 8001 is the aggregate of the parts that are the quotients arising from the division by 2 and its powers. And the divisors of 8128 are 2, 4, 8, 16, 32, 64, the sum of which added to 1, and to 8001, is equal to 8128. And so in the other instances.

Only eight perfect numbers have as yet been found, owing to the difficulty of ascertaining in very great terms, whether a number is a prime or not. And these eight are as follow, 6, 28, 496, 8128, 33550336, 8589869056, 137438691328, 2305843008139952128. By an evolution of the expression $\frac{6-92+320}{1-20+64}$ to twenty terms, the reader will see at what distance these perfect numbers are from each other. But these twenty terms are as follow, those that are perfect numbers being designated by a star:

6, 28, 496, 8128, 130816, 2096128, 33550336, 536854528,

8589869056, 137438691328, 2199022206976, 35184367894528,

562949936644096, 9007199187632128, 144115187807420416,

2305843008139952128, 36893488143124135936,

590295810341525782528, 9444732965670570950656,

151115727451553768931328.

Hence it appears that the eighth perfect number is the 16th term of the series produced by the expansion of $\dfrac{6-92+320}{1-20+\ 64.}$

As however there are only eight perfect numbers in twenty terms of this series, it is evident that Ruffus in his Commentary on the Arithmetic of Boetius, was greatly mistaken in asserting that every other term in the series is a perfect number.

It is remarkable in this series that the terms alternately end in 6 and 8. This is also true of the four first perfect numbers; but the other four end indeed in 6 and 8, yet not alternately.

The other terms also of this series, from their correspondence with perfect numbers, may be called partially perfect. For both are resolved by 2 and its powers into parts, the aggregates of which are equal to the wholes; and both are terminated by 6 and 8.

Again, in the series $1+8+32+512+8192$, &c. produce by the expansion of $\dfrac{1-8-96}{1-16,}$ the half of each of the terms after the first is a square number. Thus the half of 8, of 32, of 512, &c. viz. 4, 16, 216, are square numbers. And if each of the terms of the series $6+28+496+8128+130816$, &c. is doubled, the sum of the parts of each is a square number. Thus the sum of the parts of 12, the double of 6 is 16; the sum of the parts of 56, the double of 28, is 64; the sum of the parts of 992, the double of 496, is 1024, the root of which is 32; of the parts of 16256, the double of 8128, is 16384, the square root of which is 128; and of the parts of 216632, the double of 130816, is 262144, the square root of which is 512. And so of the rest; all the roots after the second increasing in a quadruple ratio. As this property also extends to the terms that are not perfect numbers as well as to those that are, it shows in a still greater degree the correspondence of what I call the partially perfect, with the completely perfect numbers.

Farther still, if 2 be subtracted from the number of the rank which any number after 28, holds in the series 6, 28, 496, 8128, 130816, &c. and the remainder be added to the number of the said rank, the sum will be the index of that power of 2 which by multiplication with its corresponding number in the series 3, 7, 31, 127, 511, &c. produced the perfect or partially perfect number. Thus if from 3, we subtract 2, and add 3 to the remainder 1, the sum 4 will indicate that the fourth power of 2, viz. 16 multiplied by the third term 31, will give the third term, viz. 496, in the series 6, 28, 496, 8128, &c. Thus also, if 2 be subtracted from 4, and 4 be added to the remainder, the sum 6 will indicate that the sixth power of 2, viz. 64, multiplied by the 4th term 127, will produce the 4th term 8128, of the series 6, 28, 496, 8128, &c. And so of the rest.

The rule for obtaining a number which is either perfect or partially perfect in the series 6, 28, 496, 8128, 130816, &c. any term in this series being given, in the most expeditious manner, is the following. Multiply the given perfect, or partially perfect number by 16, and add to the product twelve times the number in the duple series, from the multiplication of which with a corresponding number in the series 3, 7, 31, 127, 511, &c. the perfect, or partially perfect number is produced, and the sum will be the next number in order in the series 6, 28, 496, &c. Thus $28 \times 16 = 448$, and 448 added to 12 times 4, i.e. to 48, is equal to 496. Thus too $496 \times 16 = 7936$, and $7936 + 12 \times 16 (= 192) = 8128$. And so of the rest.

Lastly, all the perfect numbers are found in the series of hexagonal numbers; which numbers are 1, 6, 15, 28, 45, 66, &c.; and the expression which is the aggregate of them and when evolved gives all of them in order ad infinitum is

$$\frac{1+3}{1-3+3-1}.$$

CHAPTER XL

On another species of imperfectly amicable numbers.

As Ozanam in his Mathematical Recreations, does not mention what numbers are to be employed in order to find other amicable numbers after 9363584, and 9437056,* after various trials to accomplish this, I found that if any number by which two amicable numbers are obtained, is multiplied by 8, the product will be a number by which either two numbers may be obtained, the aggregate of all the parts of one of which is equal to the other, or two numbers the aggregate of the parts of one of which only arising from a division by 2 and its powers, will be equal to the other. Thus if 64 is multiplied by 8, the product will be 512. The three numbers formed in the same way as the primes that produce amicable numbers, will be 1535, 3071, and 4718591. And two numbers 4827120640, 4831837184, will be produced, the sum of the parts of the latter of which arising from a division by 2 and its powers with the addition of unity, will be equal to the former.

Again, if 512 is multiplied by 8, the product will be 4096. The three numbers corresponding to primes will be 12287,

---

* "Schooten gives the following practical rule from Descartes, for finding amicable numbers, viz. Assume the number 2, or some power of the number 2, such that if unity be subtracted from each of these three following quantities, viz. from 3 times the assumed number, also from 6 times the assumed number, and from 18 times the square of the assumed number, the three remainders may be all prime numbers; then the last prime number being multiplied by double the assumed number, the product will be one of the amicable numbers sought, and the sum of its aliquot parts will be the other."—Hutton's Mathem. Dict.

This also is Ozanam's method of finding amicable numbers, which we have already given and illustrated by examples. Mr. John Gough shows, that if a pair of amicable numbers be divided by their greatest common measure, and the prime divisors of these quotients be severally increased by unity, the products of the two sets thus augmented, will be equal.

24575, and 301989887. And the two imperfectly amicable numbers will be 2473599180800, and 2473901154304, the sum of the parts of the latter of which arising from a division by 2 and its powers with the addition of unity will be equal to the former.

Farther still, the product of 4096 multiplied by 8 will be 32768. The three numbers which are either primes or corresponding to primes, will be 98303, 196607, and 19327352831. And the two imperfectly or perfectly amicable numbers will be 1266618067910656, and 1266637395132416.

And in the last place if 32768 is multiplied by 8, the product will be 262144. The three numbers which are either primes or corresponding to primes, will be 786431, 1572863, and 1236950581247. And the two imperfectly or perfectly amicable numbers will be 648517109391294464, and 648518346340827136.

In order that the reader may become acquainted with the method of obtaining the parts of perfectly amicable numbers, I shall give an instance of it in the two numbers 9363584 and 9437056. Let the first of these numbers then be divided by 2 and the powers of 2, viz. by 4, 8, 16, 32, 64, &c. till the division is stopped by a remainder which is a prime number. These quotients with the indivisible remainder will be as below, 4681792, 2340896, 1170448, 585224, 292612, 146306, 73153. In the next place, as the two prime numbers 191 and 383, are multiplied together in order to produce the number 9363584, it is evident that these also are parts of it, and consequently they must be employed as the divisors of it. The quotient therefore of 9363584 divided by 191 is 49024; and the quotient of the same number divided by 383 is 24448. Each of these quotients also may be divided by 2 and its powers. The quotients therefore arising from the division of 49024 by 2 and its powers are 24512, 12256, 6128, 3064, 1532, 766; and the remainder is 383. But the quotients arising from a similar division of 24448 are 12224, 6112, 3056, 1528, 764, 382; and the remainder is 191. The sum therefore of all these quotients will be as below:

$$
\begin{aligned}
&4681792 \\
&2340896 \\
&1170448 \\
&585224 \\
&292612 \\
&146306 \\
&73153 \\
&49024 \\
&24448 \\
&24512 \\
&12256 \\
&6128 \\
&3064 \\
&1532 \\
&766 \\
&383 \\
&12224 \\
&6112 \\
&3056 \\
&1528 \\
&764 \\
&382 \\
&191 \\
\hline
&9436801
\end{aligned}
$$

And if to this sum, the sum of 2 and its powers are added, together with unity, viz. if $1+2+4+8+16+32+64+128 =255$ be added, the aggregate will be 9437056, the second of the amicable numbers.

In like manner if 9437056 be divided by 2 and its powers, the quotients and their aggregate will be as below:

$$
\begin{aligned}
& 4718528 \\
& 2359264 \\
& 1179632 \\
& 589816 \\
& 294908 \\
& 147454 \\
& 73727 \\
\hline
& 9363329
\end{aligned}
$$

And if to this sum 255 be added, as in the former instance, the aggregate will be 9363584, the first of the amicable numbers.

The first thing remarkable in these perfectly amicable numbers is, that the number 2 and its powers are employed in the production of all of them, and that they cannot be produced by any other number and the powers of it. For as these amicable numbers are images of true friendship, this most clearly shows that such friendship can only exist between two persons.

In the next place, the numbers 3, 6, and 18, which are used in the formation of these numbers, perspicuously indicate perfection; and are therefore images of the perfection of true friendship. For 3 and 6 are the first perfect numbers, the former from being the paradigm of *the all,* comprehending in itself beginning, middle and end, and the latter from being equal to all its parts: and 18 is produced by the multiplication of 6 by 3.

In the third place, the paucity of these numbers most beautifully adumbrates the rarity of true friendship. For between 1 and 1000 there are only two. In like manner between 284 and 20000 there are only two. And between 18416 and ten millions there are only two.

In the fourth place the greater the numbers are in the series of perfectly and imperfectly amicable numbers the nearer they approach to a perfect equality. Thus for instance, the exponent of the ratio of 220 to 284 is $1\frac{64}{220}$ and by reduction $1\frac{16}{55}$. But the exponent of the ratio of 17296 to 18416 is $1\frac{1120}{17296}$, and by reduction $1\frac{70}{1081}$. And $\frac{70}{1081}$ is much less than $\frac{16}{55}$. Again, the exponent of the ratio of 9363584 to 9437056 is $1\frac{73472}{9363584}$, and by reduction $1\frac{287}{73153}$. And $\frac{287}{73153}$ is much less than $\frac{70}{1081}$. In a similar manner it will be found that the exponents of the ratios of the succeeding amicable numbers will continually decrease; and consequently that the greater two amicable numbers become, the nearer they approach to an equality with each other. Indeed, in the amicable numbers after the first three, this is obvious by merely inspecting the numbers themselves. For in the amicable numbers 4827120640 and 4831837184, the first two numbers from the left hand to the right are the same in each, viz. 4 and 8. In the two amicable numbers 2473599180800 and 2473901154304, the first four numbers 2473 are the same in each. In the two amicable numbers 1266618067910656 and 1266637395132416, the first five numbers are the same in each. This is also the case with the two amicable numbers which immediately succeed these, viz. 648517109391294464 and 648518346340827136. And in the two amicable numbers which are next but one to these last, viz. in the numbers 170005188316757680455680 and 170005193383307194138624, the first seven numbers from the left hand to the right are the same in each; by all which it appears that the greater two amicable numbers are, the more figures in the one are the same as those in the other, and consequently that their approximation to a perfect equality is greater.

The following are the remarkable properties of the prime numbers and the numbers corresponding to prime, from which both species of amicable numbers are produced.

These numbers are as follows:

5	11	71
23	47	1151
191	383	73727
1535	3071	4718591
12287	24575	301989887
98303	196607	19327352831

In the first place 2×5 and $+1=11$, 2×23 and $+1=47$, 2×191 and $+1=383$, 2×1535 and $+1=3071$, 2×12287 and $+1=24575$, and 2×98303 and $+1=196607$. And thus the double of the first number in each rank added to unity is equal to the second number in the same rank.

In the next place, the first number of the first rank multiplied by 4 and added to 3, will be equal to the first number of the second rank. Thus also the second number 11×4 and added to $3=47$ the second number of the second rank. But 23×8 and $+7=191$, 47×8 and $+7=383$, 191×8 and $+7=1535$, 383×8 and $+7=3071$, 1535×8 and $+7=12287$, 3071×8 and $+7=24575$, 12287×8 and $+7=98303$, and 24575×8 and $+7=196607$.

Again, 47×4 and $+3=191$, 383×4 and $+3=1535$, 3071×4 and $+3=12287$, and 24575×4 and $+3=98303$.

Again, $\frac{1151}{71}=16$, with a remainder 15. $\frac{73727}{1151}=64$, with a remainder 63. $\frac{4718591}{73727}=64$, and the remainder is 63. And $\frac{301989887}{4718591}=64$, with the same remainder 63. And so of the rest ad infin. the quotient and remainder being always 64 and 63.

Hence infinite series of all these may easily be obtained, viz. of the two first terms in each rank, the first rank excepted, and of the third term in each rank the two first ranks excepted. For

$$\frac{23+7+7+7, \&c.\ ad\ infin.}{1-8} = 23+191+1535+12287, \&c.$$

$$\frac{47+7+7+7, \&\text{c. ad infin.}}{1-8} = 47+383+3071+24575, \&\text{c.}$$

And $\dfrac{73727+63+63+63, \&\text{c.}}{1-64} = 73727+4718591, \&\text{c.}$ But

these expressions when reduced will be $\dfrac{23-16}{1-9+8,}\ \dfrac{47-40}{1-9+8,}$ and

$\dfrac{73727-73664}{1-65+64.}$

Another remarkable property of these numbers is this, that the product of the two first in each rank subtracted from the third number in the same rank, leaves a remainder equal to the aggregate of those two first. Thus $5\times11=55$, and $71-55$ $=16$. But $16=5+11$. Thus too, $23\times47=1081$, and $1151-1081=70$, $=23+47$. And thus $191\times383=73153$, and 73727 $-73153=574=191+383$. And so of the rest. Hence the third less by the sum of the two other numbers, will be equal to the product of the two first. From the expressions therefore before given, and from what is now shown, it will be easy to find an expression which when evolved will give an infinite series of the products of the two first numbers in each rank. And this expression, (the first term of it being the product of the two first numbers, in the third rank, in order that it may be in the same rank with the expression $\dfrac{72737-73664}{1-65+64,}$) will be

$$\frac{73153-699337+1179656-503472}{1-74+657-1096+512.}$$

All these amicable numbers therefore in order after 17296, 18416, may be found, if the first term of the infinite series arising from the expansion of each of these expressions is multiplied by 128, the second term of each by 1024, the third term by 8192, and so on, the multipliers always increasing in an octuple ratio.

That the reader may see the truth of what we have asserted concerning this species of imperfectly amicable numbers, exemplified, the following instances are added of the resolution of two of them into parts by 2 and its powers.

In the first place the sum of the parts of the number 4831837184 is equal to 4827120640, as is evident from the following division:

2)4831837184	Divisors by 2 and its powers with the addition of unity.
2)2415918592	1
	2
2)1207959296	4
	8
2)603979648	16
	32
2)301989824	64
	128
2)150994912	256
	512
2)75497456	1024
2)37748728	2047 Total.
2)18874364	
2)9437182	
4718591	

4827118593
+ 2047

4827120640

The next instance is in the two numbers 2473901154304, 2473599180800, as below:

2)2473901154304	Divisors, with the addition of unity.
———————	
2)1236950577152	1
———————	2
2)618475288576	4
———————	8
2)309237644288	16
———————	32
2)154618822144	64
———————	128
2)77309411072	256
———————	512
2)38654705536	1024
———————	2048
2)19327352768	4096
———————	8192
2)9663676384	———
———————	16383 Total.
2)4831838192	
———————	
2)2415919096	
———————	
2)1207959548	
———————	
2)603979774	
———————	
301989887	
———————	
2473599164417	
+ 16383	
———————	
2473599180800	

The most extraordinary circumstance attending this series of numbers is, that the greater any pair of them is, the more they approximate to a perfect equality; so that if the series could be extended to infinity, the last pair of numbers would be equal to each other.

It is likewise evident from the formation of this series, that all perfectly as well as all imperfectly amicable numbers, are contained in it; so that it corresponds in this respect, to the series before delivered, in which all perfect and partially perfect numbers are contained.

CHAPTER XLI

On the geometric number, in the eighth book of the Republic of Plato.

THE obscurity of what Plato says respecting the geometric number, is so great, as to have become proverbial among the ancients; and it is not elucidated in any of those invaluable remains of Grecian philosophy, which have been transmitted to the present time. What follows, is an attempt to remove the veil, in which it has been so long concealed.

In the first place, the whole passage in the Republic respecting this number is as follows: "It is indeed difficult for a city thus constituted, to be changed; but as every thing which is generated is obnoxious to corruption, neither will such a constitution as this remain for ever, but be dissolved. And its dissolution is this. Not only with respect to terrestrial plants, but likewise in terrestrial animals, a fertility and sterility of soul as well as of body takes place, when the revolutions of the heavenly bodies complete the periphery of their respective orbits, which are shorter, to the shorter-lived, and contrarywise to such as are the contrary. And with reference to the fertility and sterility of our race, although those are wise that you have educated to be governors of cities, yet will they never by reason in conjunction with sense, observe the proper seasons, but overlook them, and sometimes generate children when they ought not. But the period to *that which is divinely generated,* is that which the perfect number comprehends; and to that which is generated by man, that period in which the augmentations surpassing and surpassed, when they shall have received three restitutions, and four boundaries of things assimilating and dissimilating, increasing and decreasing, shall render all things correspondent and effable; of which the sesquitertian progeny when conjoined with the pentad, and thrice increased, affords two harmonies. One of these, the equally equal, is a hundred times a hundred; but the other, of equal length indeed, but more oblong, is of a hundred numbers from effable diameters of pentads, each being deficient by unity, and from two numbers that are ineffable, and from a hundred cubes of the triad. But the whole geometric number of this kind, is the author of better and worse generations; of which when our governors being ignorant, join our couples together unseasonably, the children shall neither be of a good genius, nor fortunate."

In the second place, with respect to the meaning of what is here said by Plato, as to the periodical mutation of things in the sublunary region, it must be observed, that all the parts of the universe are unable to participate of the providence of divinity in a similar manner, but some of its parts enjoy this eternally, and others temporally; some in a primary, and others in a secondary degree. For the universe being a perfect whole, must have a first, a middle, and a last part. But its first parts, as having the most excellent subsistence, must always exist according to nature; and its last parts must sometimes subsist according to, and sometimes contrary to nature. Hence the celestial bodies, which are the first parts of the universe, perpetually subsist according to nature, both the whole spheres, and the multitude coordinate to these wholes; and the only alteration which they experience, is a mutation of figure, and variation of light at different periods. But in the sublunary region, while the spheres of the elements remain on account of their subsistence as wholes, always according to nature, the parts of these wholes have sometimes a natural, and sometimes an unnatural subsistence; for thus alone can the circle of generation unfold all the variety which it contains.

The different periods in which these mutations happen, are called by Plato, with great propriety, periods of *fertility* and *sterility*. For in these periods, a fertility or sterility of men, animals, and plants, takes place; so that in fertile periods, mankind will be both more numerous, and upon the whole, superior in mental and bodily endowments, to the men of a barren period. And a similar reasoning must be extended to animals and plants. The so much celebrated heroic age, was the result of one of these fertile periods, in which men transcending the herd of mankind, both in practical and intellectual virtue, abounded on the earth.

With respect to the epithet *divinely generated,* it is well observed by the Greek scholiast, "that Plato does not mean by this either the whole world, though the epithet is primarily applicable to it, nor the celestial regions only, nor the sublunary world, but *every thing which is perpetually and circularly moved,* whether in the heavens, or under the moon; so far as it is corporeal calling it *generated,* (for no body is self-subsistent), but so far as it is perpetually moved, *divine.* For it imitates the most divine of things, which possess an ever-vigilant life. But with respect to the perfect number mentioned here by Plato, we must not only direct our attention to a perfect number in vulgar arithmetic,—for this is rather numbered than number, tends to perfection and is never perfect, as being always in generation,—but we must survey the cause of this number, which is indeed intellectual, but comprehends the definite boundary of every period of the world."

In the third place, let us consider what Plato means by augmentations surpassing and surpassed; things assimilating and dissimilating, increasing and decreasing, correspondent and effable.

Augmentations surpassing, are ratios of greater inequality, viz. when the greater is compared to the less, and are multiples, superparticulars, superpartients, multiple super-particulars, and multiple-superpartients. But multiple ratio is, as we have before shown, when a greater quantity contains a less many times; superparticular ratio is when the greater contains the less quantity once, and some part of it besides; and superpartient ratio is when the greater contains the less quantity once, and certain parts of it likewise. Again, multiple-superparticular ratio is when the greater contains the less many times, and some part of it besides; and multiple-superpartient ratio, is when the greater contains the less many times, and also some of its parts. But augmentations surpassed, are ratios of less inequality, viz. when the less is compared with the greater quantity; as for instance, submultiples, subsuperparticulars, subsuperpartients, and those which are composed from these three. Those numbers are called by Plato *assimilating* and *dissimilating,* which are denominated by arithmeticians *similar* and *dissimilar.* And similar numbers are those whose sides are proportional, but dissimilar numbers those whose sides are not proportional. Plato also calls those numbers *increasing* and *decreasing,* which arithmeticians denominate *superperfect,* and *deficient,* or more than perfect and imperfect.

Things correspondent and effable, are boundaries which correspond in ratio with each other; and can be expressed in numbers either integral or fractional,—such as these four terms or boundaries 27, 18, 12, 8, which are in sesquialter and sub-sesquialter ratios; since these mutually correspond in ratio, and are effable. For effable quantities are those which can be expressed in whole numbers or fractions; and in like manner, ineffable quantities are such as cannot be expressed in either of these, and are called by modern mathematicians surds.

In the fourth place, let us consider what we are to understand by *the sesquitertian progeny when conjoined with the
pentad, and thrice increased, affording two harmonies.* By the
sesquitertian progeny, then, Plato means the number 95. For
this number is composed from the addition of the squares of
the numbers 4 and 3, (i.e. 25) which form the first sesquitertian ratio, and the number 70 which is composed from 40 and
30, and therefore consists of two numbers in a sesquitertian
ratio. Hence, as 95 is composed from 25 and 70, it may with
great propriety be called a sesquiterian progeny. This number
conjoined with 5, and thrice increased, produces ten thousand
and a million. For $100 \times 100 = 10,000$, and $10,000 \times 100 =$
1,000,000. But it must here be observed, that these two numbers, as will shortly be seen, appear to be considered by Plato
as analogous to two parallelopipedons, the former viz. ten
thousand, being formed from $10 \times 10 \times 100$, and the latter
from $1000 \times 10 \times 100$. These two numbers are called by Plato
two harmonies, for the following reason:—Simplicius, in his
commentary on Aristotle's treatise De Coelo, informs us that
a cube was denominated by the Pythagoreans *harmony,** because it consists of 12 bounding lines, 8 angles, and 6 sides;
and 12, 8, and 6 are in harmonic proportion. As a parallelopipedon, therefore, has the same number of sides, angles, and
bounding lines as a cube, the reason is obvious why the numbers 10,000, and 1,000,000 are called by Plato harmonies. Hence
also, it is evident why he says, "that the other of these harmonies, viz. a million is of equal length indeed, but more oblong."
For if we call 100 the breadth, and 10 the depth, both of
ten thousand and a million, it is evident that the latter number, when considered as produced by $1000 \times 10 \times 100$ will be
analogous to a more oblong parallelopipedon than the former.

---

* See chap. XXVIII. of this book.

Again, when he says, "that the number 1,000,000 consists of a hundred numbers from effable diameters of pentads, each being deficient by unity, and from two that are ineffable, and from a hundred cubes of the triad," his meaning is as follows. The number 1,000,000 consists of a hundred numbers (i.e. of a hundred such numbers as 10,000,) each of which is composed from effable diameters of pentads, &c. But in order to understand the truth of this assertion, the reader must recollect what has been delivered in Chap. xxxiv. of this book, viz. that there are certain numbers which are called by arithmeticians effable diameters. These also are twofold; for some are the diameters of even, and others of odd squares. And the diameters of effable even squares, when multiplied into themselves, produce square numbers double of the squares, of which they are the diameters, with an excess of unity. Thus, for instance, the number 3 multiplied into itself, produces 9, which is double of the square number 4, with an excess of unity; and therefore 3 will be the diameter of the even square 4. But the diameters of effable odd square numbers, are in power double of the squares of which they are the diameters by a deficiency of unity. This being premised, it follows that the number 10,000 will consist of a certain number of heptads; for 7 is the effable diameter of the square number 25. And from what follows it will be found that this number is 989.

But the number 10,000, not only consists of 989 heptads, but Plato also adds, "from two numbers that are ineffable," viz. from two numbers, the roots of which cannot be exactly obtained nor expressed, either in whole numbers or fractions, such as the roots of the numbers 2 and 3. The numbers 300 and 77 are also of this kind; and as we shall see appear to be the numbers signified by Plato. In the last place, he adds, "and from a hundred cubes of the triad," viz. from the number 2700; for this is equal to a hundred times 27, the cube of 3.

The numbers, therefore, that form 10,000, are as below:

$$
\begin{array}{r}
989 \\
7 \\
\hline
6{,}923 \\
300 \\
77 \\
2700 \\
\hline
10{,}000
\end{array}
$$

viz. 989 heptads, two ineffable numbers 300 and 77,* and a hundred times the cube of 3, i.e. 270. And the whole geometric number is a million.

All that Jamblichus says concerning this, which he calls the *nuptial number,* in his commentary on the Arithmetic of Nicomachus, is as follows: "This example will be useful to us for the purpose of understanding the *nuptial number* in the Republic of Plato. For he there says, that from two parents who are good, a good offspring will entirely be born; but the contrary, from two of a contrary character. And that from a mixture of good and bad parents, the progeny will be in every respect bad, but never good. For from the conjunction of odd numbers by themselves, with the addition of unity, which in the composition precedes them, square numbers are produced, which from such numbers have the nature of good. But the cause of this is equality, and prior to this *this one.* From a conjunction, however, of even numbers, the duad being the leader, numbers longer in the other part are produced, which

* The reader, who may have my Plato and Aristotle in his possession, is requested to correct, by the above numbers, an error in the developement of this geometric number, which is given in the Republic of the former, and the Politics of the latter. This error originated from mistating the product of a hundred times 27 to be 270, instead of 2,700.

have a contrary nature, because this is also the case with their generators. But again, the cause of this is inequality, and prior to this, the indefinite duad. And if a mixture should be made, and as I may say, a marriage of the even and the odd, the offspring will partake of the nature of each of these, whether their generators differ by unity, or by some greater number. For the numbers produced, are either such as are longer in the other part, or such as are oblong. And again, from squares mingled with each other, squares are generated; from numbers longer in the other part, such as resemble them are produced; but from such as are mixed, squares are never generated, but numbers that are entirely heterogeneous. And this is what the most divine Plato says respecting the male and female governors of his Republic, when they have not been nourished in the mathematical disciplines, or though they have been nurtured in them, yet have engaged in wedlock in a confused and disorderly manner, from which the progeny being depraved, will be the principle of sedition and discord to the whole polity."

Let there be given a series of square numbers from unity, and under them a series of numbers longer in the other part, from the duad or two, as below:

1	4	9	16	25	36	49	64	81	100
2	6	12	20	30	42	56	72	90	110

Then, if 2 is compared to 1, the ratio is duple, and is the root of the duple ratio. But 6 to 4 is sesquialter, and 12 to 9 sesquitertian, and by thus proceeding, the superparticular ratio, the sesquiquartan, sesquiquintan and others will be found, the differences exceeding each other by unity. For the difference between 2 and 1 is 1, between 6 and 4 is 2, between 12 and 9 is 3, and so on, the excess being always unity.

In the next place, the terms of one series being compared

with each other, it will be found, that the square numbers differ from each other, when assumed in a continued series, by 3. But the difference between the numbers longer in the other part, is 4.

The difference of two numbers longer in the other part, to the difference of two squares, is superpartient; but those ratios have only the appellations pertaining to odd numbers. Thus, for instance, the difference between 6 and 2 is 4, but the difference between 4 and 1 is 3, therefore, the difference 4 to the difference 3 is sesquitertian. Again, the difference between 12 and 6 is 6, but between 9 and 4 is 5, therefore the ratio of the difference 6 to the difference 5, is sesquiquintan, and so of the rest.

The numbers which are generated from the first similar, or the square 4, are all similars and squares. Thus 4 times 4 is 16, four times 9 is 36, four times 16 is 64; all which are square numbers, and of a similar nature. But the numbers which are generated from dissimilar terms, are all dissimilar, as 12 which is generated from 2 and 6, and 72 which is generated from 6 and 12, and so of the rest. And the number produced by the multiplication of a dissimilar number 6, with a similar number 4, will be the dissimilar oblong 24, and will be in the rank of evil numbers.*

In the gnomons of squares, and the gnomons of numbers longer in the other part, the following analogy occurs.

---

* Good numbers, according to Plato, are such as always subsist after the same manner, and preserve equality; and such are square numbers which are generated from odd gnomons, and are placed by the Pythagoreans in the series of things that are good. But evil numbers are those that are longer in the other part, and oblongs. From good numbers, therefore, good numbers are produced. Thus from 3 multiplied into itself, the square number is generated; from 4 the square 16; and from 5 the square 25, which are also generated from the circumposition of odd gnomons. But from the multiplication of 3 and 4, i.e. from the conjunction of good and evil, 12 is produced, which is longer in the other part, and is therefore evil. And so in other instances.

$$1 \quad 3 \quad 5 \quad 7 \quad 9 \quad 11 \quad 13 \quad 15$$
$$2 \quad 4 \quad 6 \quad 8 \quad 10 \quad 12 \quad 14 \quad 16$$

If three gnomons of squares are assumed, 1, 3, 5, the sum of them is 9, and the sum of the gnomons 2 and 4, of two numbers longer in the other part, is 6, which is subsesquialter to 9. If four gnomons of squares are assumed, 1, 3, 5, 7, the sum of them is 16, and the sum of the three gnomons 2, 4, and 6 of numbers longer in the other part is 12; but 16 to 12 is a sesquitertian ratio. And by proceeding in this way, the other ratios will be found to be sesquiquartan, sesquiquintan, &c.

If squares are compared, and the numbers longer in the other part which are media between them, the ratio of the first analogy is duple, i.e. of 1, 2, 4; of the second analogy 4, 6, 9, is sesquialter; of the third 9, 12, 16, is sesquitertian, and so on.

But if numbers longer in the other part are compared with squares as media, the ratios will be found to be allied and connected, viz. the duple with the sesquialter, as in 2, 4, 6; the sesquialter with the sesquitertian, as in 6, 9, 12; the sesquitertian with the sesquiquartan, as in 12, 16, 20, and so on. Moreover, every square and similar number, with a subject number longer in the other part, and dissimilar, produces a triangular number. Thus 1+2=3, 4+6=10, 9+12=21, &c. all which sums are triangular numbers. Likewise, if the first dissimilar is added to the second similar number, or the second dissimilar to the third similar number, the sums will also be triangular numbers. Thus 2+4=6, 6+9=15, 12+16=28, &c. And thus much respect to what Jamblichus says concerning the nuptial number.

PYTHAGORAS

BOOK THREE

CHAPTER I

On the manner in which the Pythagoreans philosophized about numbers.

THE Pythagoreans, turning from the vulgar paths, and delivering their philosophy in secret to those alone who were worthy to receive it, exhibited it to others through mathematical names. Hence they called forms, numbers, as things which are the first separated from impartible union; for the natures which are above forms, are also above separation.* The all-perfect multitude of forms, therefore, they obscurely signified through the duad; but they indicated the first formal principles by the monad and duad, as not being numbers; and also by the first triad and tetrad, as being the first numbers, the one being odd, and the other even, from which by addition the decad is generated; for the sum of 1, 2, 3, and 4, is ten. But after numbers, in secondary and multifarious lives, introducing geometrical prior to physical magnitudes; these also they referred to numbers, as to formal causes and the princi-

---

* Forms subsist at the extremity of the intelligible triad, which triad consists of *being, life,* and *intellect.* But being and life, with all they contain, subsist here involved in impartible union. See my Proclus on the Theology of Plato.

ples of these; referring the point indeed, as being impartible to the monad, but a line as the first interval to the duad; and again, a superficies, as having a more abundant interval to the triad; and a solid to the tetrad. They also called, as is evident from the testimony of Aristotle, the first length the duad; for it is not simply length, but the *first* length, in order that by this they might signify *cause*. In a similar manner also, they denominated the *first* breadth, the triad; and the *first* depth the tetrad. They also referred to formal principles all psychical knowledge. And intellectual knowledge indeed, as being contracted according to impartible union, they referred to the monad; but scientific knowledge, as being evolved, and as proceeding from cause to the thing caused, yet through the inerratic, and always through the same things, they referred to the duad; and opinion to the triad, because the power of it is not always directed to the same thing, but at one time inclines to the true, and at another to the false. And they referred sense to the tetrad, because it has an apprehension of bodies; for in the duad indeed, there is one interval from one monad to the other; but in the triad there are two intervals from any one monad to the rest; and in the tetrad there are three. They referred, therefore, to principles every thing knowable, viz. beings, and the gnostic powers of these. But they divided beings not according to breadth, but according to depth; into intelligibles, objects of science, objects of opinion, and sensibles. In a similar manner, also they divided knowledge into intellect, science, opinion, and sense. The extremity, therefore, of the intelligible triad, or animal itself, as it is called by Plato in the Timæus, is assumed from the division of the objects of knowledge, manifesting the intelligible order, in which forms themselves, viz. the first forms and the principles of these, are contained, viz. the idea of the one itself, of the first length, which is the duad itself, and also the ideas of the first breadth and the first depth; (for in common the term *first* is adapted to all of them), viz. to the triad itself, and the tetrad itself.

Again, the Pythagoreans and Plato did not denominate idea from one thing, and ideal number from another. But since the assertion is eminently true, that all things are similar to number, it is evident that number, and especially every ideal number, was denominated on account of its paradigmatic peculiarity. If any one, however, wishes to apprehend this from the appellation itself, it is easy to infer that idea was called, from rendering as it were its participants similar to itself, and imparting to them *form, order, beauty,* and *unity;* and this in consequence of always preserving the same form, expanding its own power to the infinity of particulars, and investing with the same species its eternal participants. *Number* also, since it imparts proportion and elegant arrangement to all things, was allotted this appellation. For the ancients, says Syrianus,* call to *adapt* or *compose* αρσαι *arsai,* whence is derived αριθμος *arithmos number.* Hence αναρσιον *anarsion* among the Greeks signifies *incomposite.* Hence too, those Grecian sayings, *you will adapt the balance, they placed number together with them,* and also *number and friendship.* From all which number was called by the Greeks *arithmos,* as that which measures and orderly arranges all things, and unites them in amicable league.

Farther still, some of the Pythagoreans discoursed about inseparable numbers alone, i.e. numbers which are inseparable from mundane natures, but others about such as have a subsistence separate from the universe, in which as paradigms they saw those numbers are contained, which are perfected by nature. But others, making a distinction between the two, unfolded their doctrine in a more clear and perfect manner.

* In Aristot. Metaphys. Lib. 13.

If it be requisite, however, to speak concerning the difference of these monads, and their privation of difference, we must say that the monads which subsist in quantity, are by no means to be extended to essential numbers; but when we call essential numbers monads, we must assert that all of them mutually differ from each other by *difference* itself, and that they possess a privation of difference from *sameness*. It is evident also, that those which are in the same order, are contained through mutual comparison, in *sameness* rather than in difference, but that those which are in different orders are conversant with much diversity, through the dominion of *difference*.

Again, the Pythagoreans asserted that nature produces sensibles by numbers; but then these numbers were not mathematical but physical; and as they spoke symbolically, it is not improbable that they demonstrated every property of sensibles by mathematical names. However, says Syrianus, to ascribe to them a knowledge of sensible numbers alone, is not only ridiculous, but highly impious. For they received indeed, from the theology of Orpheus, the principles of intelligible and intellectual numbers, they assigned them an abundant progression, and extended their dominion as far as to sensibles themselves. Hence that proverb was peculiar to the Pythagoreans, that *all things are assimilated to number*. Pythagoras, therefore, in THE SACRED DISCOURSE, clearly says, that "number is the ruler of forms and ideas, and is the cause of gods and dæmons." He also supposes that *"to the most ancient and artificially ruling deity, number is the canon, the artificial reason, the intellect also, and the most undeviating balance of the composition and generation of all things."* αυτος μεν πυθαγορας, εν τω ιερω λογω, διαρρηδην μορφων και ιδεων κραντορα τον αριθμον ελεγεν ειναι, και θεων και δαιμονων αιτιον· και τω πρεσβυτατω και κρατιστευοντι τεχνιτη θεω κανονα, και λογον τεχνικον, νουν τε και σταθμαν αχλινεστασταν τον αριθμον υπειχε συστασιος και γενεσεως των παντων. Syrianus adds, "But Philolaus declared that number is the governing and self begotten bond of the eternal permanency of mundane natures." φιλολαυς δε, της των κοσμικων αιωνιας διαμονης την κρατιστενουσαν και αυτογενη συνοχην ειναι απεφηνατο τον αριθμον. "And Hippasus, and all those who were destined to a quinquennial silence, called number the judicial instrument of the maker of the universe, and the first paradigm of mundane fabrication." οι δε περι ιππασον ακουσματικοι ειπον κριτικον κοσμουργου θεου οργανον, και παραδειγμαπρωτον κοσμοποιϊας. But how is it possible they could have spoken thus sublimely of number, unless they had considered it as possessing an essence separate from sensibles, and a transcendency fabricative, and at the same time paradigmatic?

CHAPTER II

On mathematical and physical number.

As in every thing, according to the doctrine of Aristotle, one thing corresponds to matter, and another to form, in any number, as for instance the pentad, its five monads, and in short its quantity, and the number which is the subject of participation, are derived from the duad itself; but its form, i.e. the pentad itself, is from the monad: for every form is a monad, and unites its subject quantity. The pentad itself, therefore, which is a monad, proceeds from the principal monad, or that which ranks as the highest principle after *the ineffable one,* forms its subject quantity, which is itself formless, and connects it to its own form. For there are two principles of mathematical numbers in our souls, the monad which comprehends in itself all the forms of numbers, and corresponds to the monad in intellectual natures, and the duad which is a certain generative principle of infinite power, and which on this account, as being the image of the never-failing and intelligible duad, is called indefinite. While this proceeds to all things, it is not deserted in its course by the monad, but that which proceeds from the monad continually distinguishes and forms boundless quantity, gives a specific distinction to all its orderly progressions, and incessantly adorns them with forms. And as in mundane natures, there is neither any thing formless, nor any vacuum among the species of things, so likewise in mathematical number, neither is any quantity left innumerable, for thus the forming power of the monad would be vanquished by the indefinite duad, nor does any medium intervene between the consequent numbers, and the well-disposed energy of the monad.

Neither, therefore, does the pentad consist of substance and accident, as a white man; nor of genus and difference, as man of animal and biped; nor of five monads mutually touching each other, like a bundle of wood; nor of things mingled, like a drink made from wine and honey; nor of things sustaining position, as stones by their position complete the house; nor lastly, as things numerable, for these are nothing else than particulars. But it does not follow that numbers themselves, because they consist of indivisible monads, have nothing else besides monads; (for the multitude of points in continued quantity is an indivisible multitude, yet it is not on this account that there is a completion of something else from the points themselves) but this takes place because there is something in them which corresponds to matter, and something which corresponds to form. Lastly, when we unite the triad with the tetrad, we say that we make seven. The assertion, however, is not true: for monads conjoined with monads, produce indeed the subject of the number 7, but nothing more. Who then imparts the heptadic form to these monads? Who is it also that gives the form of a bed to a certain number of pieces of wood? Shall we not say that the soul of the carpenter, from the art which he possesses, fashions the wood, so as to receive the form of a bed, and that the numerative soul, from possessing in herself a monad which has the relation of a principle, gives form and subsistence to all numbers? But in this only consists the difference, that the carpenter's art is not naturally inherent in us, and requires manual operation, because it is conversant with sensible matter, but the numerative art is naturally present with us, and is therefore possessed by all men, and has an intellectual matter which it instantaneously invests with form. And this is that which deceives the multitude, who think that the heptad is nothing besides seven monads. For the imagination of the vulgar, unless it first sees a thing unadorned, afterwards the supervening energy of the adorner, and lastly, above all the thing itself, perfect and formed, cannot be persuaded that it has two natures, one formless, the other formal, and still further, that which beyond these imparts form; but asserts that the subject is one, and without generation. Hence, perhaps, the ancient theologists and Plato ascribed temporal generations to things without generation, and to things which are perpetually adorned, and regularly disposed, privation of order and ornament, the erroneous and the boundless, that they might lead men to the knowledge of a formal and effective cause. It is, therefore, by no means wonderful, that though seven sensible monads are never without the heptad, these should be distinguished by science, and that the former should have the relation of a subject, and be analogous to matter, but the latter should correspond to species and form.

Again, as when water is changed into air, the water does not become air, or the subject of air, but that which was the subject of water becomes the subject of air, so when one number unites itself with another, as for instance the triad with the duad, the species or forms of the two numbers are not mingled, except in their immaterial reasons, in which at the same time that they are separate, they are not impeded from being united, but the quantities of the two numbers which are placed together, become the subject of the pentad. The triad, therefore, is one, and also the tetrad, even in mathematical numbers: for though in the ennead or number nine, you may conceive a first, second, and third triad, yet you see one thing thrice assumed; and in short, in the ennead there is nothing but the form of the ennead in the quantity of nine monads. But if you mentally separate its subjects, (for form is impartible) you will immediately invest it with forms corresponding to its division; for our soul cannot endure to see that which is formless, unadorned, especially as she possesses the power of investing it with ornament.

Since also separate numbers possess a demiurgic or fabricative power, which mathematical numbers imitate, the sensible world likewise contains images of those numbers by which it is adorned; so that all things are in all, but in an appropriate manner in each. The sensible world, therefore, subsists from immaterial and energetic reasons,* and from more ancient causes. But those who do not admit that nature herself is full of productive powers, lest they should be obliged to double things themselves, these wonder how from things void of magnitude and gravity, magnitude and gravity are composed; though they are never composed from things of this kind which are void of gravity and magnitude, as from parts. But magnitude is generated from essentially impartible element; since form and matter are the elements of bodies; and still much more is it generated from those truer causes which are considered in demiurgic reasons and forms. Is it not therefore necessary that all dimensions, and all moving masses, must from these receive their generation? For either bodies are unbegotten like incorporeal natures, or of things with inter-

---

* i.e. Productive principles.

val things without interval are the causes, of partibles impartibles, and of sensibles and contraries, things insensible and void of contact: and we must assent to those who assert that things possessing magnitude are thus generated from impartibles. Hence the Pythagorean Eurytus, and his followers, beholding the images of things themselves in numbers, rightly attributed certain numbers to certain things, according to their peculiarity. In consequence of this, he said, that a particular number is the boundary of this plant, and again, another number of this animal; just as of a triangle 6 is the boundary, of a square 9, and of a cube 8. As the musician too, harmonizes his lyre through mathematical numbers, so nature through her own natural numbers, orderly arranges, and modulates her productions.

Indeed, that numbers are participated by the heavens, and that there is a solar number, and also a lunar number, is manifest according to the adage, even to the blind. For the restitutions of the heavenly bodies to their pristine state (αποκαταστασεις) would not always be effected through the same things, and in the same manner, unless one and the same number had dominion in each. Yet all these contribute to the procession of the celestial spheres, and are contained by their perfect number. But there is also a certain natural number belonging to every animal. For things of the same species would not be distinguished by organs after the same manner, nor would they arrive at puberty and old age about the same time, or generate, nor would the foetus be nourished or increase, according to regular periods, unless they were detained by the same measure of nature. According to the best of the Pythagoreans also, Plato himself, number is the cause of better and worse generations. Hence though the Pythagoreans sometimes speak of the squares and cubes of natural numbers, they do not make them to be monadic, such as the number 9, and the number

27, but they signify through these names from similitude, the progression of natural numbers into, and dominion about, generations. In like manner, though they call them equal or double, they exhibit the dominion and symphony of ideas in these numbers. Hence different things do not use the same number, so far as they are different, nor do the same things use a different, so far as they are the same.

In short, physical numbers are material forms divided about the subject which receives them. But material powers are the sources of connection and modification to bodies. For form is one thing, and the power proceeding from it another. For form itself is indeed impartible and essential; but being extended, and becoming bulky, it emits from itself, as if it were a blast, material powers which are certain qualities. Thus, for instance, in fire, the form and essence of it is impartible, and is truly the image of the cause of fire: for in partible natures, the impartible has a subsistence. But from form which is impartible in fire, and which subsists in it as number, an extension of it accompanied with interval, takes place about matter, from which the powers of fire are emitted, such as heat, or refrigeration, or moisture, or something else of the like kind. And these qualities are indeed essential, but are by no means the essence of fire. For essences do not proceed from qualities, nor are essence and power the same thing. But the essential every where precedes power. And from this being one the multitude of powers proceeds, and the distributed from that which is undistributed; just as many energies are the progeny of one power.

CHAPTER III

On the monad.

THE monad, as we learn from the extracts preserved by Photius from Nicomachus, was called by the Pythagoreans intellect, male and female, God, and in a certain respect matter. They also said, that it in reality mingled all things, is the recipient and capacious of all things, is Chaos, confusion, commixtion, obscurity, darkness, a chasm, Tartarus, Styx, and horror, and void of mixture, a subterranean profundity, Lethe, a rigid virgin, and Atlas. It is likewise called by them the axis, the Sun, and Pyralios, Morpho, the tower of Jupiter, and spermatic reason. Apollo likewise, the prophet, and ambiguous.

With respect to the first of these appellations, intellect, the reason why the Pythagoreans thus denominated the monad will be evident if it is considered that forms or ideas were called by them numbers, and that as the monad contains in itself the cause of numbers, so intellect is the source of all ideas. As the monad too comprehends in itself the multitude which it produces, and with which it accords, so intellect comprehends in itself all the forms which proceed from it, and with which it is coordinate. But they appear to have called the monad male and female, from containing in itself causally, the odd and the even, the former of which corresponds to the male, and the latter to the female, or according to the anonymous author in Theologumenis Arithmeticis, it was so called as being the seed of all things. Hence we are informed by Theo of Smyrna, (p. 30) that Aristotle in his treatise called Pythagoric, said, "that *the one* partakes of both these natures; for being added to the odd it makes the even number, and to the even, the odd number, which it could not do, if it did not participate of both these." And he further informs us that Archytas also was of the same opinion. As God too is the cause of all multitude, the reason is obvious why they called the monad God. They also very properly denominated it *in a certain respect,* and not wholly matter, from its similitude to divinity. For God is the first, and matter the last of things, and each subsists by a negation of all things. Hence matter is said to be

dissimilarly similar to divinity. It is similar, so far as it alone
subsists by a negation of all things. But it is dissimilarly similar, because divinity is better and beyond all things, but matter
is worse than, and below all things.

Again, when they said that the monad in reality mingled
and is the recipient of all things, this likewise was asserted by
them from the analogy of the monad to deity; for all things
are mingled by and comprehended in the ineffable nature of
divinity. But they called it chaos from resembling the infinite,
for chaos, according to Pythagoras,* is analogous to infinity, in
the same manner as ether is said by him to correspond to
bound. And bound and infinity are the two great principles of
things immediately posterior to the ineffable. For the same
reason they called it a chasm. But they called it confusion,
commixture, obscurity, and darkness, because in the ineffable
principle of things of which it is the image, all things are pro-
foundly one without any separation or distinction, as being all
things prior to all, and in consequence of being involved in unfathomable depths, are concealed in unknown obscurity and
darkness. Hence, as we are informed by Damascius in his admirable MS. treatise περι αρχων, the Egyptians asserted nothing
of the first principle of things, but celebrated it as a thrice unknown darkness transcending all intellectual perception. ανυμν-
ηκασιν πρωτην αρχην σκοτος υπερ πασαν νοησιν, σκοτος αγνωστον, τρις
τουτο επιφημιζοντες. As Tartarus too subsists at the extremity
of the universe, in a descending series, it is dissimilarly similar
to the ineffable which is the extremity of things in an ascending series. But when they called the monad Styx, it was in
consequence of looking to its immutable nature. For Styx, according to its first subsistence, is the cause by which divine natures retain an immutable sameness of essence; for this is the
occult meaning of the fabulous assertion, that the Gods swear

---

* See the notes to my translation of Aristotle's Metaphysics.

by Styx, viz. they continue through this invariably the same. They appear to have called the monad, horror, from considering that the ineffable is perfectly unknown, and unconnected with our nature; for the perception of any sensible thing of this kind, is attended with terror. But they denominated it void of mixture, from the simplicity of the nature of the ineffable and a subterranean profundity from its unfathomable depths, which are beyond all knowledge. As with respect to the ineffable likewise, knowledge, as Damascius beautifully observes, is refunded into ignorance, the monad, which is the image of it, is very appropriately called Lethe or oblivion. But from the purity of its nature, the monad is denominated a rigid virgin. And it is called Atlas, because the ineffable supports, connects, and separates all things; for of this the fabulous pillars of Atlas are an image.

Besides these appellations, the Pythagoreans also called the monad Apollo, as we are informed by Plutarch and Plotinus, from its privation of multitude. They likewise denominated it Prometheus, according to the anonymous author of Theologum. Arithmet. because it in no respect runs to the anterior part, απο του προσω μηδενι τροπω θειν; for there is nothing beyond the ineffable. The same author, likewise, informs us that they called it "essence, the cause of truth, the simple paradigm, the order of symphony; in the greater and the less, the equal; in intension and remission, the middle; in multitude the moderate; in time the present now. And besides these, a ship, a chariot, a friend, life, and felicity." For as *the one* is all things prior to all, it is preeminently the most excellent of things, but this, according to *the one,* i.e. without departing from the ineffable simplicity of its nature. They also denominated it form, because, as Simplicius observes (in Phys. lib. 1.) form circumscribes and bounds every thing to which it accedes. But they called it Proteus, as we are informed by the above mentioned anonymous author, in consequence of comprehending the peculiarities of all things in itself, ουκ απιθανως δε και πρωτεα προσηγορευον αυτην, τον εν Αιγυπτω παμμορφον ηρωα, τα παντων ιδιωματα περιεχουσαν. They also denominated it Jupiter, because what *the one,* or the ineffable principle of things is to all the orders of the Gods, that Jupiter is to all the divine orders posterior to him, as is beautifully observed by Proclus in Theol. Plat. lib. 5. They likewise called it Mnemosyne the mother of the Muses, because as the Muses generate all the variety of reasons with which the world is replete, and are the causes of the perfection of the universe, Mnemosyne will be analogous to *the one* which is the source of all multitude. It may also be said that as Mnemosyne is memory, and memory is stability of knowledge, the monad is thus denominated, as being the image of *the one* which is the stable root of all knowledge, and of all things. But they called it Vesta, or the fire in the centre of the earth, which as Simplicius observes (de Cælo lib. 2.) possesses a fabricative power, nourishes the whole earth from the middle, and excites whatever in it is of a frigid nature. So that as a producing centre it is analogous to *the one.** On this appellation, there is the following remarkable passage in the before mentioned anonymous author. "In addition to these things, also, they say, that a certain fiery cube of the nature of unity, is situated about the middle of the four elements, the middle position of which Homer also knew, when he says,

> As far beneath the unseen region hurl'd,
> As earth is distant from the etherial world.

Empedocles, Parmenides, and nearly most of the ancient wise men, appear to accord in these things with the Pythagoreans;

---

* From this passage of Simplicius, it is evident how much they are mistaken, who suppose that by the fire at the centre, the Pythagoreans meant the sun, and who in consequence of this ascribe the system of Copernicus to Pythagoras, as the author. See my Introduction to the Timæus in vol. II. of my translation of Plato, and the note on the Hymn to Vesta, in my translation of the Orphic hymns.

for they say that the monadic nature, after the manner of Vesta, is established in the middle, and on this account preserves that seat in equilibrium." προς τουτοις φασι περι το μεσον των τεσσαρων στοιχειων κεισθαι τινα εναδικον διαπυρον κυβον, ου την μεσοτητα της θεας (lege θεσεως) ειδεναι και Ομηρον λεγοντα

τοσσον ενερθ’ αϊδος, οσον ουρανος εστ’ απο γαιης.

εοικασι δε κατα γε ταυτα κατηκολουθηκεναι τοις πυθαγορειοις, οι τε περι Εμπεδοκλεα και Παρμενιδην, και σχεδον οι πλειστοι των παλαι σοφων, φαμενοι, την μοναδικην φυσιν, Εστιας τροπον, εν μεσω ιδρυσθαι· και δια τουτο ισορροπον φυλασσειν την αυτην εδραν.

In the last place, they called the monad multinominal, as we are informed by Hesychius; and this with the greatest propriety, because *the ineffable one,* of which the monad is the image, is, as we have observed, all things prior to all.

CHAPTER IV

On the duad.

THE duad was called by the Pythagoreans, as we learn from Nicomachus, "audacity, matter, the cause of dissimilitude, and the interval between multitude and the monad. This alone produces equality from composition and mixture, on which account also it is equal. But it is likewise unequal, defect, and abundance, and is alone unfigured, indefinite, and infinite. It is also alone the principle and cause of the even, yet is neither evenly-even, nor unevenly-even, nor evenly-odd. But many of these things are proximate to the physical peculiarity of the duad. It is likewise the fountain of all symphony, and among the Muses is Erato. It is also harmony, patience, and a root, though not in a certain respect in energy. It is power too, the feet of Ida abounding with fountains, a summit and Phanes.

It is also Justice, and Isis, Nature and Rhea, the mother of Jupiter, and the fountain of distribution. It was likewise called by them Phrygia, Lydia, Dindymene, Ceres, and Eleusinia, Diana and Cupid, Dictynna, Aeria, Asteria, Disamos, and Esto. Also Venus, Dione, Mychæa, Cytherea, ignorance, ignobility, falsehood, difference, indistinction, strife, dissension, Fate and Death."

Prior, however, to a development of these appellations, it will be requisite to observe concerning the duad, that the Pythagoreans, before they evinced the multitude subsists in intelligibles, necessarily investigated the cause of the multitude which is there, and found that among the genera of being it is *difference,* which subsists according to *non-being;* but that in causes most eminently the first, it is the indefinite duad, which, says Syrianus, Pythagoras in the Sacred Discourse calls Chaos, and which he associates with intellect; for he assigns this appellation to the monad, which is the first of the two great principles* after *the ineffable one.*

This duad is indeed every where the cause of multitude, so far as it produces things from *the one* with their proper differences. But so far as it is a principle, there is also in the several orders of beings a proper monad; and a duad connate to this found, and which generates a number accommodated to itself.

Every number too, subsists from these two principles, the monad and duad; but the odd number is rather characterized by the property of the monad, but the even by the property of the duad. In angles, also, the right angle subsists rather according to the monad, but the acute and obtuse, according to the indefinite duad, in which exuberance and defect are most ap-

---

* These two great principles are not only called the monad and duad, but also bound and infinity.

parent. Of figures, likewise, those which are characterized by equality, sameness, and similitude, have greater relation to the monad; but those in which inequality, difference, and dissimilitude are predominant, are more allied to the duad. In short, every figure subsists from these two principles: for the sphere, circle, equilateral triangle, square and cube, participate of the duad by their quantity, and their possession of interval. And again, beams of timber, altars, scalene triangles, and oblong figures accord with the monad, from which they receive their form.

Again, the Pythagoreans, says Syrianus, considered accidents, and saw that the same principles had an analogous subsistence in these; and that they had their proper monad and duad; the former being the cause of identity to them, and the latter of difference and multitude. In natural reasons also, or productive seminal principles, they placed effective causes. There is therefore, in nature, one productive principle generative of all colours, and another which is indeed primarily perfected from this, but which produces together with it the multitude and diversity of colours: and these are the monad and duad of colours. In other accidents also, which are perfected through natural reasons, there will be found a monad and duad analogous to these.

Having premised thus much, let us direct our attention in the next place, to the appellations of the duad. With respect to the appellation audacity, therefore, we are informed by the anonymous author that the duad was so called "because it first separated itself from the monad." For as the descent of the soul into body, and her abandoning an intellectual and divine life, for an irrational and mortal condition of being may be called audacity, as being in a certain respect an improper boldness, so with reference to the transcendant excellence of the monad, a departure from it as the paternal profundity and the adytum of god-nourished silence, as it is called in the Chaldean oracles, may be said, metaphorically speaking, to be an audacious undertaking. But the duad was called matter, as being indefinite, and the cause of bulk and division, as Simplicius observes in his comment on the Physics. And it is the cause of dissimilitude, as being in its first subsistence *the infinite,* from which dissimilitude is suspended, in the same manner as similitude is suspended from bound. But it is the interval between multitude and the monad, because it is yet perfect multitude, but is as it were parturient with it, and almost unfolding it into light. Of this we see an image in the duad of arithmetic. For as Proclus beautifully observes in his Comment on the 20th &c. definition of the first book of Euclid's Elements: "The duad is the medium between unity and number. For unity, by addition, produces more than by multiplication; but number, on the contrary, is more increased by multiplication than by addition; and the duad, whether multiplied into, or compounded with itself, produces an equal quantity." The duad was also called equal, because, says the anonymous author, "two and two are *equal* to twice two:" that is, the addition of two to itself, is equal to the multiplication of it by itself. But it is unequal, defect and abundance, as the same author observes, according to the conception of matter. For he adds, the Pythagoreans call matter homonymously with this, the indefinite duad, because so far as pertains to itself, it is deprived of morphe, form, and a certain definition, and is defined and bounded by reason and art. It is likewise alone unfigured, because, as the anonymous writer observes, "From the triangle and the triad polygonous figures proceed in energy, *ad infinitum;* from the monad all figures subsist at once according to power; but from two things, whether they are right lines, or angles, a right-lined figure can never be composed."* But

---

* The latter part of this extract in the original is defective; for it is υπο δε

the duad was called indefinite and infinite, because in its first subsistence it is infinity, and therefore has no appropriate bound. And as we have shown that it was called equal, it is not wonderful that it was denominated the cause of the even, and consequently as the cause of it, was said to be neither evenly-even, nor unevenly-even, nor evenly-odd.

Again, it was called the fountain of all symphony, because the symphony diapason, which is most harmonic, is formed from a duple ratio. But is was denominated *Erato*, "because, says the anonymous author, it attracts to itself through *love* the accession of the monad, as of form, and thus generates the remaining effects," την γαρ της μοναδος, ως ειδους προσοδον δι ερωτα επισπωμενη, τα λοιπα αποτελεσματα γεννα. As the fountain of all symphony, it is evident why it was called harmony. But it was denominated patience, because, says the anonymous writer, it is the first multitude that sustains or endures separation, viz. a separation from the adytum of the monad. It is also a root, though not in a certain respect in energy, because it is the mother of number with which it is parturient, but is not number in perfect energy. It was likewise denominated power, because the first infinity is the first power. But it is the feet of Ida abounding with fountains, because it is the root of the region of ideas, or an intelligible essence. For the foot of a mountain is the same as the root of it; and mount Ida, as Proclus observes in his Apology for Homer, signifies the region of ideas. It is also called Phanes, or intelligible intellect, as being the occult power of it. But it may be said generally, that it is Justice, Isis, Nature, Rhea, &c. because, as being of a feminine nature, it is the fountain of all the divinities that are of a female characteristic. It likewise appears that it was

δυο οντες ευθειων ποτε, ειτε γονιων, ευθυγραμμον συνισταται σχημα. Instead of which it is necessary to read, as in my translation, υπο δε δυο οντες ειτε ευθειων, ειτε γονιων, ου ποτε ευθυγραμμον συνισταται σχημα.

called Cupid for the reason above assigned, for its being denominated Erato, viz. from *desiring* the accession of the monad. But it is ignorance, from its subsistence as infinity, about which there is an all-perfect ignorance. And it is ignobility, falsehood, difference, &c. as being the leader of the worse co-ordination of things.

CHAPTER V

On the triad.

NICOMACHUS, in the extracts from him preserved by Photius, observes of the triad conformably to the Pythagoreans, as follows: "The triad is the first odd number in energy, is the first perfect number, is a middle and analogy. It causes the power of the monad to proceed into energy and extension. But it is also the first of numbers, and is properly a system of monads. Hence afterwards, the Pythagoreans refer this number to physiology. For it is the cause of that which has triple dimensions, gives bound to the infinity of number, is similar and the same, homologous and definite. The triad also is intellect, and is the cause of good counsel, intelligence, and knowledge. It is also the most principal of numbers, and is the mistress and composition of all music. It is likewise especially the mistress of geometry, possesses authority in whatever pertains to astronomy and the nature and knowledge of the heavenly bodies, and connects and leads them into effect. Every virtue also is suspended from this number, and proceeds from it. In the next place with respect to its mythological appellations, it is Saturn and Latona, and the horn of Amalthea. It is also Ophion, Thetis, and Harmony, Hecate, Erana, and Charitia, and among the Muses, Polymnia. It is likewise Pluto and Loxia, the bear, and Helice, and the constellation which is never merged in the deep. It is Damatrame and Dioscoria, Metis and Trigemina, Triton, and the perfect of the sea, Tritogeneia and Achelous, Naetis and Agyiopeza, Curetide and Cratæide, Symbenia and marriage, Gorgonia and Phorcia, Trisamos and Lydios."

Thus far Nicomachus. That the triad then is the first odd number in energy, will be evident from considering that it is in reality the first number; for number is more increased by multiplication than by addition, as we have before observed from Proclus, and this is the case with the triad, but is not so with the duad or the monad. That it is also the first perfect number is evident from this, that three things, as Aristotle* observes, are all, and the all is perfect from having a beginning, middle, and end. But the triad is a middle and analogy, because all analogy or proportionality consists of three terms at least, and analogies were by the ancients called middles. It also causes the power of the monad to proceed into energy, and extension, because the monad considered as unproceeding is hyparxis, or the summit of essence, but it is prolific through power, and in the third place, it unfolds multitude into light through energy. That it is likewise the first of numbers we have before shown. And it appears to me that it was said to be a system of monads, because every system has a first, middle, and last. But it gives bound to the infinity of number, because it is all-perfect. Hence too, from its all-perfect nature, it is similar and the same, homologous and definite. As energy also it is intellect; for intellect is the first energy. But it is the cause of good counsel, intelligence, and knowledge, "because," as the anonymous author observes, "men correctly employ present circumstances, foresee such as are future, and acquire experience from such as are past." It is also the most principal, because it is the first of numbers. And it is the mistress and composition of all music, because harmony contains three symphonies, the diapason,

* De Coelo. lib. i. cap. 1.

the diapente, and the diatessaron. It may likewise be said to be especially the mistress of geometry, because the triangle is the principle of all figures. With respect to the triad possessing authority in whatever pertains to astronomy and the nature and knowledge of the heavenly bodies, and that it connects and leads them into effect, this will be evident from considering that there are three quaternions of the celestial signs, viz. the fixed, the moveable, and the common. In every sign also, there are three faces and three decans, and three lords of every triplicity. And among the planets there are three fortunes. According to the Chaldeans likewise, there are three etherial worlds prior to the sphere of the fixed stars. And we are informed by the anonymous author, "that every traduction of divine and mortal natures is effected by *emission, reception,* and *restoration;* etherial natures after a certain manner disseminating; the region which surrounds the earth as it were receiving; and restoration taking place through things which have an intermediate subsistence.

Οτι και η συμπασα διεξαγωγη θειωντε και θνητων εκ τεπροεσεως, και υποδοχης, και τριτον ανταποδοσεως κρατυνεται. σπερμαινοντων μεν τροπον τινα των αιθεριων. υποδεχομενων δε ωσανει των περιγειων. αν ταποδοσεως δε δια των αναμεσων τελουμενων.

With respect to the mythological appellations of this number, as no author that is extant has unfolded their recondite meaning, I shall only observe, that the several divinities by the names of which it is celebrated, were doubtless referred to it so far as each of them is of a perfective nature.

CHAPTER VI

On the tetrad.

THE tetrad, as we learn from Nicomachus, was called by the Pythagoreans, "the greatest miracle, a God after another man-

ner (than the triad,) a manifold, or rather, every divinity. It is
also the fountain of natural effects, and is the key-bearer of nature. It is the introducer and cause of the constitution and
permanency of the mathematical disciplines. It is likewise the
nature of Aeolus, Hercules, and elevation, most robust, masculine, and virile. It is Mercury and Vulcan, Bacchus and Sori-
tas, Maiadeus or Maiades. For the tetrad is the son of Maia,
i.e. of the duad. It is also Eriunius, Socus, and Dioscorus,
Bassareus and Bimater, having the duad for its mother. It is
also of a feminine form, is effective of virility, and excites Bacchic fury. It is likewise Harmonita or Harmonia, and among
the Muses, Urania."

With respect to the first of these appellations, "the greatest
miracle," it is necessary to observe, that the tetrad in its first
subsistence is the extremity of the intelligible triad, which is
called by Orpheus Phanes and Protogonus, and by Plato
animal itself (αυτοζωον). In this the first ideas of all things are
contained; and this, as we are informed by Proclus, is the first
effable deity, all beyond it being perfectly ineffable. Hence all
the intellectual orders of Gods are said by Orpheus to have
been *astonished* on surveying this deity unfolding himself into
light from mystic and ineffable silence;

Θαυμαζον καθορωντες εν αιθερι φεγγος αελπτον,
τω μεν απεστιλβε χροος αθανατοιο φανητος.

Procl. lib. 2. in Tim.

Hence as an astonishing, admirable, and unexpected deity, the
tetrad may be mythologically said to be the greatest miracle.
But it is a God after another manner than the triad, because in
the triad the first perfect is beheld, but in the tetrad all mundane natures are comprehended according to the causality of
principle. From its all-comprehending nature likewise, it is a
manifold, or rather, every divinity. As too, it *causally* contains
all mundane natures, it may very properly be called the *foun-*

tain of natural effects. Because likewise it opens and shuts the recesses of generation, it is denominated, as the anonymous author observes, *the key-bearer of nature,* as is also the mother of the Gods who is represented with a key. But it is the introducer and cause of the constitution and permanency of the mathematical disciplines, because these are four in number, viz. arithmetic and geometry, music and astronomy; and also because the first numbers and the first forms subsist in the intelligible tetrad. It is likewise said to be the nature of Aeolus, on account of the variety of its peculiarity, according to the anonymous writer, and because without this it would be impossible for the orderly and universal distribution of things to subsist. With respect to the other appellations of the tetrad, as Meursius in his Denarius Pythagoricus has given but few extracts from the anonymous writer, though his treatise professedly contains an explanation of these names, and as I cannot find a satisfactory development of them in any ancient writer, the appellation Harmonia excepted, I shall not attempt any elucidation of them. But the tetrad was very properly called by the Pythagoreans harmony, because the quadruple ratio forms the symphony disdiapason.

They also called the tetrad the first depth, because they considered a point as analogous to the monad, a line to the duad, a superficies to the triad, and a solid to the tetrad. They likewise denominated it justice, because, as we are informed by Alexander Aphrodisiensis (in Metaphys. major. cap. 5.) they were of opinion that the peculiarity of justice is compensation and equability, and finding this to exist in numbers, they said that the first evenly-even number is justice. For they asserted that which is first in things which have the same relation, to be especially that which it is said to be. But the tetrad is this number, because since it is the first square, it is divided into even numbers, and is even. The tetrad also was called by the

Pythagoreans every number, because it comprehends in itself all the numbers as far as to the decad, and the decad itself; for the sum of 1. 2. 3. and 4, is 10. Hence both the decad and the tetrad were said by them to be every number; the decad indeed in energy, but the tetrad in capacity. The sum likewise of these four numbers was said by them to constitute the tetractys, in which all harmonic ratios are included. For 4 to 1, which is a quadruple ratio, forms, as we have before observed, the symphony disdiapason; the ratio of 3 to 2, which is sesquialter, forms the symphony diapente; 4 to 3, which is sesquitertian, the symphony diatessaron; and 2 to 1, which is a duple ratio, forms the diapason.

Having however mentioned the tetractys, in consequence of the great veneration paid to it by the Pythagoreans, it will be proper to give it more ample discussion, and for this purpose to show from Theo of Smyrna,* how many tetractys there are: "The tetractys," says he, "was not only principally honoured by the Pythagoreans, because all symphonies are found to exist within it, but also because it appears to contain the nature of all things." Hence the following was their oath: "Not by him who delivered to our soul the tetractys, which contains the fountain and root of everlasting nature." But by him who delivered the tetractys they mean Pythagoras; for the doctrine concerning it appears to have been his invention. The above mentioned tetractys therefore, is seen in the composition of the first numbers 1. 2. 3. 4. But the second tetractys arises from the increase by multiplication of even and odd numbers beginning from the monad. Of these, the monad is assumed as the first, because, as we have before observed, it is the principle of all even, odd, and evenly-even numbers, and the nature of it is simple. But the three successive numbers receive their composition according to the even and the odd; because every num-

* In Mathemat. p. 147.

ber is not alone even, nor alone odd. Hence the even and the odd receive two tetractys, according to multiplication; the even indeed, in a duple ratio; for 2 is the first of even numbers, and increases from the monad by duplication. But the odd number is increased in a triple ratio; for 3 is the first of odd numbers, and is itself increased from the monad by triplication. Hence the monad is common to both these, being itself even and odd. The second number however, in even and double numbers is 2; but in odd and triple numbers 3. The third among even numbers is 4; but among odd numbers is 9. And the fourth among even numbers is 8; but among odd numbers is 27.

$$\left\{ \begin{array}{llll} 1. & 2. & 4. & 8. \\ 1. & 3. & 9. & 27. \end{array} \right\}$$

In these numbers the more perfect ratios of symphonies are found; and in these also a tone is comprehended. The monad however, contains the productive principle of a point. But the second numbers 2 and 3 contain the principle of a side, since they are incomposite, and first, are measured by the monad, and naturally measure a right line. The third terms are 4 and 9, which are in power a square superficies, since they are equally equal. And the fourth terms 8 and 27 being equally equally equal, are in power a cube. Hence from these numbers, and this tetractys, the increase takes place from a point to a solid. For a side follows after a point, a superficies after a side, and a solid after a superficies. In these numbers also, Plato in the Timæus constitutes the soul. But the last of these seven numbers, i.e. 27, is equal to all the numbers that precede it; for $1+2+3+4+8+9=27$. There are therefore, two tetractys of numbers, one of which subsists by addition, but the other by multiplication, and they comprehend musical, geometrical, and arithmetical ratios, from which also the harmony of the universe consists.

But the third tetractys is that which according to the same

analogy or proportion comprehends the nature of all magnitude. For what the monad was in the former tetractys, that a point is in this. What the numbers 2 and 3, which are in power a side, were in the former tetractys, that the extended species of a line, the circular and the right are in this; the right line indeed subsisting in conformity to the even number, since it is terminated* by two points; but the circular in conformity to the odd number, because it is comprehended by one line which has no end. But what in the former tetractys the square numbers 4 and 9 were, that the twofold species of planes, the rectilinear and the circular are in this. And what the cube numbers 8 and 27 were in the former, the one being an even, but the other an odd number, that the two solids, one of which has a hollow superficies, as the sphere and the cylinder, but the other a plane superficies, as the cube and the pyramid, are in this tetractys. Hence, this is the third tetractys, which gives completion to every magnitude, from a point, a line, a superficies, and a solid.

The fourth tetractys is of the simple bodies fire, air, water and earth, which have an analogy according to numbers. For what the monad was in the first tetractys, that fire is in this. But the duad is air. The triad is water. And the tetrad is earth. For such is the nature of the elements according to tenuity and density of parts. Hence fire has to air the ratio of 1 to 2; but to water, the ratio of 1 to 3; and to earth, the ratio of 1 to 4. In other respects also they are analogous to each other.

The fifth tetractys is of the figures of the simple bodies. For the pyramid indeed, is the figure of fire; the octaedron of air; the icosaedron of water; and the cube of earth.

The sixth tetractys is of things rising into existence through

* Instead of περιττουται, it is necessary to read περατουται, the necessity of which emendation, I wonder the learned Bullialdus did not observe.

the vegetative life. And the seed indeed is analogous to the monad and a point. But if it increases in length it is analogous to the duad and a line; if in breadth, to the triad and a superficies; but if in thickness, to the tetrad and a solid.

The seventh tetractys is of communities; of which the principle indeed, and as it were monad is man; the duad is a house; the triad a street; and the tetrad a city. For a nation consists of these. And these indeed are the material and sensible tetractys.

The eighth tetractys consists of the powers which form a judgment of things material and sensible, and which are of a certain intelligible nature. And these are, intellect, science, opinion and sense. And intellect indeed, corresponds in its essence to the monad; but science to the duad; for science is the science of a certain thing. Opinion subsists between science and ignorance; but sense is as the tetrad. For the touch which is common to all the senses being fourfold, all the senses energize according to contact.

The ninth tetractys is that from which the animal is composed, the soul and the body. For the parts of the soul indeed, are the rational, the irascible, and the epithymetic, or that which desires external good; and the fourth is the body in which the soul subsists.

The tenth tetractys is of the seasons of the year, through which all things rise into existence, viz. the spring, the summer, the autumn, and the winter.

And the eleventh is of the ages of man, viz. of the infant, the lad, the man, and the old man.

Hence there are eleven tetractys. The first is that which subsists according to the composition of numbers. The second, according to the multiplication of numbers. The third subsists according to magnitude. The fourth is of the simple bodies.

The fifth is of figures. The sixth is of things rising into existence through the vegetative life. The seventh is of communities. The eighth is the judicial power. The ninth is of the
parts of the animal. The tenth is of the seasons of the year.
And the eleventh is of the ages of man. All of them however
are proportional to each other. For what the monad is in the
first and second tetractys, that a point is in the third; fire in the
fourth; a pyramid in the fifth; seed in the sixth; man in the
seventh; intellect in the eighth; and so of the rest. Thus for
instance, the first tetractys is 1. 2. 3. 4. The second is the monad, a side, a square, and a cube. The third is a point, a line,
a superficies, and a solid. The fourth is fire, air, water, earth.
The fifth the pyramid, the octaedron, the icosaedron, and the
cube. The sixth, seed, length, breadth and depth. The seventh,
man, a house, a street, a city. The eighth, intellect, science,
opinion, sense. The ninth, the rational, the irascible, and the
epithymetic parts, and the body. The tenth, the spring, summer, autumn, winter. The eleventh, the infant, the lad, the
man, and the old man.

The world also which is composed from these tetractys is
perfect, being elegantly arranged in geometrical, harmonical,
and arithmetical proportion; comprehending every power, all
the nature of number, every magnitude, and every simple and
composite body. But it is perfect, because all things are the
parts of it, but it is not itself a part of any thing. Hence, the
Pythagoreans are said to have first used the before mentioned
oath, and also the assertion that "all things are assimilated to
number."

The Pythagoreans likewise, as we learn from the anonymous
author, gave a fourfold distribution to the goods both of the
soul and the body. For those of the former are prudence, tem-
perance, fortitude, and justice; but those of the body which
correspond to these, are, acuteness of sensation, health, strength

and beauty. And in external things, prosperity, renown, power and friendship, are the objects of desire.

The celebrated four causes also of Aristotle, are referred to the tetrad, divinity as the cause *by which* υφ'ου, or the efficient cause, matter *from which* εξ ου, form *through which* δι ου, and the effect *with reference to which* προς ο.

The anonymous author further observes, that in the tetrad accumulation and abundance are considered, in the same manner as multitude in the triad, and hence, says he, we proclaim the living thrice blessed on account of their felicity, but the dead who have exchanged this life for the next in the best manner, four times blessed. And thus much for the tetrad.

CHAPTER VII

On the pentad.

THE pentad, as we learn from the Nicomachean extracts, was called by the Pythagoreans the privation of strife, and the unconquered, alliation or change of quality, light and justice, and the smallest extremity of vitality. Likewise Nemesis and Bubastia, vengeance and Venus, Gamelia and Androgynia, Cythereia and Zonæa, circular and a demigoddess, the tower of Jupiter, Didymæa, and a stable axis. They likewise magnificently celebrate it as immortal and Pallas, Cardiatis and the leader, Acreotis and equilibrium, unmarried and Orthiatis, and of the Muses Melpomene.

Of these names the four first are thus explained by the anonymous author. "The pentad," says he, "is change of quality, because it changes that which is triply extended or which has length, breadth and depth into the sameness of a sphere, in consequence of moving circularly* and producing light. Whence also it is called light. But it is the privation of strife, because it constitutes and unites all things which were before separated by interval, and on account of the association and friendship of the two forms (of numbers, i.e. of the even and the odd, the pentad consisting of 3 and 2). And it is justice, because the pentad in the most eminent degree unfolds justice into light." But Alexander Aphrodisiensis in his Comment on the 7th chapter of the first book of Aristotle's Metaphysics, assigns the following reason why the pentad was called by the Pythagoreans *the unconquered.* "Because," says he, "in the first right-angled triangle whose sides are effable,† one of the sides is 3, another is 4, and the base is 5, and the base is in power equal to both the other sides; hence is was said by the Pythagoreans that it was victorious, and the two other sides were conquered. The pentad therefore, was denominated by them unconquered as not being surpassed, and as being superior." The anonymous author too, unfolds the meaning of this appellation as follows: "The Pythagoreans," says he, "called the pentad unconquered, not only because the fifth element, ether, which is arranged analogous to the pentad, and which has an invariable sameness of subsistence, terminates the strife and mutation of the elements which subsist under it as far as to the earth, but also it amicably connects and unites the first two differing, and not similar species of numbers, the odd and the even (i.e. 2 and 3.) becoming itself the system of their association."

The same author likewise thus explains the reason why the pentad was called the smallest extremity of vitality. "Since," says he, "according to physiologists there are three things

---

* For 5 is eminently a circular and spherical number, in every multiplication terminating in, or restoring itself.

† See this explained in the chapter on the properties of the heptad.

which are productive of life after corporification, viz. the vegetable, the psychical, and the rational power; and the rational
indeed, is arranged according to the hebdomad, but the psychical power according to the hexad, the vegetable power necessarily falls under the arrangement of the pentad; so that the pentad is a certain least extremity of vitality."

He also informs us that the reason why the Pythagoreans
called the pentad Nemesis, was because it distributes in an appropriate manner things celestial and divine, and the natural
elements. The pentad was likewise called Justice by the Pythagoreans for two reasons, as we are informed by Proclus on
Hesiod, because it pertains to justice either to punish trans-
gression, and take away inequality of possession, or to equalize
what is less, and to benefit. But they denominated it Venus,
according to the anonymous author, because the male and the
female numbers are complicated with each other. And after
the same manner, he adds, they called it Gamelia, because the
pentad first comprehends the form of every number, viz. 2 the
first even, and 3 the first odd number. Hence it is denominated marriage, as consisting of the male and the female. And
they doubtless called it Androgynia, because being an odd
number it is of a masculine characteristic. But they called it
circular, because, as we have before observed, it is eminently a
circular and spherical number. They likewise denominated it
a demigoddess, as the anonymous writer informs us, not only
because it is the half of the decad which is a divine number,
but also because in its proper diagram it is arranged in the
middle.* And Didymus, or Didymæa, double, because it divides the decad, which is otherwise indivisible, into two parts.
But they called it, he adds, immortal and Pallas, from containing a representation of the fifth essence (ether, over which
Pallas presides).

* Viz. it is in the middle of the series 1. 2. 3. 4. 5. 6. 7. 8. 9.

He further informs us, that they denominated it Cardiatis, or Cordialis, according to a similitude of the heart in animals, which is arranged in the middle. But they called it, he adds, Providence and Justice, because it equalizes things unequal; justice being a medium between excess and defect, just as 5 is the middle of all the numbers that are equally distant from it on both sides as far as to the decad, some of which it surpasses, and by others is surpassed, as may be seen in the following arrangement:

$$1 \quad 4 \quad 7$$
$$2 \quad 5 \quad 8$$
$$3 \quad 6 \quad 9$$

For here, as in the middle of the beam of a balance, 5 does not depart from the line of the equilibrium, while one scale is raised, and the other is depressed.

In the following arrangement also, viz. 1. 2. 3. 4. 5. 6. 7. 8. 9, it will be found that the sum of the numbers which are posterior, is triple the sum of those that are prior to 5; for $6+7+8+9=30$; but $1+2+3+4=10$. If therefore the numbers on each side of 5 represent the beam of a balance, 5 being the tongue of it, when a weight depresses the beam, an obtuse angle is produced by the depressed part with the tongue, and an acute angle by the elevated part of the beam. Hence, it is worse to do than to suffer an injury: and the authors of the injury verge downward as it were to the infernal regions; but the injured tend upward as it were to the Gods, imploring the divine assistance. Hence the meaning of the Pythagoric symbol is obvious, "Pass not above the beam of the balance." Since however injustice pertains to inequality, in order to correct this, equalization is requisite, that the beam of the balance may remain on both sides without obliquity. But equalization is effected by addition and subtraction. Thus if 4 is added to 5, and 4 is also taken from 5, the number 9 will be produced on one side, and 1 on the other, each of which is equally distant from 5. Thus too, if 3 is added to 5, and is also subtracted from it, on the one side 8 will be produced, and on the other 2. If 2 is added to 5, and likewise taken from it, 7 and 3 will be produced. And by adding 1 to 5 and subtracting 1 from it, 6 and 4 will be the result; in all which instances the numbers produced are equidistant from 5, and the sum of each couple is equal to 10.

We are likewise informed by Plutarch in his treatise On the Generation of the Soul according to Plato, that the Pythagoreans called the pentad τροφος, which signifies a sound, because they were of opinion that the first of the intervals of a tone which is capable of producing a sound is the fifth.

The same Plutarch also in his treatise On Eι at Delphi, farther informs us that the pentad was called by the Pythagoreans nature, "because," says he, "by the multiplication of itself, it again terminates in itself. For as nature receiving wheat in the seed, and becoming expanded in the middle produces many figures and forms, through which she brings her work to the (desired) end, but at last exhibits wheat, restoring the principle at the end of the whole mutation, thus also, while other numbers, when multiplied into themselves, terminate by increase in other numbers, five and six alone as often as they are multiplied into themselves, exhibit and preserve themselves."

CHAPTER VIII

On the hexad.

THE Pythagoreans, as we learn from the extracts from Nicomachus, denominated the hexad, "the form of form, the only number adapted to the soul, the distinct union of the parts of the universe, the fabricator of the soul, and the producing cause of the vital habit. Hence also, it is harmony, the perfection of parts, and is more properly Venus herself. It is also Zygia and nuptial, and Androgynæa. It is likewise Zygitis, benevolence, peace, friendship, health, Acmon, and truth. Among the Fates likewise they make it to be Lachesis; and they call it the principle, and the half of the whole. They also denominate it fardarting and Trivia, pertaining to two times, and Persea, triformed, Amphitrite and Anchidice, among the Muses Thalia, and Panacea."

With respect to the first of these appellations the *form of form,* Meursius has unfortunately omitted to assign from the anonymous author, the reason of its being so called, in the true spirit of a mere verbalist contenting himself with extracting from that author the words, ειδος ουν ειδους ουκ αν διαμαρτοιμεν αυτην ηγουμενοι, i.e. "We shall not therefore err in conceiving that the hexad is the form of form." Perhaps however, it was thus denominated because the perfect is that which character-izes all forms or ideas, and 6 is the first perfect number in en-ergy. But the hexad was said by the Pythagoreans to be the only number adapted to the soul, because soul from being the connecting medium or bond of intelligibles and sensibles is most eminently allied to Venus, who, as we are informed by Proclus in his MS. Commentary on the Parmenides, "imparts communion in multitude to intelligibles and all beings," την εν τω πληθει κοινωνιαν παρεχομενη τοις τε νοητοις, και πασι τοις ουσιν. From the anonymous author also we learn that the hexad was called the distinct union of the parts of the universe, because soul is as it were the animated form of formless matter. He adds, that no number can be more adapted to soul than the hexad, or can more properly be said to be the fabricator of soul, because it is found to be effective of the vital *habit,* from whence also it derives its appellation, ευρισκομενη και της ζωτικης εξεως εμποιητικη, παρ ο εξας. And that it is called harmony, be-cause every soul is harmonic.

The same writer also observes, "that the hexad was called the perfection of parts by the Pythagoreans, who in thus denominating it followed Orpheus, whether because six alone of all the numbers within the decad is equal to its members or parts; or because the whole and the universe is divided according to this number, and is through it elegantly arranged." With respect to its being denominated Venus herself, we learn from Martianus Capella lib. 7. that it was thus called, "because it may be shown that it is the source of harmony. For 6 to 12, says he, forms the symphony diapason; 6 to 9 the symphony diapente; and 6 to 8 the symphony diatessaron; whence it is said to be Venus the mother of harmony."

Again, with respect to the epithets nuptial (γαμηλια) and Androgynæa, these in the anonymous author are γαμος marriage, and αρρενοθηλυς; and concerning these he observes "that the hexad is generated by the power and multiplication of the first odd and the first even number which are male and female; and hence it is called αρρενοθηλυς, i.e. *male and female.* It is likewise called marriage, because it is itself equal to its parts. But the work of marriage is to produce offspring similar to the parents." The epithet φιλοτησια benevolence, is in the anonymous author φιλιωσις friendship and love, "which," says he, "it is appropriately called, because it connects together the male and the female." The anonymous author further informs us, "that the hexad was called health and beauty on account of the entireness and symmetry of its parts." For health is symmetry and a subsistence according to nature of the parts of the body.

From the same author likewise we learn, "that it was called *Acmon,* viz. as it were *unwearied,* (την οιον ακαματον) because the most principal triangles of the mundane elements participate of it, each of them becoming six, if they are distributed by three perpendiculars."

With respect to the appellation *truth,* perhaps it was so called because truth is the harmonious conjunction of that which knows with that which is known; and the hexad, as we have before shown, is most eminently harmonic.

Again, according to the anonymous author it was called far-darting εχατηβελετις, Trivia, and pertaining to two times; the first of these because the triad which is *Hecate* being *hurled forth* (Βολησασαν) and as it were composed (i.e. joined with another triad) generates the hexad. "But it was called Trivia," says he, "perhaps from the nature of the goddess. And it is probable that it was thus denominated, because this number is first allotted the motions which take place in the three intervals (length, breadth and depth,) each of which receives a twofold division from circumstances; (viz. motion according to length, is either backwards or forwards, according to breadth, is either on the right hand or the left, and according to depth, is either upwards or downwards.) But it was denominated pertaining to two times, from the distribution of the whole of time being effected by six signs of the zodiac above, and six under the earth. Or it was thus called, because time is allied to the triad, since it consists of three parts, and the hexad is formed from two triads."

With respect to the epithets Persea and triformed, the hexad appears to have been thus denominated for the same reason that it was called Trivia; for it is well known that Diana is tri-formed, and this goddess is called Persia by Orpheus in the introduction to his hymns. But we are informed by the anonymous writer that the hexad was called Amphitrite, because it has a triad on each side of it; and Anchidice, because it is especially proximate to the pentad, which as we have before shown was called by the Pythagoreans δικη *dice,* or Justice.

Lastly, the same author informs us, that it was called Thalia and Panacea, the former on account of the harmony of its composition; for I conjecture this to be the meaning of the words δια την των ετερων αρμονιαν, "through the harmony of the other," since the same author adds, "that much prior to this it was called κοσμος the world, because the world, in the same manner as 6, is often seen to consist of contraries according to an harmonious arrangement." And six consists by multiplication of the two contrary numbers 2 and 3, one of which is even and the other odd, and one of which is analogous to the male, but the other to the female. But is was called Panacea, on account of what has been before said of it under the appellation of health, or because it is as it were παναρχεια *panarcea,* all-sufficiency, being sufficiently supplied with parts to the perfection of its whole.

CHAPTER IX

On the heptad.

THE heptad, as we are informed by the anonymous writer, and Etymologici Auctor, was so called from the verb *sebo* denoting veneration (απο του σεβω) being a certain septas, as divine, and motherless, and a virgin, σεπτας τις ουσα, ως θεια, και αμητωρ, και παρθενος. And the appellations given to it by the Pythagoreans, as we learn from the extracts from Nicomachus are as follow: "Fortune and opportunity, Minerva, Mars and Acreotis, Agelia and Atrytone, Phylacitis, and Obrimopatra, or sprung from a powerful father, Tritogenia and Glaucopis or azure-eyed, Alalcomenia and Panteuchia, Ergane and Polyarete or much-implored, integrity of parts, and the horn of Amalthea, Aegis and Osiris, dream and voice, sound, and of the Muses Clio. To which may also be added judgment and Adrastia."

Of these epithets, Fortune, opportunity, Minerva, Tritogenia and voice, are explained as follows by the anonymous writer:

"The heptad is called Minerva, because similar to what is said of the goddess in fables, it is a certain virgin and unmarried; being neither begotten from a mother, which is the even number, nor by a father which is the odd number; except, that as Minerva was produced from the summit of the father of all things, so the heptad proceeds from the monad which is the head or summit of number. And it is as it were a certain virile Minerva. But the number which may be easily divided is feminine. It is also called opportunity, because its energies in decision with respect to health or disease, generation or corruption, are accomplished in a short time. And it is Fortune, because similar to what is said in fables of that goddess, it governs mortal affairs, and after a certain manner casually and opportunely occurs and decides. It is likewise denominated voice, because there are seven elementary sounds not only of the human voice, but also of every instrumental, mundane, and harmonic sound. And this not only because the first harmonic sounds are emitted, as we learn, by the seven planets, but also because the first diagram with musicians is the heptachord. But it is denominated Tritogenia, because the forms or parts of the soul being three, viz. the intellective, the irascible and the epithymetic, four most perfect virtues are produced belonging to these parts, just as of the three intervals (length, breadth and depth,) there are four boundaries in corporeal increase, (viz. a point, a line, a superficies and a solid)."

With respect to the epithet Agelia, the same anonymous writer likewise informs us, "that the heptad was thus called from being collected and congregated, (απο του συνειλησθαι, και συνηχθαι) the nature of it being uniform, since it is entirely indissoluble except into that which is homonymous.* Or it is so called because all physical effects are *led* through it to perfection. (ἡ απο του παντα αγαγεναι δἰ αυτης τα φυσικα αποτελεσματα

---

* Viz. Except into a *seventh* part which is 1.

εἰς τελείωσιν.) Or rather, which is more Pythagoric, it is thus denominated, because the most celebrated of the Babylonians, together with Ostanes and Zoroaster, very properly call the starry spheres *herds*, (αγελαι); whether because these alone among corporeal magnitudes are perfectly carried about a centre, or in conformity to the Oracles because they are considered by them as in a certain respect the bonds and collectors of physical reasons, which they likewise call in their sacred discourses *herds,* and by the insertion of a *gamma* angels. Hence, in a similar manner, they denominate the stars and dæmons which rule over each of these herds (or starry spheres) angels and archangels: and these are seven in number."

The same author further informs us that the heptad was called Phylacitis, or of a guardian nature, not only because the above mentioned angels and archangels are seven leaders, but also because the stars which guard the universe and preserve it in a connected and perpetual permanency are seven in number."

With respect to the epithets Obrimopatra and Glaucopis, it is evident that the heptad was thus called from its alliance to Minerva. This is also the case with the epithets Panteuchia and Ergane. For Minerva considered as one of the Curetes was celebrated by the former of these appellations, which signifies that she is furnished with every kind of armour. Hence the epithet παντευχος *panteuchos* is given to her by the Chaldæan Oracles, and by Plato in the Laws she is said to be adorned with every kind of armour, πανοπλια παντελει κοσμηθεισα. And Ergane or the artificer is well known to be an epithet of Minerva.

Again, the heptad perhaps as well as the triad was called the horn of Amalthæa, from its alliance to the monad, as being the source of every divine good. But it appears to have been called Aegis, because Minerva is celebrated as the ægis-bearing goddess, and this, as Proclus informs us On the Timæus, because the all-connecting chain of Fate is moved by this goddess, from whom also its plastic energies proceed. Lastly, the heptad was called, as we are informed by the anonymous writer, Telesphoros and judgement, the former because the seventh month is prolific, and the latter because a judgment is formed of diseases on the seventh day.

CHAPTER X

On the ogdoad.

"The number eight," says the anonymous writer, "is the first cube in energy, and is the only evenly-even number within the decad." The power of this number also is so great, that, according to the Grecian proverb, "All things are eight;" which proverb according to the above mentioned author originated from all things being comprehended in the eighth celestial sphere.

According to the extracts from Nicomachus, the names given to this number by the Pythagoreans are as follows: "Universal harmony and Cadmeia, mother and Rhea, the producing cause of females and Cybele, Cybebe and Dindymene, and the tutelar goddess, love and friendship, Metis, conception, and Oreia, Themis, law, immature, and of the Muses Euterpe."

With respect to the first of these epithets universal harmony, Camerarius* informs us, (from the anonymous author above quoted I have no doubt) that the Pythagoreans distinguished musical ratios by this number, and explained the mundane system according to those ratios as follows: The ratio of 9 to 8 is sesquioctave. This forms a tone, and is attributed to the moon.

---

* In Nicomach. Arithmet.

The ratio of 12 to 9 is sesquitertian, and the ratio of 12 to 8 is sesquialter. These ratios are given to the planet Mercury. In like manner 16 to 12 is sesquitertian, and 16 to 8 is duple. These ratios they attribute to Venus. The ratio of 18 to 12 is sesquialter, and of 18 to 9 is duple. These are ascribed to the sun. The ratio of 21 to 9 which is duple sesquitertian, is attributed to the planet Mars. The ratios of 24 to 18 which is sesquitertian, of 24 to 12 which is duple, of 24 to 8 which is triple, of 18 to 12 and also of 12 to 8, each of which is sesquialter, are ascribed to Jupiter. The ratios of 32 to 24 which is sesquitertian, and of 32 to 8 which is quadruple, are attributed to Saturn. And in the last place, the ratios of 36 to 24 which is sesquialter, of 36 to 18 which is duple, of 36 to 9 which is quadruple, and of 24 to 18 which is sesquitertian, are ascribed to the eighth or inerratic sphere, which comprehends all the rest. Hence the ogdoad was called by the Pythagoreans Cadmeia, because Harmony is said to have been the wife of Cadmus. And Cadmus, as we learn from Olympiodorus, is the sublunary world.

With respect to the epithets mother, Rhea, Cybele, and Dindymene, the ogdoad was doubtless thus denominated from being the first cube, and a cube is the element of earth which is participated by Rhea who is the same divinity as Ceres, and was called Cybele and Dindymene. As Rhea too is the vivific goddess, the life of which she is the source must be of a feminine characteristic; and hence the reason is obvious why the ogdoad is celebrated as the producing cause of females. As to the epithet Cybele, the mother of the gods was called from being the cause of divine inspiration to mystics.* The anonymous writer likewise informs us, that this number was called *Euterpe,* because it is the *most mutable* (μαλιστα ευτρεπτος) of all the numbers within the decad, being evenly-even, and this

---

* Etymologici Auctor.

as far as to the monad which is naturally indivisible.*

From Macrobius too we learn that "the ogdoad was called by the Pythagoreans justice, because it is the first number that is so resolved into evenly-even numbers, viz. into two fours, that each of these can nevertheless be divided into numbers equally evenly-even, i.e. into two twos. Its composition also is of the same quality as its analysis; for it is twice two twice. Since therefore its composition proceeds by an even equality, and its analysis equally returns as far as to the monad, which does not receive division in an arithmetical ratio, the ogdoad deservedly obtains the appellation of justice on account of its equal division."

CHAPTER XI

On the ennead.

ACCORDING to the extracts from Nicomachus, the ennead was celebrated by the Pythagoreans as "flowing round the other numbers within the decad like the ocean. It was also called by them the horizon, Prometheus and Concord, Perseia and Halios, freedom from strife and similitude, Vulcan and Juno, the sister and wife of Jupiter, Hecaergus and Pæan, Nysseis and Agyica, Enyalius and Agelia, Tritogenia and Persuasion, Curetis and Proserpine, Hyperion, and of the Muses Terpsichore."

Of these appellations, ocean and the horizon are unfolded as follows by the anonymous writer: "That there can be no number beyond the ennead, but that it circulates all numbers within itself, is evident from the regression of numbers. For the natural progression of them is as far as to 9, but after it their retrogression takes place. For 10 becomes as it were again the

---

* Viz. It can be divided by 2 as far as to unity.

monad. Thus if from each of the numbers 10, 11, 12, 13, 14, 15, 16, 17, 18, and 19, the number 9 is subtracted, the numbers that remain will be 1, 2, 3, 4, 5, 6, 7, 8, 9, 10. And vice versa the progression will receive an increase by the addition of 9. For if to each of the numbers 1, 2, 3, 4, 5, &c. 9 is added, the numbers produced will be 10, 11, 12, 13, 14, &c. Likewise by subtracting from 20, twice 9, from 30, thrice 9, from 40, four times 9, from 50, five times 9, &c. the numbers 2, 3, 4, 5, 6, &c. will be produced. By taking likewise from 100, eleven times 9, we again return to the monad. And after the same manner we may proceed to infinity. Hence it is not possible there should be any elementary number beyond the ennead. Hence the Pythagoreans called it ocean and the horizon, because all numbers are comprehended by and revolve within it. Hence too, it was called by them Halios, (παρα το αλιζειν) concord, and Perseia, because it congregates all numbers, and collects them into one, and does not permit the conspiration of the numbers beyond it to be dissipated."

With respect to the appellation Prometheus, we are informed by the anonymous writer, that the ennead was thus called, "from not suffering a number to proceed in the anterior part of it." (viz. from not suffering any number besides the nine that are in the place of units to be anterior to it.) απο του μη εαν τινα προσω αυτης χωρειν αριθμον. He adds: "And this reasonably; for being triply perfect, it does not admit of any increase; but consisting of two cubes, viz. 1 and 8, and being also a square, it is the only number as far as to itself that has a triangle* for its side."

The same author likewise informs us, that the ennead was called freedom from strife, on account of the retribution and permutation of numbers from it as far as to the monad. By

* I.e. a triangular number.

this I suppose he alludes to the equalization by addition and subtraction mentioned in the chapter on the pentad. But he says, it was perhaps denominated similitude, because 9 is the first odd square number. For the form of the odd number is said to be assimilative through the whole of itself; but the form of the even number is dissimilar. And again, the square number is assimilative; but that which is longer in the other part is dissimilar. Perhaps also it was thus denominated, because it is especially similar to its side. For as its side has the third place in the natural series of numbers, so likewise the ennead is the third number in a progression according to analogy.* He farther observes, that it was called Vulcan because the ascent of numbers is as far as to 9, in the same manner as the ascent of things which are decomposed by fire is as far as to the sphere of fire (i.e. the summit of the air.) But it was denominated Juno, because the sphere of air is arranged according to this number. And it was called the sister and wife of Jupiter, on account of its conjunction with the monad; but Hecaergus or far-darting, from preventing the farther progression of number. (απο του ειργειν την εκας προβασιν του αριθμου.) The epithet Nysseis is with the anonymous writer Nysseiotas; and he informs us the ennead was thus denominated from piercing† (απο του επινυσσαν) and from being arranged as a certain boundary of the progression of number.

With respect to the appellation Enyalius, which signifies Mars, we are informed by Martianus Capella, that the ennead was thus called because it is the extremity of the first series of numbers (i.e. of the numbers within 10); and that the end of all things is from Mars. As to the epithets Curetis and Proserpine, we learn from the anonymous author, that the ennead

* Viz. in the triple progression 1, 3, 9, 27, 81, &c.

† Νυσσα signifies a goal, and therefore the verb επινυσσω alludes here to an arrow or dart having arrived at its destined boundary by piercing the mark.

had these appellations in consequence of consisting of three triads; the triad harmonizing both with the Curetes and Proserpine. From the same author also we learn that it was called Hyperion, from having proceeded into a magnitude transcending the other numbers (within the decad); and Terpsichore from turning, and causing the retrogression and convergency of productive principles to circulate like a dance. (απο του τρεπειν και ως χορον ανακυκλουν την των λογων παλιμπετειαν, και συνευσιν.) This author likewise informs us, that it was called Telesphorus, or *bringing to an end,* because it gives perfection and consummation to the offspring that are produced in nine months; and also that it was denominated *perfect* because it is generated from the triad which is perfect. The ennead likewise may be said to be the perfector as we learn from Proclus in Tim. p. 298, "because it gives completion to the fabrication of generation." For, says he, "this number is adapted to generation (i.e. the sublunary region); since it proceeds from the monad as far as to the last numbers without retrogresion; and this is the peculiarity of generation." And thus much for the appellations of the ennead.

CHAPTER XII

On the decad.

THE decad according to the extracts from Nicomachus was denominated by the Pythagoreans "the world, heaven, fate, eternity, strength, faith, necessity, Atlas, unwearied, God, Phanes, the sun, Urania, memory and Mnemosyne."

The anonymous author informs us that the first of these appellations *the world,* was given to the decad, "from *all* things being arranged according to it both universally and partially." But as Protospatharius observes (in Hesiodi Dies) it was called the *decad,* from *containing* every number in itself, (ως δεχομενην παντα αριθμον εφ' εαυτου.) Proclus likewise informs us, "that the decad, as the Pythagorean hymn says, in mundane; and that divine number proceeds from the undecaying retreats of the monad, till it arrives at the divine tetrad which generated the mother of all things, the universal recipient, venerable, the boundary of all things, immutable and unwearied, and which both the immortal Gods and earth-born men denominate the sacred decad." Proclus adds, "that by the monad and its undecaying retreats in these verses, that uniform and occult cause *the one* being, (i.e. being characterized by *the one,* and which is the summit of the intelligible order) is signified; but that the divine tetrad is the evolution into light of intelligible multitude, which the duad that is between the monad and tetrad unfolds; and that the decad is the world, which receives the images of all the divine numbers, which are supernally imparted to it."*

The decad was called heaven, as we learn from the anonymous writer, "from being the most perfect boundary of number, whence also it was denominated the *decad,* being as it were δεχας, *the recipient,* just as heaven is the receptacle of all things." With respect to the epithet fate, we are informed by the same author, "that the decad was thus called, because there is no peculiarity either in numbers, or in things that exist according to the composition of number, which is not spermatically contained in the decad and in the numbers within it. But it extends connectedly and consecutively to the numbers posterior to itself. Hence it is fate, as being a certain connected

---

* Προεισι γαρ ο θειος αριθμος, ως φησιν ο Πυθαγορειος εις αυτον υμνος, μοναδος εκ κευθμωνος ακηρατου εστ' αν ικηται τετραδα επι ζαθεην, η δη τεκε μητερα παντων, πανδεχεα, πρεσβειραν, ορον περι πασι τιθεισαν, ατροπον, ακαματον, δεκαδα κλειουσι μιν αγνην αθανατοι τε θεοι και γηγενεεις ανθρωποι.

Procl. in Tim. p. 269.

But the last line is from Syrianus in Aristot. Metaphys.

and well-ordered digression (from the monad)." As the decad likewise contains every number in itself, and number is infinite, perhaps it was on this account called eternity; for eternity is infinite life. I say perhaps, for Meursius stupidly omits the reasons assigned by the anonymous writer for these appellations, as well as for those of faith and necessity. As to the epithet Atlas, the anonymous writer observes, "that the decad is so called in allusion to the Titan Atlas, who is fabled to bear the heavens on his shoulders. For Homer says of him,

> And the long pillars which on earth he rears,
> End in the starry vault and prop the spheres.

But the decad preserves the reason or productive principle of the spheres, being as it were a certain diameter, and convolving and enclosing these in the most connected manner."

With respect to the epithet Phanes, as the decad is denominated the world, and as Phanes who subsists at the extremity of the intelligible order is the paradigm of the world, the reason is obvious why the decad is thus called. To which we may add that Phanes who is the αυτοζωον or animal itself of Plato, contains in himself the first ideas, which are four, and 4 is paradigmatically or causally 10. From the anonymous writer we learn that it was called strength, because mundane natures are corroborated by it, and because it appears to rule over other numbers. It is also a certain defensive enclosure and receptacle of all reasons or productive principles, whence it is called the *key-bearer*, (κλειδουχος). According to Cedrenus likewise "it was denominated κλαδουχος, or the *branch-bearer*, because all the numbers (posterior to it) germinate from it as certain branches." Again, according to Anatolius, as we learn from the anonymous writer, "the decad was denominated strength and all-perfect, because it bounds every number, comprehending within itself every nature of the even and the odd, the moveable and the immoveable, the evil and the good." And

lastly, according to Chalcidius on the Timæus of Plato, the decad was called by the Pythagoreans the first square, because it
consists of the first four numbers, 1, 2, 3, and 4.

We have already observed that all numbers revolve within
the number 9, and that on this account it was called by the
Pythagoreans the ocean and the horizon; so that it is in reality
paronymous to the monad. This being the case, it may seem
wonderful that the decad also should be considered as analogous to the monad. The reason however of this is, that the
first offspring of a monad is likewise a monad, which contains
in a more expanded manner all that subsists more contractedly,
and as it were spermatically in the prior monad. Hence both
the ennead and the decad are monads; but in the former all
numbers subsist more unitedly, and the latter with more
abundant diffusion and separation.

CHAPTER XIII

On the properties of the monad.

HAVING thus unfolded the meaning of most of the appellations given by the Pythagoreans to numbers as far as to the decad, I shall in the next place present the reader with such properties of these numbers as have been discovered partly by the
ancients and partly by myself; and shall begin as order requires
with the properties of the monad.

We have shown then from Aristotle in his Pythagorics that
the monad is virtually i.e. causally, both odd and even; for
added to the odd it produces the even number, and to the even
the odd number. In the next place, Plutarch in his Platonic
Questions observes, that the monad is a triangular number (in
power); for if any triangular number is multiplied by 8, and

unity is added to the product, the sum will be a square number. Thus $3 \times 8 = 24$, and $24 + 1 = 25$, a square number. Thus too, $6 \times 8 = 48$, and $48 + 1 = 49$. But this likewise happens to the monad; for $8 \times 1 = 8$, and $8 + 1 = 9$, which is a square number.

Again, it is well known to mathematicians, that if any pentagonal number is multiplied by 24, and unity is added to the product, the sum will be a square number. Thus $5 \times 24 = 120$, and $120 + 1 = 121$, the square of 11. Thus too, $12 \times 24 = 288$, and $288 + 1 = 289$, the square of 17. And so in other instances. And this also happens to the monad; for $24 \times 1 = 24$, and $24 + 1 = 25$, the square of 5. The monad therefore is also virtually in power or causally a pentagonal number.

Thus too, I have found it may be shown that the monad is a triangular, quadrangular, pentagonal &c. pyramid. Thus for instance, the numbers 1, 4, 10, 20, 35, &c. are triangular pyramids.* The numbers 1, 5, 14, 30, 55, &c. are quadrangular pyramids. The numbers 1, 6, 18, 40, 75, &c. are pentagonal; and the numbers 1, 7, 22, 50, 95, &c. are first hexagonal pyramids.

But 4×1 and $+1 = 5$ the second ⎫
4×4 and $+1 = 17$ the 5th ⎬ hexagonal gnomon.
4×10 and $+1 = 41$ the 11th ⎭
&c.

5×1 and $+1 = 6$ the second ⎫
5×5 and $+1 = 26$ the 6th ⎬ heptagonal gnomon.
5×14 and $+1 = 71$ the 15th ⎭
&c.

7×1 and $+1 = 8$ the second ⎫
7×6 and $+1 = 43$ the 7th ⎬ enneagonal gnomon.
7×18 and $+1 = 127$ the 17th ⎭
&c.

* See the Table in the first book of the Arithmetic of Maurolycus.

$8\times$ 1 and $+1=$ 9 the second }
$8\times$ 7 and $+1=$ 57 the 8th   } decagonal gnomon.
8×22 and $+1=177$ the 23rd }
&c.

Again, the numbers 1, 2, 3, 4, 5, 6, &c. are triangular gnomons, and I have found it may be demonstrated that the monad is virtually each of these. For,

2×1 and $+1=$ 3 }
2×2 and $+1=$ 5 }
2×3 and $+1=$ 7 } the gnomons of squares.
2×4 and $+1=$ 9 }
2×5 and $+1=11$ }
&c.

3×1 and $+1=$ 4 }
3×2 and $+1=$ 7 }
3×3 and $+1=10$ } the gnomons of pentagons.
3×4 and $+1=13$ }
3×5 and $+1=16$ }
&c.

4×1 and $+1=$ 5 }
4×2 and $+1=$ 9 }
4×3 and $+1=13$ } the gnomons of hexagons.
4×4 and $+1=17$ }
4×5 and $+1=21$ }
&c.

5×1 and $+1=$ 6 }
5×2 and $+1=11$ }
5×3 and $+1=16$ } the gnomons of heptagons.
5×4 and $+1=21$ }
5×5 and $+1=26$ }
&c.

6×1 and $+1=$ 7 }
6×2 and $+1=13$ }
6×3 and $+1=19$ } the gnomons of octagons.
6×4 and $+1=25$ }
6×5 and $+1=31$ }
&c.

And so of the rest, which abundantly proves that the monad is causally every number.

CHAPTER XIV

On the properties of the duad, and triad.

THE duad, as it is beautifully observed by Proclus in his Commentaries on Euclid, is the medium between the monad and number. For unity, says he, by addition produces more than by multiplication; but number, on the contrary, is more increased by multiplication than by addition; and the duad, whether multiplied into, or added to itself, produces an equal quantity. Hence some of the ancients derive its appellation from τou δυναι, because number begins from hence to enter into multitude. Hence too, it was called Rhea, which signifies a certain flux, because from hence the streams, i.e. the progressions of multitude are derived. Again, the duad, as Martianus Capella observes, is the mother of the elements; for 4 is the offspring of 2. And it is also the first form of the even number. The hebdomad likewise 64 which is both a square and a cube, is produced by a continued multiplication by 2 from unity, as we shall show when we discuss the properties of the number 7. As Theo of Smyrna also observes,* matter, every sensible nature, generation, motion, increase, composition, association and relation, subsist according to the duad. And lastly, as is evident from the preceding chapter, if 2 is multiplied by any triangular gnomon, and unity is added to the product, the sum will always be the gnomon of a square.

Again, from the junction of the duad with the monad the triad is generated, which says Theo of Smyrna, is the first number that has a beginning, middle and end. He *adds,*

* Mathemat. p. 156.

"Hence it is the first number of which the word *all* is enunciated. For we do not enunciate *the all* of the numbers less than
three, but we say one, and both. By this number also we make
compacts, manifesting by this that we request every good. We
likewise call those that are in every respect miserable, thrice-
wretched, and those that are in every respect blessed, thrice-
blessed. The first origin also of a superficies is from this number. For the first subsistence of it is in a triangle; and on this
account there are three genera of a triangle, viz. the equilateral, the isosceles, and the scalene. There are likewise three
species of angles, the right, the acute, and the obtuse. And the
right angle indeed is defined by the nature of unity, and consists of the equal and the similar. Hence all right angles are
equal to each other, being media between the acute and obtuse,
the surpassing and the surpassed. But the other angles are infinite and indefinite; for they consist from excess and defect. The
triad also from the composition of the monad and duad with
itself produces 6, which is the first perfect number, being equal
to its parts. And this perfect number when added to the first
square, which is 4, produces the decad."

According to the Pythagoreans likewise, as we have before
observed,* every transmission of divine and mortal concerns is
accomplished through emission and reception, and in the third
place is strengthened through restoration. Thus after a certain
manner the etherial bodies disseminate; but terrestrial natures
receive as it were (the etherial effluxions); and a restoration†
is effected through the intermediate natures.

* See chap. 5.

† Bullialdus, from whom this information is derived, and who obtained it
from the anonymous author of Theologum. Arithmet. is very much mistaken in
the meaning of the word αντατοδοσις *restoration,* in this place. For he says,
"per αντατοδοσιν intelligere oportet effectus productos a causis." So far however is this word from signifying in this passage effects produced by causes, that
it signifies the restoration of parts to the wholes from which they were derived.

Again, of any two numbers whatever, either one of the two, or their sum, or their difference is divisible by 3. Thus of the two numbers 6 and 5, 6 is divisible by 3; of 11 and 5 the difference 6 is divisible by 3; and of 7 and 5 the sum 12 is divisible by 3. The square of 3 also, viz. 9, has this property, that 4, the sum of its aliquot parts 1, 3, is the square of 2.

Farther still, if any triangular gnomon is multiplied by 3 and unity is added to the product, the sum will be the gnomon of a pentagon, as is evident from what is delivered in the 13th chapter. And lastly, if any gnomon of a square, viz. if any one of the numbers 1, 3, 5, 7, 9, &c. is multiplied by 3, and unity is added to the product, the sum will be a pentagonal gnomon, as we have before shown in the chapter on polygonous numbers. Thus for instance,

$$\left. \begin{array}{l} 3\times1 \text{ and } +1= \ 4 \text{ the 2nd} \\ 3\times3 \text{ and } +1=10 \text{ the 4th} \\ 3\times5 \text{ and } +1=16 \text{ the 6th} \\ 3\times7 \text{ and } +1=22 \text{ the 8th} \end{array} \right\} \text{ pentagonal gnomon.}$$

CHAPTER XV

On the properties of the tetrad, pentad, and hexad.

HAVING already said so much about the tetrad in the chapter on its appellations, there remains but little more to observe concerning it from the ancients; Theo in the extract we have given from him respecting the tetractys having nearly exhausted the subject. I have therefore only to add farther, that the square of this number has a space equal to the length of the sides. For the sides are 4 in number, each of which is 4, and the square of it is 16. It is also produced as well by the addi-

---

For in every order of things there are μονη, προοδος, and επιστροφη, i.e. permanency in, progression from, and a return to causes

tion of 2 to itself, as by the multiplication of 2 into itself, and
on both these accounts, as we are informed by Camerarius, and
as we have before observed, it was called by the Pythagoreans
justice; the essence of justice consisting in equality. I have
also found that if 4 multiplies any one of the series of squares
1, 4, 9, 16, 25, &c. and unity is added to the product, the sum
will be an hexagonal gnomon. For,

$$4\times1 \text{ and } +1= 5 \text{ the 2nd}$$
$$4\times4 \text{ and } +1=17 \text{ the 5th} \left.\right\} \text{ hexagonal gnomon.}$$
$$4\times9 \text{ and } +1=37 \text{ the 10th}$$

&c.

Likewise, that if 4 multiplies any gnomon of a square, and
unity is added to the product the sum will be also an hexagonal
gnomon. For,

$$4\times1 \text{ and } +1= 5 \text{ the 2nd}$$
$$4\times3 \text{ and } +1=13 \text{ the 4th} \left.\right\} \text{ hexagonal gnomon.}$$
$$4\times5 \text{ and } +1=21 \text{ the 6th}$$

&c.

And again, that if 4 multiplies any pentagon, and unity is
added to the product the sum will likewise be an hexagonal
gnomon. Thus,

$$4\times 1 \text{ and } +1= 5 \text{ the 2nd}$$
$$4\times 5 \text{ and } +1=21 \text{ the 6th} \left.\right\} \text{ hexagonal gnomon.}$$
$$4\times12 \text{ and } +1=49 \text{ the 13th}$$
$$4\times22 \text{ and } +1=89 \text{ the 23rd}$$

&c.

Farther still, that if 4 multiplies any gnomon of a pentagon,
and unity is added to the product, the sum will also be an
hexagonal gnomon. For,

$$4\times 1 \text{ and } +1= 5 \text{ the 2nd}$$
$$4\times 4 \text{ and } +1=17 \text{ the 5th} \left.\right\} \text{ hexagonal gnomon.}$$
$$4\times 7 \text{ and } +1=29 \text{ the 8th}$$
$$4\times10 \text{ and } +1=41 \text{ the 11th}$$

&c.

Again, if 4 multiplies any triangular number, and unity is added to the product, the sum will be an hexagonal gnomon. For,

$$\left. \begin{array}{l} 4\times\ 1 \text{ and } +1= 5 \text{ the 2nd} \\ 4\times\ 3 \text{ and } +1=13 \text{ the 4th} \\ 4\times\ 6 \text{ and } +1=25 \text{ the 7th} \\ 4\times10 \text{ and } +1=41 \text{ the 11th} \end{array} \right\} \text{ hexagonal gnomon.}$$

&c.

And in the last place, if 4 multiplies any one of the numbers in a natural series 1, 2, 3, 4, 5, &c. and unity is added to the product, the sum will likewise be an hexagonal gnomon, as is evident from what is delivered at the end of the 13th chapter.

With respect to the pentad, in the first place, as Martianus Capella observes, whether it is associated with other odd numbers, or with those of its own kind, it always presents itself to the view. Thus $5\times5=25$; $3\times5=15$; $7\times5=35$; and $9\times5=45$; in all which products the terminating figure is 5. He adds, "There are five zones of the earth. In man also there are five senses. And there are five species of inhabitants of the earth, viz. men, quadrupeds, reptiles, flying and swimming animals." There are likewise five descending (καταφοραι) meteors; viz. snow, dew, hail, rain, and frost. And there are as many ascending (αναφοραι) from the earth and water; viz. vapour, smoke, clouds, mists, and the wind called typhon, or a whirlwind.

Again, from what I have shown in the 13th chapter, it is evident that if 5 multiplies any quadrangular pyramid, and unity is added to the product, the sum will be an heptagonal gnomon. For,

$$\left. \begin{array}{l} 5\times\ 1 \text{ and } +1= 6 \text{ the 2nd} \\ 5\times\ 5 \text{ and } +1=26 \text{ the 6th} \\ 5\times14 \text{ and } +1=71 \text{ the 15th} \end{array} \right\} \text{ heptagonal gnomon.}$$

&c.

From what is there shown also it follows, that if 5 multiplies any triangular gnomon, and unity is added to the product, the sum will be an heptagonal gnomon. For,

5×1 and $+1=\;\;6$ the 2nd
5×2 and $+1=11$ the 3rd
5×3 and $+1=16$ the 4th } heptagonal gnomon.
5×4 and $+1=21$ the 5th
5×5 and $+1=26$ the 6th
&c.

Farther still, I have found that if 5 multiplies any hexagonal gnomon, and unity is added to the product the sum will also be an heptagonal gnomon. For,

$5\times\;\;1$ and $+1=\;\;6$ the 2nd
$5\times\;\;5$ and $+1=26$ the 6th } heptagonal gnomon.
$5\times\;\;9$ and $+1=46$ the 10th
5×13 and $+1=66$ the 14th
&c.

Likewise, if 5 multiplies any hexagon, and unity is added to the product, the sum will be an heptagonal gnomon. Thus,

$5\times\;\;1$ and $+1=\;\;6$ the 2nd
$5\times\;\;6$ and $+1=31$ the 7th } heptagonal gnomon.
5×15 and $+1=76$ the 16th
&c.

Again, if 5 multiplies any one of the squares 1, 4, 9, 16, &c. and unity is added to the product the sum will also be an heptagonal gnomon. For,

5×1 and $+1=\;\;6$ the 2nd
5×4 and $+1=21$ the 5th } heptagonal gnomon.
5×9 and $+1=46$ the 10th
&c.

And in the last place, if 5 multiplies any gnomon of a square, and unity is added to the product, the sum will be an heptagonal gnomon. For,

5×1 and $+1=\;\;6$ the 2nd
5×3 and $+1=16$ the 4th } heptagonal gnomon.
5×5 and $+1=26$ the 6th
&c.

With respect to the hexad, it is the first perfect number in energy, being equal to the sum of its parts. Hence, it after a manner comprehends in itself 3 which is prior to it, and is remarkable also for its perfection. For 2+2+2=6. The sum likewise of any three numbers that surpass each other by unity, may be divided by 3 or 6. The area also of the first rectangular triangle whose sides are commensurable is 6, as will be shown in the next chapter, On the hebdomad. For the sides of this triangle are 3, 4, and 5; by which numbers the Pythagoreans demonstrate as follows among other things, that the offspring of nine and seven months are vital, but not those of eight months. If 4 is multiplied by 5 the product is 20. Five also multiplied by itself is 25. The sum of these two numbers added together is 45; which sum being multiplied by the number of the space 6, produces 270. This number, if it is considered as so many days, and is reduced to months by dividing it by 30, will give 9 months. Again, if 5 is multiplied by 4 the product is 20, and the product of 5 by 3 is 15. But the sum of these two is 35; which sum multiplied by 6 the number of the triangular area produces 210. This number also being considered as so many days, and divided by 30, will be reduced to 7 months.* Farther still, if 5 is multiplied by 3 the product is 15; and 5 multiplied by itself is 25. The sum of these two is 40; and this multiplied by 6 is 240. But this divided by 30 will be reduced to 8 months, when the number 240 is considered as days. The offspring however of 8 months are not vital, because 8 consists of the two odd numbers 5 and 3, which

---

* It may also be shown as follows, that the times of a vital birth depend on the hexad. Let 6 and 12 be taken, which are in a duple ratio, and let there also be assumed the two harmonic media 8 and 9. The sum of these four numbers is 35, which multiplied by 6 produces 210, the time of seven months. Again, let 6 and 18 be taken, which are in a triple ratio, and let the two harmonic media likewise, 9 and 12, be assumed. The sum of these four is 45, which multiplied by 6 exhibits the sum of 270 days, the time of nine months.

have a masculine property.* The male however by itself, or the female by itself, is unable to generate. But in the numbers 9 and 7, the odd and the even are mingled together, viz. the male and the female. For 5+4=9, and 4+3=7.† The hexad likewise is a certain foundation or root of arithmetical proportion. For the least numbers in which arithmetical proportion consists are 1, 2, 3, and the sum of these is 6.

The hexad also in the same manner as the pentad, always restores itself in the multiplication of itself by itself, but unlike the pentad it has not the same number always preceding. Thus for instance in all the multiplications of 5 into itself, 2 always precedes the last number. Thus 5 multiplied into itself as far as to the 5th power, produces the series 5, 25, 125, 625, 3125. And so in other instances ad infinitum. But 6 in the multiplications of itself by itself, always has either 1, or 3, or 5, or 7, or 9, viz. it always has some one of the odd numbers within the decad preceding the last term, as is evident in the following series 6, 36, 216, 1296, 7776, 46656.

According to the Pythagoreans likewise, after 216 years, which number is the cube of 6, there is a regeneration of things; and this is the periodic time of the metempsychosis.

In the hexad too, as Theo of Smyrna observes, the harmonic medium first consists. For the sesquitertian of it, viz. 8, being assumed, and also the double of it 12, the numbers 6, 8, and 12, will be in harmonic proportion; for as 6 is to 12 so is the difference between 8 and 6, to the difference between 8 and 12, viz. so is 2 to 4. If likewise, the sesquialter of it 9 is assumed,

---

* Any two numbers likewise of which 8 consists, are either both of them odd, or both of them even. Thus 1 and 7, and 5 and 3 are both of them odd; but 2 and 6, and 4 and 4, are both of them even.

† In like manner of any two numbers of which 9 and 7 consist, one is odd and the other even. Thus 1+8=9, 2+7=9, 3+6=9, and 4+5=9. And again 1+6=7, 2+5=7, and 3+4=7.

and the double of it 12, the numbers 6, 9, and 12, will be in arithmetical proportion. And if the half of it is taken, and afterwards the double, the numbers 3, 6, and 12, will be in geometrical proportion. The four numbers themselves likewise, 6, 8, 9, and 12, are in geometrical proportion; for $6 \times 12 = 72 = 8 \times 9$. The hexad also, says Martianus Capella, is the number that generates harmonies. For 6 to 12 is the symphony diapason; 6 to 9 is the symphony diapente; and 6 to 8 is the symphony diatessaron. He adds, "The hexad likewise associated with the square and solid quaternary, i.e. with 4, measures the hours of the day and night; for $6 \times 4 = 24$."

Farther still, from what I have shown in the 13th chapter, it is evident that if 6 multiplies any triangular gnomon, and unity is added to the product, the sum will be an octagonal gnomon. And I have also found that if 6 multiplies any heptangular gnomon, and unity is added to the product, the sum will be an octangular gnomon. For,

$$\left. \begin{array}{l} 6 \times \ 1 \text{ and } +1 = \ 7 \text{ the 2nd} \\ 6 \times \ 6 \text{ and } +1 = 37 \text{ the 7th} \\ 6 \times 11 \text{ and } +1 = 67 \text{ the 12th} \\ 6 \times 16 \text{ and } +1 = 97 \text{ the 17th} \end{array} \right\} \text{ octangular gnomon.}$$
&c.

And by a similar process with the squares 1, 4, 9, 16, &c. the gnomons of squares 1, 3, 5, 7, &c. and the heptagons 1, 7, 18, &c. octangular gnomons will be produced. For,

$$\left. \begin{array}{l} 6 \times 1 \text{ and } +1 = \ 7 \text{ the 2nd} \\ 6 \times 4 \text{ and } +1 = 25 \text{ the 5th} \\ 6 \times 9 \text{ and } +1 = 55 \text{ the 10th} \end{array} \right\} \text{ octangular gnomon.}$$
&c.

$$\left. \begin{array}{l} 6 \times 1 \text{ and } +1 = \ 7 \text{ the 2nd} \\ 6 \times 3 \text{ and } +1 = 19 \text{ the 4th} \\ 6 \times 5 \text{ and } +1 = 31 \text{ the 6th} \end{array} \right\} \text{ octangular gnomon.}$$
&c.

$6\times\ 1$ and $+1=\ \ 7$ the 2nd
$6\times\ 7$ and $+1=\ 43$ the 8th $\Big\}$ octangular gnomon.
6×18 and $+1=109$ the 19th
&c.

CHAPTER XVI

On the properties of the hebdomad.

THE hebdomad possesses many admirable properties, and is of a venerable nature as its name implies. Concerning these properties much has been transmitted to us by the ancients, but they have been discussed by none so copiously as by Philo the Jew, who in his treatise De Mundi Opificio, has written the following eulogium on this number:

"I know not whether any one can sufficiently celebrate the nature of the hebdomad, which is too excellent to be described by the power of words; yet it is not proper to be silent though what is said about it is of the most wonderful nature, but we should endeavour, if we cannot relate all and its most principal excellencies, to render manifest at least such of its properties as are accessible by our reasoning power. The hebdomad then, is spoken of in a twofold respect; one indeed, subsisting within the decad, which is seven times measured by the monad alone, and consists of seven monads; but the other is external to the decad, of which the principle is entirely the monad, according to double, or triple, or in short, analogous numbers; and such are the numbers of 64 and 729; the former indeed increasing by a duplication from unity, but the other by a triplication. Each species however ought not to be negligently considered. The second species indeed, has a most manifest prerogative. For the hebdomad which is compounded from double, or triple, or analogous numbers from the monad, is both a cube and a square, comprehending both species, viz. of the incorporeal and corporeal essence; the species of the incorporeal indeed, according to the superficies which is formed by squares; but of the corporeal according to the other dimension (depth) which is formed by cubes. But the credibility of what is said is most manifest in the above mentioned numbers. For the hebdomad 64 which is immediately increased from unity in a duple ratio, is a square produced by the multiplication of 8 by 8; and it is also a cube, the side or root of which is 4. And again, the hebdomad which is increased in a triple ratio from the monad, viz. 729, is a square indeed, formed by the multiplication of 27 by itself, and is also a cube, the side of which is 9.* By always making too a hebdomad the principle instead of the monad, and increasing according to the same analogy as far as to the hebdomad, you will always find that the increased numbers is both a square and a cube. The hebdomad therefore compounded in a duple ratio from 64, will be 4096,† which is both a square and a cube; a square indeed, having for its side 64; but a cube, the side of which is 16.

Let us now pass to the other species of the hebdomad which is comprehended in the decad, and which exhibits an admirable nature no less than the former hebdomad. This therefore is composed of one, two and four, which possess two most harmonic ratios, the duple and the quadruple; the former of which forms the symphony diapason, and the latter the symphony disdiapason. This hebdomad also comprehends other divisions, consisting after a manner of certain conjugations. For it is in the first place indeed, divided into the monad and hexad, afterwards into the duad and pentad, and lastly into the triad and tetrad. But this analogy or proportion of num-

---

* Thus $1 \times 2 \times 2 \times 2 \times 2 \times 2 \times 2 = 64$; and $1 \times 3 \times 3 \times 3 \times 3 \times 3 \times 3 = 729$.

† For $64 \times 2 \times 2 \times 2 \times 2 \times 2 \times 2 = 4096$. And thus also the hebdomad compounded in a triple ratio from 64 will be 46656, which is both a square and a cube; for the square root of it is 216, and the cube root is 36.

bers is also most musical. For 6 has to 1 a sextuple ratio; and the sextuple ratio produces the greatest interval in tones, by which the most sharp is distant from the flattest sound, as we shall demonstrate when we make a transition from numbers to harmonies. Again, the ratio of 5 to 2 exhibits the greatest power in harmony, nearly possessing an equal power with the diapason, as is most clearly exhibited in the harmonic canon. But the ratio of 4 to 3 forms the first harmony the sesquitertian, which is diatessaron.

Another beauty likewise of this hebdomad presents itself to the view, and which is to be considered as most sacred. For since it consists of the triad and the tetrad, it exhibits that which is undiverging and naturally in a direct line in things. And it must be shown after what manner this is effected. The rectangular triangle which is the principle of qualities, consists of the numbers 3, 4 and 5.* But 3 and 4 which are the essence of this hebdomad, form the right angle. For the obtuse and the acute exhibit the anomalous, the irregular and the unequal; since they admit of the more and the less. But the right angle does not admit of comparison, nor is one right angle more right than another, but it remains in the similar, and never changes its proper nature. If however the right angled triangle is the principle of figures and qualities; but the essence

---

* Viz. The first rectangular triangle whose sides are commensurable consists of the numbers 3, 4, and 5. For the area of such a triangle is 6, being equal to half the product of the two sides 3 and 4, i.e. to $\frac{3 \times 4}{2}$. But the sides of any rectangular triangle, whose area is less than 6, will be incommensurable. Thus, if 5 is the area of a rectangular triangle, it will be equal to $\frac{2 \times 5}{2}$ or to $\frac{1 \times 10}{2}$. Hence the two least sides will be either 2 and 5, or 1 and 10; and the hypothenuse will either be $2\sqrt{29}$, or $2\sqrt{101}$, each of which is incommensurable. This also will be the case if the area is 4, or 3, or 2. And as the commensurable is naturally prior to the incommensurable, the rectangular triangle, whose sides are 3, 4, and 5, will be the principle of the rest. Hence too, it is evident why 3 and 4 form the right angle.

of the hebdomad 3 and 4 necessarily impart the right angle, this hebdomad may justly be considered as the fountain of every figure and of every quality. To what has been said also, it may be properly added, that 3 is the number of a plane figure, since a point is arranged according to the monad, but a line according to the duad, and a superficies according to the triad. But 4 is the number of a solid, by the addition of unity giving depth to superficies. Hence it is manifest, that the essence of the hebdomad is the principle of geometry and stereometry: and in short, it is the principle of incorporeal and corporeal natures.

There is also naturally so much of what is adapted to sacred concerns in the hebdomad, that it has a pre-eminence with reference to all the numbers that are within the decad. For of these some beget, not being themselves begotten; but others are begotten indeed, but do not beget; and others both beget and are begotten. The hebdomad however alone is beheld in no part of these; which may be confirmed by demonstration as follows: Unity therefore generates all the numbers that are posterior to it, but is by no means generated by any number. Eight is indeed generated by twice four, but generates no number within the decad. Again, 4 ranks among those natures that both beget and are begotten. For it generates 8 by being multiplied by 2, and is generated by twice two. But 7 alone, as I have said, is neither naturally adapted to generate, nor to be generated. Hence other philosophers indeed assimilate this number to Victory, who is motherless and a virgin, and who is said to have sprung to light from the head of Jupiter. But the Pythagoreans assimilate it to the leader and ruler of all things. For that which neither generates nor is generated, remains immoveable; for generation subsists in motion, since that also which is generated is not without motion. For that which generates is in motion, in order that it may generate, and also that which is generated, in order that it may be generated. But the most ancient principle and leader of things, of whom the hebdomad may appropriately be said to be the image, alone neither moves nor is moved. Philolaus bears testimony to the truth of what I say in the following words: "God," says he, "is the leader and ruler of all things, being always one, stable, immoveable, himself similar to himself, and different from other things." In intelligibles therefore, the hebdomad exhibits the immoveable and the impassive; but in sensibles it evinces a mighty and most connective power, by which and by the periods of the moon, all terrestrial things are naturally adapted to be benefited. The manner however in which this is effected must be considered.

The number 7 being added to unity, and the numbers that follow it, generates 28, a perfect number, and equal to its parts.* But the number thus generated is apocatastatic of the moon, i.e. has the power of restoring it to its pristine state, at the time in which the moon begins to receive a sensible increase of its figure, and to which by decreasing it returns. It increases indeed, from the first lunarform illumination till it is bisected, during seven days. Afterwards, in the same number of days it becomes full-orbed. And again, running back as it were from the goal through the same path, from being full-orbed, it becomes again bisected in seven days, and from this, in the same number of days it acquires its first form, and thus gives completion to the number 28.

The hebdomad also is called by those who employ names properly *telesphoros,* or *the perfector,* because all things acquire perfection through this number. The truth of this however, may be inferred from every organic body employing three intervals or dimensions, i.e. length, breadth and depth, and four boundaries, a point, a line, a superficies, and a solid, from the

* For $1+2+3+4+5+6+7=28$.

composition of which the hebomad is formed. It would however be impossible for bodies to be measured by the hebdomad, according to the composition of three dimensions and four boundaries, unless it happened that the ideas of the first numbers, viz. of one, two, three and four, in which the decad is founded, comprehended the nature of the hebdomad. For these numbers have indeed four boundaries, the first, the second, the third, and the fourth; but three intervals; the first interval being from 1 to 2, the second from 2 to 3, and the third from 3 to 4. Independent also of these things, the ages from infancy to old age, most clearly exhibit the perfective power of the hebdomad, since they are measured by it. In the first seven years therefore, the teeth shoot forth. In the second is the time in which there is an ability of emitting prolific seed. In the third there is an increase of the beard. And in the fourth there is an accession of strength. The season of marriage is in the fifth. But in the sixth is the acme of intelligence. In the seventh there is an amelioration and an increase both of intellect and reason. But in the eighth, perfection in each. In the ninth there is equity and mildness, the passions for the most part becoming gentle. And in the tenth age, is the desirable end of life, the organic parts being still entire. For extreme old age is wont to supplant and afflict. Solon also the Athenian legislator, enumerates human life by the above mentioned hebdomads. But Hippocrates the physician says there are seven ages, viz. of the infant, the child, the lad, the young man, the man, the elderly man, and the old man; and these are measured by hebdomads, but do not extend beyond seven. His words however are as follow: "In the nature of man there are seven seasons, which they call ages, the infant, the child, the lad, &c. And infancy indeed continues to the shedding of the teeth; but the child, to the generation of the seed which extends to twice seven years. The lad continues till the beard becomes rough with hairs; but the young man, as far as to the increase of the whole body, which extends to four times seven years. The man continues as far as to fifty years wanting one, i.e. to seven times seven years; but the elderly man as far as to fifty-six years, i.e. to seven times eight years. And all the years that follow this pertain to the old man."

It is also said with respect to the peculiar composition of the hebdomad, as having an admirable order in its nature, since it consists of three and four, that the third number from the monad in a duple ratio is a square, but the fourth number in the same ratio is a cube, and that the seventh is a cube and at the same time a square.* Hence the seventh number is truly perfective, announcing both equalities, the superficial through a square, according to an alliance with the triad, and the solid through a cube, according to an alliance with the tetrad. But the hebdomad consists of the triad and the tetrad. The hebdomad however is not only perfective, but, as I may say, is most harmonic, and after a certain manner is the fountain of the most beautiful diagram which comprehends all harmonies, i.e. the diatessaron, the diapente, and the diapason; and likewise all analogies, viz. the arithmetical, the geometrical, and besides these, the harmonic. But the *plinthion*† consists of the numbers 6, 8, 9, and 12. And 8 is indeed to 6 in a sesquitertian ratio, according to which the harmony diatessaron subsists. But 9 is to 6 in a sesquialter ratio, according to which the harmony diapente subsists. And 12 is to 6 in a duple ratio, which forms the harmony diapason. It contains likewise, as I have said, all analogies; the arithmetical indeed, in the numbers 6, 9, and 12; for as the middle number surpasses the first by 3,

* Thus in the numbers 1, 2, 4, 8, 16, 32, 64, which are in a duple ratio, 4 is a square, 8 is a cube, and 64 is both a square and a cube. Thus also in the numbers 1, 3, 9, 27, 81, 243, 729, which are in a triple ratio, 9 is a square, 27 a cube, and 729 is both a square and a cube. And this will also be the case with numbers in a quadruple, quintuple, &c. ratio.

† See chap. 32, of the 2nd book.

it is also surpassed by the last number by 3. But it contains the geometrical analogy in the four numbers 6, 8, 9, and 12. For as 8 is to 6, so is 12 to 9; the ratio being sesquitertian. And it contains the harmonic analogy in the three numbers 6, 8, and 12. There is however a twofold criterion of harmonic analogy; one indeed, when as is the last term to the first, so is the difference between the last and middle, to the difference between the middle and first term. Of this, the most evident credibility may be derived from the proposed numbers 6, 8, and 12. For the last is double of the first term; and 12 exceeds 8 by 4, and 8 exceeds 6 by 2. But 12 : 6 :: 4 : 2. The other criterion however of harmonic analogy is, when the middle term by an equal part surpasses and is surpassed by the extremes. For 8 being the middle term, surpasses the first by a third part of the first term; for 8—6=2 the third part of 6; but it is surpassed by the last term by an equal part of the last; for 12—8=4, which is the third of 12. These things indeed necessarily thus subsist with respect to the venerable nature of this diagram, whether it may be proper to call it plinthion, or to give it some other appellation. So many ideas, and still more than these, does the hebdomad exhibit in things incorporeal and intelligible.

But the nature of it likewise extends to every visible essence, pervading through heaven and earth, which are the boundaries of the universe. For what part of the world is there, which is not enamoured of the hebdomad, being tamed by the love and desire of it? They say therefore, in the first place, that heaven is begirt with seven circles, the names of which are, the arctic, antarctic, the summer tropic, the winter tropic, the equinoctial, the zodiac, and besides these, the galaxy. For the horizon belongs to us; according to the acuteness of our vision, or the contrary, our sensible perception being circumscribed by it in a greater or less degree. The planets indeed, an army proceeding in a course contrary to that of the fixed stars, being arranged in seven orders, exhibit an abundant sympathy with the air and the earth. For these they vary by what are called the annual seasons, producing infinite mutations in each of them, by serene and cloudy weather, and by violent storms of wind. Again, they cause rivers to overflow, and to be diminished, plains to become stagnant water, or on the contrary, to have a squalid appearance. They likewise produce the mutations of the sea, its fluxes and refluxes. For sometimes the gulfs of the sea when it resounds through its reciprocations form profound shores; and a little after, the sea returning becomes most deep and navigable not by bearing small burdens, but an innumerable multitude of large ships. The planets likewise generating all terrestrial animals, plants and fruits, increase and bring them to perfection, preparing the nature in each to run its course; so that new flowers may succeed the old, and may arrive at their acme; in order to supply animals that are in want with an exuberant abundance. Moreover, the bear which is said to be the precursor of sailors consists of seven stars; to which pilots looking out through ten thousand paths in the sea, attempting a thing incredible, and greater than human judgment could expect to accomplish. For by looking to the above mentioned stars as leading lights, regions have been discovered unknown before, islands indeed, by the inhabitants of the continent, and continents by islanders. For it was necessary that the profound recesses both of the earth and sea, should be unfolded by the most pure essence of the heavens to the animal which is dear to divinity.

In addition also to what has been said, the choir of the pleiades derives its completion from a hebdomad of stars, the risings and occultations of which become the causes of mighty goods to all things. For when these set furrows are cut for the purpose of semination; and when they are about to rise, they become the joyful messengers of harvest. But when they rise, they excite the glad husbandmen to the collection of necessary aliment; who well pleased deposit the food they have collected for diurnal use. The sun too, the leader of the day, by producing two equinoxes in every year, in spring and in autumn; the vernal in Aries, but the autumnal in Libra, procures the most manifest credibility of divine majesty about the hebdomad. For each of the equinoxes takes place in the seventh month, at which times the law orders the greatest and most public festivals to be celebrated; since in both these, the fruits of the earth arrive at perfection; in spring indeed, corn and other seminations; but in autumn the produce of the vine, and of most other trees. Since also terrestrial are suspended from celestial natures according to a certain physical sympathy, the productive principle of the hebdomad originating supernally descends as far as to us, that mortal genera may be partakers of its advent.

Our soul also, the ruling part excepted, is divided into seven parts, viz. the five senses, the vocal organ, and the generative power; all which as in admirable machines, being drawn by the ruling part as if by secret strings, at one time are at rest, and at another time, in motion, and each according to appropriate habitudes and motions. In a similar manner likewise, if any one endeavors to explore the internal and external parts of the body, he will find that in each of these there are seven. The parts therefore, that are obvious are these, the head, the breast, the belly, the two hands and the two feet. But the internal parts which are called the viscera are, the stomach, the heart, the lungs, the spleen, the liver, and the two kidneys. Again, the most ruling part in the animal, the head, employs seven most necessary parts, two eyes, an equal number of ears, two nostrils, and in the seventh place the mouth, through which, as Plato says, there is an ingress of mortal, but an egress of immortal natures. For meat and drink indeed enter into it, which are the corruptible nutriment of the corruptible body; but from the reason of the immortal soul, there is an egress of immortal laws, through which the rational life is governed. The subjects also of the judicial power of the sight, the most excellent of the senses participate according to genus of the number seven. For there are seven things that are seen, body, interval, magnitude, colour, motion, and permanency; and besides these, nothing else. It happens likewise, that all the mutations of voice are seven, the acute, the grave, the circumflex, in the fourth place, the rough, in the fifth, the smooth, in the sixth the long, and in the seventh the short sound.

Moreover, it happens that there are seven motions, the upward, the downward, to the right hand, to the left hand, before, behind, and the circular, which becomes in the highest degree manifest from leaping. It is also said, that the secretions through the body are subject to this number. For tears indeed are poured forth through the eyes; the purifications from the head through the nostrils; but the saliva which we eject, through the mouth. There are also two evacuations for carrying off superfluities; the one before, but the other behind. The sixth secretion, is the effusion of the sweat through the whole body. And the seventh is the most natural emission of the seed through the genitals. Again, the menstrual purgations in women, are for the most part supplied in seven days; and the infant in the womb is naturally adapted to be animated in seven months, as an event most paradoxical. For offspring that are born in the seventh month live; but those that are born in the eighth month for the most part die. Severe diseases of our body likewise, and especially when from the bad temperature of the corporeal powers, we are afflicted with continued fevers, are principally decided on the seventh day. For this day forms a judgment of the contest about the soul, to some decreeing safety, but to others death.

But the power of this number not only extends to the above

mentioned particulars, but also to the best of the sciences, to grammar and music. For the lyre indeed consisting of seven chords, analogous to the choir of the seven planets, produces the most noble harmonies, and is nearly the leader of all instrumental music. Among the elements also of the grammatical art, the vowels truly so called are seven, since they are seen to produce a sound from themselves, and when they are conjoined with other letters, they form articulate sounds. For they supply indeed, what is wanting in the semivowels, by furnishing entire sounds; but they turn and change the natures of the mutes, by inspiring them with proper power, in order that things which were before ineffable may become effable. Hence those who first gave names to letters, as being wise men, appear to me to have denominated this number επτα, from the veneration and inherent sanctity pertaining to it, (απο του περι αυτον σεβασμου, και της προσουσης σεμνοτητος.) But the Romans adding the letter σ, which is wanting in the Greek, more clearly exhibit its origin, by calling it *septem,* from, as I have said, veneration and sanctity."

Again, according to Herophilus, as we are informed by Theo of Smyrna,* the human intestine is 28 cubits long, i.e. four times seven; and 28 is a perfect number. The moon also is said to impart from the etherial to the sublunary regions celestial powers while she uses the tetrad and the hebdomad. The increase likewise and decrease of things, and especially of such as are humid, follow the phases of the moon. Hence, a Greek poet cited by Baptista Camotius, in his Comment on the Metaphysics of Theophrastus, says of the moon, "that when she increases she augments, and when she decreases, injures all things."

This number too is the shortest boundary of the birth of children. And according to the Theban Hephæstion, the long-

* Mathemat. p. 162.

est boundary of the duration in the womb of those children that are born in the tenth month is 288 days and 8 hours. The mean duration is 273 days and 8 hours. And the shortest duration is 258 days and 8 hours. But of those that are born in the seventh month, the longest duration in the womb is 206 days and 8 hours; the least duration is 176 days and 8 hours; and the mean duration is 191 days and 8 hours. The ancient physicians likewise, as we learn from the anonymous writer, observe, that seven hours prior to the birth the navel of the foetus is spontaneously separated from the mother; within which space of time the foetus is able to support life, without receiving any nutriment from the mother.*

Again, Plato, says Theo Smyrnæus, following nature constitutes the soul from seven numbers. These numbers are 1, 2, 3, 4, 8, 9, 27, concerning the remarkable properties of which, I refer the reader to Plutarch's treatise On the Generation of the Soul according to Plato in the Timæus.

Farther still, conformably to what I have shown in the preceding numbers, if 7 multiplies a triangular gnomon, and unity is added to the product, the sum will be an enneagonal gnomon. For,

$$7\times1 \text{ and } +1= 8 \text{ the 2nd}$$
$$7\times2 \text{ and } +1=15 \text{ the 3rd}$$
$$7\times3 \text{ and } +1=22 \text{ the 4th}$$
$$7\times4 \text{ and } +1=29 \text{ the 5th}$$

} enneagonal gnomon.

&c.

By a similar process likewise with octagons, with squares, with pentagonal column. triang. pyramids, with square gnomons, and with the gnomons of octangles, enneagonal gnomons will be produced. Thus,

* Vid. Notas Bulliald. in Theon. Mathemat. p. 284.

$7\times$ 1 and $+1=$ 8 the 2nd ⎫
$7\times$ 8 and $+1=$ 57 the 9th ⎬ enneagonal gnomon.
7×21 and $+1=$148 the 22nd ⎭
&c.

7×1 and $+1=$ 8 the 2nd ⎫
7×4 and $+1=$29 the 5th ⎬ enneagonal gnomon.
7×9 and $+1=$64 the 10th ⎭
&c.

$7\times$ 1 and $+1=$ 8 the 2nd ⎫
$7\times$ 6 and $+1=$ 43 the 7th ⎬ enneagonal gnomon.
7×18 and $+1=$127 the 19th ⎭
&c.

7×1 and $+1=$ 8 the 2nd ⎫
7×3 and $+1=$22 the 4th ⎬ enneagonal gnomon.
7×5 and $+1=$36 the 6th ⎭
&c.

$7\times$ 1 and $+1=$ 8 the 2nd ⎫
$7\times$ 7 and $+1=$50 the 8th ⎬ enneagonal gnomon.
7×13 and $+1=$92 the 14th ⎭
&c.

CHAPTER XVII

On the ogdoad, ennead, and decad.

THE ogdoad, says Martianus Capella, is perfect, because it is covered by the hexad;* for every cube has six superficies. Likewise it derives its completion from odd numbers in a following order. For the first odd number is 3 and the second 5, and 3+5=8. Thus also the cube which is formed from the triad, viz. 27, is composed of three odd numbers in a following order, viz. of 7, 9, and 11. Thus too, the third cube which is formed from the tetrad, viz. 64, derives its completion from four odd numbers in a following order, viz. from 13, 15, 17,

---

* In my edition which is Lugd. 1619, the original is, "Perfectus item quod a septenario tegitur;" but instead of *septenario*, it is evident it should be *senario*.

19; for the sum of these is 64. And thus all cubes will be found to consist of as many odd numbers as there are unities in its root. Moreover, this octonary cube is the first of all cubes, in the same manner as the monad is the first of all numbers." Thus far Capella.

Again, in the chapter On the properties of the monad, we have shown from Plutarch that if 8 multiplies any triangular number, and unity is added to the product, the sum will be a square number. And we have also shown that if the triple of 8, i.e. 24, multiplies any pentagonal number, and unity is added to the product, the sum will also be a square.

Farther still, conformably to what we have shown of the former numbers within the decad, if 8 multiplies any triangular or enneangular gnomon, or any gnomon of a square, or any square, or first hexangular pyramid, or any enneagon, and unity is added to the product, the sum will be a decagonal gnomon. For,

$$8 \times 1 \text{ and } +1 = 9 \text{ the 2nd}$$
$$8 \times 2 \text{ and } +1 = 17 \text{ the 3rd} \Big\} \text{ decagonal gnomon.}$$
$$8 \times 3 \text{ and } +1 = 25 \text{ the 4th}$$
&c.

$$8 \times 1 \text{ and } +1 = 9 \text{ the 2nd}$$
$$8 \times 8 \text{ and } +1 = 65 \text{ the 9th} \Big\} \text{ decagonal gnomon.}$$
$$8 \times 15 \text{ and } +1 = 121 \text{ the 16th}$$
&c.

$$8 \times 1 \text{ and } +1 = 9 \text{ the 2nd}$$
$$8 \times 3 \text{ and } +1 = 25 \text{ the 4th} \Big\} \text{ decagonal gnomon.}$$
$$8 \times 5 \text{ and } +1 = 41 \text{ the 6th}$$
&c.

$$8 \times 1 \text{ and } +1 = 9 \text{ the 2nd}$$
$$8 \times 4 \text{ and } +1 = 33 \text{ the 5th} \Big\} \text{ decagonal gnomon.}$$
$$8 \times 9 \text{ and } +1 = 73 \text{ the 10th}$$
&c.

$$8 \times 1 \text{ and } +1 = 9 \text{ the 2nd}$$
$$8 \times 7 \text{ and } +1 = 57 \text{ the 8th}$$
$$8 \times 22 \text{ and } +1 = 177 \text{ the 23rd}$$

decagonal gnomon.

&c.

$$8 \times 1 \text{ and } +1 = 9 \text{ the 2nd}$$
$$8 \times 9 \text{ and } +1 = 73 \text{ the 10th}$$
$$8 \times 24 \text{ and } +1 = 193 \text{ the 25th}$$

decagonal gnomon.

&c.

With respect to the properties of the ennead, in the first place it consists of the three numbers 2, 3, and 4, which are in a natural order, and in which the ratio of symphonies are contained. For the ratio of 4 to 3 is sesquitertian, and forms the symphony diatessaron. The ratio of 3 to 2 is sesquialter, and forms the symphony diapente. And the ratio of 4 to 2 is duple, in which the diapason consists.

Again, if 9 multiplies any triangular, square, or decagonal gnomon, or any square or decagon, and unity is added to the product, the sum will be an endecagonal gnomon. For,

$$9 \times 1 \text{ and } +1 = 10 \text{ the 2nd}$$
$$9 \times 2 \text{ and } +1 = 19 \text{ the 3rd}$$
$$9 \times 3 \text{ and } +1 = 28 \text{ the 4th}$$

endecagonal gnomon.

&c.

$$9 \times 1 \text{ and } +1 = 10 \text{ the 2nd}$$
$$9 \times 3 \text{ and } +1 = 28 \text{ the 4th}$$
$$9 \times 5 \text{ and } +1 = 46 \text{ the 6th}$$

endecagonal gnomon.

&c.

$$9 \times 1 \text{ and } +1 = 10 \text{ the 2nd}$$
$$9 \times 9 \text{ and } +1 = 82 \text{ the 10th}$$
$$9 \times 17 \text{ and } +1 = 154 \text{ the 18th}$$

endecagonal gnomon.

&c.

$$9 \times 1 \text{ and } +1 = 10 \text{ the 2nd}$$
$$9 \times 4 \text{ and } +1 = 37 \text{ the 5th}$$
$$9 \times 9 \text{ and } +1 = 82 \text{ the 10th}$$

endecagonal gnomon.

&c.

9×1 and $+1=$ 10 the 2nd ⎫
9×10 and $+1=$ 91 the 11th ⎬ endecagonal gnomon.
9×27 and $+1=244$ the 28th ⎭
&c.

In the next place, with respect to the properties of the decad, it must be observed, that though the monad is the form of all arithmetical forms, yet it is chiefly the form of the decad. For what the monad is simply to all the series of numbers, that the decad is to the following hundreds, thousands, and millions; whence according to a secondary progression, it is denominated unity. Again, as this number is the ultimate perfection of beings, it contains all things in its omniform nature. For all proportion subsists within this number; the arithmetical in a natural progression of numbers from unity; the geometrical in the numbers 1, 2, 4, and 1, 3, 9; and the harmonical in the numbers 2, 3, 6, and 3, 4, 6.

Again, it will be found that if 10 multiplies any gnomon of a triangle, square, or endecagon, or any square, or endecagon, and unity is added to the product the sum will always be a duodecagonal gnomon. For,

10×1 and $+1=11$ the 2nd ⎫
10×2 and $+1=21$ the 3rd ⎬ duodecagonal gnomon.
10×3 and $+1=31$ the 4th ⎭
&c.
10×1 and $+1=11$ the 2nd ⎫
10×3 and $+1=31$ the 4th ⎬ duodecagonal gnomon.
10×5 and $+1=51$ the 6th ⎭
&c.
10×1 and $+1=$ 11 the 2nd ⎫
10×10 and $+1=101$ the 11th ⎬ duodecagonal gnomon.
10×19 and $+1=191$ the 20th ⎭
&c.
10×1 and $+1=11$ the 2nd ⎫
10×4 and $+1=41$ the 5th ⎬ duodecagonal gnomon.
10×9 and $+1=91$ the 10th ⎭
&c.

$$10 \times 1 \text{ and } +1 = 11 \text{ the 2nd}$$
$$10 \times 11 \text{ and } +1 = 111 \text{ the 12th}$$ } duodecagonal gnomon.
$$10 \times 30 \text{ and } +1 = 301 \text{ the 31st}$$
&c.

CHAPTER XVIII

Additional observations on numbers.

THE Pythagoreans, says Plutarch, in his treatise On Isis and Osiris, adorned numbers and figures with the appellations of the Gods. For they called indeed an equilateral triangle Minerva Coryphagenes, (or born from the summit) and Tritogeneia, because it is divided by three perpendiculars drawn from the three angles. But they called unity or *the one,* Apollo, being persuaded to give it this appellation for an obvious reason, (i.e. because Apollo signifies a privation of multitude, and from the simplicity of the monad.*) They also denominated the duad, strife and audacity; but the triad, justice. For since injuring and being injured, subsist according to excess and defect, justice through equality obtains a middle situation. But what is called the tetractys, being the number 36, was according to common report the greatest oath among them, and was denominated the world, in consequence of being composed of the first four even, and the first four odd numbers.†

Again, in the same treatise he says, "It is fabled by the

---

* In the original πειθουσα προφασει, και διπλοτατοις μοναδος, which is evidently erroneous and unintelligible, owing to the word διπλοτατοις. Hence Baxter, not being able to correct this passage, does not attempt to translate it, but merely says, "he restores it to the margin whence it was taken." The whole however will be intelligible, if for διπλοτατοις we read, as in the above translation, απλοτητι της.

† Baxter, who is always a bad translator and critic where philosophy and science are concerned, absurdly translates what is here said by Plutarch of the number 36, as follows, "Because it is made up of the even number 4, and of four odd numbers summed up together." And then adds in a note, "i.e. four times 9."

Egyptians that the death of Osiris happened on the 17th day of the month, at which time it is especially evident that the moon is at the full. Hence the Pythagoreans call this day *antiphraxis, obstruction,* or *opposition,* and utterly abominate this number. For 17 falling as a middle number, between the square 16, and 18 an oblong number, (which are the only plain numbers that have their ambits equal to the spaces contained by the ambits) it opposes and disjoins them from each other, and being divided into unequal portions forms the sesquioctave ratio;" (viz. by a division into 9 and 8.)

But that the ambits of these two numbers 16 and 18 are equal to their areas is evident. For 16 is a square each side of which is 4, and the number of the sides is 4. And 18 may be conceived to be a parallelogram the four sides of which are 6, 6, 3, 3, the sum of which is 18.

It is observed by Martianus Capella, that if the number 5 either multiplies itself, or any odd number, the product always ends in 5. And I have observed of 6, which when multiplied by itself always ends in 6, that if it multiplies an even number, the product will always end in that even number itself, which it multiplies, or the final number of it. Thus $2\times6=12$; $4\times6=24$; $6\times6=36$; $8\times6=48$; $10\times6=60$; $12\times6=72$; $14\times6=84$; $16\times6=96$; $18\times6=108$, &c. And this shows the superiority of the odd to the even number. For 5 vanquishes the odd number which it multiplies, by causing it to terminate in itself; but 6 is vanquished by the even number which it multiplies, and terminates in it.

Jamblichus in his Commentary on the Arithmetic of Nicomachus, p. 47, observes of the number 6, "that besides being a perfect number, it is the first evenly-odd number, and the first of the numbers that are longer in the other part. He adds, that it was called *marriage* by the Pythagoreans, because the first conjunction of the male and female subsists from mixture* according to this number. In consequence also of the entireness and symmetry which it contains, they called it health and beauty."

The following properties of 6 and 8 are remarkable, and have I believe escaped the notice of both ancient and modern mathematicians. They respect the formation of squares by the continual addition of these numbers to themselves, together with unity.

Thus for instance $1+6+6+6+6=25$, i.e. $1+\overline{6\times4}=25$, and $25+\overline{6\times16}=121$, $121+\overline{6\times28}=289$, and $289+\overline{6\times40}=529$. And so of the rest. That is, 1 added to four times 6 is equal to 25; this added to 16 times 6 is equal to 121; and 121 added to 28 times 6 is equal to 289, &c. In which it is observable, that the square roots of the numbers thus produced differ from each other by 6. For the roots are 5, 11, 17, 23, &c. But the difference of the multiplying numbers is always 12. Thus the first multiplier is 4, the second 16, the third 28, and the fourth 40, the difference between each of which is 12.

Again, with respect to 8, $1+8=9+\overline{8\times2}=25$, $+\overline{8\times3}=49$, $+\overline{8\times4}=81$, $+\overline{8\times5}=121$, $+\overline{8\times6}=169$. Here the roots of the squares are the odd numbers 3, 5, 7, 9, 11, 13, &c. which differ from each other by 2; and the multiplying numbers are 2, 3, 4, 5, 6, &c.

$1+4+4$, &c. will likewise produce the same square numbers as $1+8+8$, &c.

---

* In the original χαταρασεως, but is should evidently be as in my translation χαταχρασεως. Tenellius, from not seeing this error, has made nonsense of the passage. For his translation is: "Item *connubium* vocari a Pythagoræis, quia per se primum fit conjunctio maris et feminæ ex conflictu."

ADDITIONAL NOTES

P. 3. *The motion of the stars likewise is celebrated as being accompanied with harmonic modulations.*—"The Pythagoreans," says Simplicius, in his Commentary on the 2nd book of Aristotle's treatise On the Heavens, "said, that an harmonic sound was produced from the motion of the celestial bodies, and they scientifically collected this from the analogy of their intervals; since not only the ratios of the sun and moon, of Venus and Mercury, but also of the other stars, were discovered by them." Simplicius adds, "Perhaps the objection of Aristotle to this assertion of the Pythagoreans, may be solved according to the philosophy of those men, as follows: All things are not commensurate with each other, nor is every thing sensible to every thing, even in the sublunary region. This is evident from dogs who scent animals at a great distance, and which are not smelt by men. How much more, therefore, in things which are separated by so great an interval as those which are incorruptible from the corruptible, and celestial from terrestrial natures, is it true to say, that the sound of divine bodies is not audible by terrestrial ears? But if any one like Pythagoras, who is reported to have heard this harmony, should have his terrestrial body exempt from him, and his luminous and celestial vehicle,* and the senses which it contains purified, either

---

* The soul has three vehicles, one etherial, another aerial, and the third this terrestrial body. The first which is luminous and celestial is connate with the essence of the soul, and in which alone it resides in a state of bliss in the stars. In the second it suffers the punishment of its sins after death. And from the third it becomes an inhabitant of earth.

through a good allotment, or through probity of life, or through a perfection arising from sacred operations, such a one will perceive things invisible to others, and will hear things inaudible by others. With respect to divine and immaterial bodies however, if any sound is produced by them, it is neither percussive nor destructive, but it excites the powers and energies of sublunary sounds, and perfects the sense which is co-ordinate with them. It has also a certain analogy to the sound which concurs with the motion of terrestrial bodies. But the sound which is with us in consequence of the sonorific nature of the air, is a certain energy of the motion of their impassive sound. If then air is not passive there, it is evident that neither will the sound which is there be passive. Pythagoras however, seems to have said that he heard the celestial harmony, as understanding the harmonic proportions in numbers, of the heavenly bodies, and that which is audible in them. Some one however may very properly doubt why the stars are seen by our visive sense, but the sound of them is not heard by our ears? To this we reply that neither do we see the stars themselves; for we do not see their magnitudes, or their figures, or their surpassing beauty. Neither do we see the motion through which the sound is produced; but we see as it were such an illumination of them, as that of the light of the sun about the earth, the sun himself not being seen by us. Perhaps too, neither will it be wonderful, that the visive sense, as being more immaterial, subsisting rather according to energy than according to passion, and very much transcending the other senses, should be thought worthy to receive the splendour and illumination of the celestial bodies, but that the other senses should not be adapted for this purpose. Of these however, and such like particulars, if any one can assign more probable causes, let him be considered as a friend, and not as an enemy."

P. 3. *And it cannot be doubted that arithmetic naturally surpasses astronomy, since it appears to be more ancient than geometry and music, which are prior to it.*—This also was the opinion of the Pythagoreans, whose doctrine concerning the division of these four mathematical sciences was, according to Proclus in his Commentary on Euclid, p. 10, as follows: "The Pythagoreans gave a fourfold division to the whole mathematical science, attributing one of its parts to the *how-many,* but the other to the *how-much.* They also gave to each of these parts a twofold division. For they said that discrete quantity, or the how-many, either has a subsistence by itself, or is surveyed according to habitude to something else. And that continued quantity, or the how-much, is either stable, or in motion. They likewise said that arithmetic surveys the discrete quantity which subsists by itself, but music that which subsists with reference to something else. And that geometry considers the continued quantity which is immoveable, but spherics (or astronomy) that which is of itself, or essentially, moveable. They affirmed besides, that discrete and continued quantity, did not consider either magnitude or multitude simply, but that which in each of these is definite. For sciences alone speculate the definite, rejecting as vain the apprehension of infinite quantity. When however these men who were universally wise, assigned this distribution, we must not suppose they directed their attention to that discrete quantity which is found in sensibles, or to that continued quantity which appears to subsist about bodies; for it is the business of physiology, I think, to survey these, and not of the mathematical science. But since the demiurgus assumed the union and division of wholes, and the sameness together with the difference of them, for the purpose of giving completion to the soul, and besides these, permanency and motion, and as Timæus teaches us, constituted the soul from these genera, we must say, that the discursive energy of reason abiding according to its diversity, its division of productive principles, and its multitude, gives subsistence to arithmetic; but that according to the union of multitude, and communion with itself, it produces geometry. Understanding itself likewise to be both one and many, it produces numbers, and the knowledge of these. But it procures for itself music, according to the bond by which it is held together. Hence arithmetic is more ancient than music, since the soul was first divided in a fabricative way, and afterwards was bound together by harmonic ratios, as Plato narrates in the Timæus. And again, the discursive energy of reason being established according to a permanent energy in itself, unfolds from itself geometry, and the fabricative principles of all figures.* But according to its inherent motion, it produces the spheric science. For it also is moved according to circles; but is established in invariable sameness, according to the causes of circles. On this account, here also geometry precedes spherics, just as permanency is prior to motion.

"Since however the scientifically-reasoning power generates these sciences, not by looking to its evolution of forms which possesses an infinite power, but to the generic comprehension of bound, hence the Pythagoreans say that the mathematical sciences taking away the infinite, are now conversant with finite quantity. For intellect has established in the scientifically-reasoning power all the principles both of multitude and magnitude; since this power wholly consists with reference to itself of similar parts, is one and indivisible, and again divisible. Unfolding into light likewise the world of forms, it participates of bound and infinity essentially from intelligibles. But it perceives intellectually indeed from its participation of bound, and generates vital energies, and various productive principles from the nature of infinity. The intellections therefore of the reasoning power, constitute these sciences according to the bound which they contain, and not according to the infinity of life. For they bring with them an image of intellect, but not of life.

* I.e. a right and circular line.

Such therefore is the doctrine of the Pythagoreans, and their division of the four mathematical sciences."

P. 11. *Again, the evenly-even number is that which may be divided into two equal parts, and each of these parts into two other equal parts, and each of these may be divided in a similar manner, and the division of the parts may be continued till it is naturally terminated by indivisible unity.*

Euclid is blamed by Asclepius in his MS. Commentary on the first book of Nicomachus, for his definition of the evenly-even number, as follows: εντευθεν τοινυν ελεγχεται ο Ευκλειδης κακως ορισαμενος εν τω εβδομω Βιβλιω τον αρτιακις αρτιον αριθμον. φησι γαρ οτι αρτιακις αρτιος αριθμος εστιν ο υπο αρτιου αριθμου μετρουμενος κατα αρτιον αριθμον. ταυτω γαρ τω λογω και οι αρτιοι μονως, και μη οντες αρτιακις αρτιοι ευρεθησονται. i.e. "Hence therefore Euclid is reprehended, who badly defines the evenly-even number in his 7th book. For he says that the evenly-even number is that which is measured by the even number, according to the even number. For by this definition, even numbers alone, and not such as are evenly-even will be found." In like manner Euclid is blamed by Jamblichus, for the same definition. And indeed justly. For as Bullialdus observes in his Notes on Theo, p. 232, 6 for instance measures 24, by the even number 4. But 24 is not an evenly-even number. For the division is terminated before it arrives at unity; since 24 is divided into 12, 12 into 6, and 6 into 3; but here the division ends, and can proceed no farther. Euclid therefore, he adds, is deservedly blamed, because his definition is imperfect, and more confined than it ought to be.

P. 16. *The unevenly-even number is composed,* &c.—Jamblichus, a man of a most acute genius, as Bullialdus justly calls him, again blames Euclid in his Commentaries on the Arithmetic of Nicomachus, for confounding evenly-odd with unevenly-even numbers, and for not distinguishing one of these from evenly-even numbers. And certainly, as Bullialdus observes, Euclid ought to have distinguished odd numbers from the unevenly-even, and these again from the evenly-even, which are confounded by him.

P. 68. Chap.6 *A square number,* &c.—In this and the two following chapters, the generation of squares, pentagons, hexagons, &c. is delivered. And in the first place it is necessary to observe, that another generation of squares is delivered by ancient authors, and is called by them διαυλος, or, *a circuitous course from the same to the same.* For in this method, says Jamblichus on Nicomachus, "the monad becomes both the barrier and the goal in each composition. For from it the progression begins in the generation of every square, from the barriers as it were, as far as to the goal, which is the side of the square." Thus for instance in order to produce a square whose side is 4, let numbers be disposed from unity, as from the barriers of a Circus, as far as to 4, and from 4 again in a retrograde order as far as to unity, as below:

$$1 \quad 2 \quad 3 \quad 4 \quad 3 \quad 2 \quad 1$$

For the sum of all these is 16, a square number, the side of which is 4. Thus too, in order to produce a square whose side is 5, numbers must be disposed from unity in a similar manner as follows:

$$1 \quad 2 \quad 3 \quad 4 \quad 5 \quad 4 \quad 3 \quad 2 \quad 1$$

For the sum of these is 25, and consequently the side is 5. And so in all other instances.

But numbers will be thus disposed, if a number is distributed into units, and in this distributed form multiplied into itself, as may be seen below:

```
1 +1 +1 +1
1 +1 +1 +1
─────────────
1 +1 +1 +1
   +1 +1 +1 +1
      +1 +1 +1 +1
         +1 +1 +1 +1
─────────────────────
1 +2 +3 +4 +3 +2 +1
```

```
1 +1 +1 +1 +1
1 +1 +1 +1 +1
─────────────────
1 +1 +1 +1 +1
   +1 +1 +1 +1 +1
      +1 +1 +1 +1 +1
         +1 +1 +1 +1 +1
            +1 +1 +1 +1 +1
─────────────────────────────
+1 +2 +3 +4 +5 +4 +3 +2 +1
```

For the purpose of facilitating the knowledge of the generation of polygonous numbers, the following Table is added:

A Table of Polygons

The Gnomons of Triangles . . .	1	2	3	4	5	6	7	8	9	10	11	12
Triangles collected	1	3	6	10	15	21	28	36	45	55	66	78
The Gnomons of squares	1	3	5	7	9	11	13	15	17	19	21	23
Squares collected	1	4	9	16	25	36	49	64	81	100	121	144
The Gnomons of Pentagons . . .	1	4	7	10	13	16	19	22	25	28	31	34
Pentagons collected	1	5	12	22	35	51	70	92	117	145	176	210
The Gnomons of Hexagons . . .	1	5	9	13	17	21	25	29	33	37	41	45
Hexagons collected	1	6	15	28	45	66	91	120	153	190	231	270
The Gnomons of Heptagons . . .	1	6	11	16	21	26	31	36	41	46	51	56
Heptagons collected	1	7	18	34	55	81	112	148	189	235	286	342
The Gnomons of Octagons	1	7	13	19	25	31	37	43	49	55	61	67
Octagons collected	1	8	21	40	65	96	133	176	225	280	341	408
The Gnomons of Enneagons . . .	1	8	15	22	29	36	43	50	57	64	71	78
Enneagons collected	1	9	24	46	75	111	154	204	261	325	396	474
The Gnomons of Decagons . . .	1	9	17	25	33	41	49	57	65	73	81	89
Decagons collected	1	10	27	52	85	126	175	232	297	370	451	540

Jamblichus has extracted the following particulars respecting this table from the *Epanthemata* or *Arithmetical Flowers* of Thymaridas:

Polygons are formed from triangles. The first triangle in power 1, is the difference of the first polygons in energy in the descending series in the table. Thus for instance, the first triangle in energy is 3, the first square is 4, the first pentagon is 5, the first hexagon is 6, &c. and the difference between these is 1. Likewise the first triangle in energy 3, is the difference of the second polygons in energy 6, 9, 12, 15, &c. in the descending series. And all the gnomons of heptagons have the same final numbers, as the first and second have, viz. 1 and 6.

In the series of hexagons, all the perfect numbers are found, as 6, 28, &c. Likewise, all hexagons are triangles, one triangle in the series of triangles being alternately omitted, as 1, 6, 15, 28, 45, &c. The perfect numbers also contained in the series of hexagons are triangular, as 6, 28, &c. In the series of pentagons, two of them are alternately even numbers, and two are odd. And of the even one number is evenly-odd, but the other is unevenly-even. Thus 1 and 5 are odd, but 12 and 22 even. And afterwards alternately 12 is unevenly-even, but 22 is evenly-odd.

In the descending series of these numbers, after the series of units, the first polygons differ by unity, as 3, 4, 5, 6; the second by 3, as 6, 9, 12, &c.; the third by 6, as 10, 16, 22, &c.; the fourth by 10, as 15, 25, 35, &c.; and the fifth by 15, as 21, 36, 51, &c.; so that all these differences are in the series of triangles.

All the second and third polygons from unity, have superparticular ratios, as 3, 4, 5, 6, and also 6, 9, 12, 15. But the fourth polygons from unity have superpartient ratios as 10, 16, 22, 28.

Every square is composed from the triangle above it, and the next antecedent triangle, as 9 from the triangles 6 and 3. Every pentagon is composed from the triangle above it and twice the antecedent triangle, as 12 from 6 and twice 3. Every hexagon from the triangle above it, and thrice the antecedent triangle, as 15 from 6 and thrice 3. And so on, the number of the preceding triangle being increased by unity. The pentagon 12 is composed from the square 9 and the preceding square 4, the first triangle unity being subtracted from the sum. The hexagon 15 consists of the pentagon 12 placed above it, and the antecedent pentagon 5, the two triangles of unity being subtracted from the sum. The heptagon 18 consists of the hexagon 15 placed above it, and the preceding hexagon 6, the three triangles of unity being subtracted from the sum. The square 16 consists of the triangle 10 and 6. The pentagon 22 consists of the square 16 and the triangle 6. The hexagon 28, of the pentagon 22, and the triangle 6. The heptagon 34, of the hexagon 28, and the triangle 6. The square 16 consists of the triangles 10 and 6, precisely and entirely. But the pentagon 22 consists of the squares 16 and 9, less by once the first triangle in energy 3. The hexagon 28, consists of the pentagons 22 and 12, less by twice the first triangle in energy, i.e. less by 6. And the heptagon 34, consists of the hexagons 28 and 15, less by thrice the first triangle in energy, i.e. less by 9.

P. 79. *The numbers called heteromekeis,* &c.—Because these numbers depart from that equality which is in squares, the Pythagoreans arranged them in the co-ordination of things evil; but they arranged squares in the co-ordination of things good. The reason however of this arrangement is, that all square numbers or figures are similar to themselves, and have equal sides, which are in the same ratio to each other. Hence they are at rest, and do not depart from unity. But numbers and figures longer in the other part, are dissimilar to each other, and have also a dissimilar ratio of their sides. For as in the natural series of numbers 1, 2, 3, 4, 5, 6, &c. the ratio of the last to the next antecedent term, becomes by proceeding less and less, so in numbers longer in the other part, the more they increase the less is the ratio of the greater side to the less. Thus for instance, 12 is a number longer in the other part, the greater side of which is 4, but the less 3. Hence the former has to the latter a sesquitertian ratio, which is less than a sesquialter ratio, because $\frac{1}{3}$ is less than $\frac{1}{2}$. Euclid never distinguishes numbers longer in the other part from such as are oblong, and comprehends all the species of them under the general name of planes; for which he is reprehended by the acute Jamblichus as follows: "This again Euclid not perceiving, confounds the diversity and variety of explanation. For he thought that the number which is longer in the other part, is simply that which is produced by the multiplication of two unequal numbers, and does not distinguish it from the oblong number. If any one however should grant him this, it would happen that contraries which are naturally incapable of subsisting together, would be found in the same subject. For his definition comprehends both square numbers and such as are longer in the other part."

P. 131. *Perfect numbers.*—As every perfect is a triangular number, the side of which is the prime number from which the perfect number is formed; if that prime be squared, it will be equal to the sum of the perfect number itself, and the triangular number immediately preceding it. Thus $7 \times 7 = 49$, and $49 = 21 + 28$. Thus too $31 \times 31 = 961$, and $961 = 465 + 496$. And so of the rest.

P. 125. *In the series* $1 + \frac{1}{3} + \frac{1}{6} + \frac{1}{10} + \frac{1}{15}$, &c.—It is remarkable likewise, that the sum of any finite number of terms in the series $\frac{1}{3} + \frac{1}{6} + \frac{1}{10} + \frac{1}{15}$, &c. may be obtained by multiplying the last term by the denominator of the term next to the last. Thus the sum of $\frac{1}{3} + \frac{1}{6}$ is equal to $3 \times \frac{1}{6} = \frac{3}{6} = \frac{1}{2}$. Thus too the sum of $\frac{1}{3} + \frac{1}{6} + \frac{1}{10}$ is equal to $6 \times \frac{1}{10} = \frac{6}{10}$. And thus also the sum of $\frac{1}{3} + \frac{1}{6} + \frac{1}{10} + \frac{1}{15}$ is equal to $\frac{10}{15}$. And so of the rest.

FINIS.